elementary mathematics for teachers

To Joanna and Jane

elementary mathematics
for teachers

charles f. brumfiel and eugene f. krause

University of Michigan

addison-wesley publishing company

reading, massachusetts · menlo park, california · london · don mills, ontario

This book is in the
Addison-Wesley series in introductory mathematics

preface

The purpose of this book is to provide a coherent, modern analysis of elementary mathematics. It is intended primarily for prospective elementary teachers, but the point of view adopted makes it suitable for a "cultural mathematics" course at the junior college or beginning college level.

The mathematical development of an individual is a chain of successive abstractions. Between the child's largely physical activity of counting blocks and the professional mathematician's almost totally cerebral researches there are a number of well-defined stages. Retracing the steps of this abstraction process provides the organization for the book, the framework into which the mathematics fits.

This is, however, a mathematics book and not a treatise on the psychology of learning or the methods of teaching. No compromise has been made with mathematical honesty. Both the practical and the theoretical aspects of elementary mathematics are examined with great care in the text and in the exercise lists. Occasionally we found it impossible to restrain ourselves from noting an implication for teaching. Prospective teachers may find such remarks useful. We hope their instructors will not find them too trivial or objectionable.

The material in this text has been tested in both pre-service and in-service elementary teacher training courses at the University of Michigan. The reaction of the students has been encouraging. For most of them it provided the first opportunity to look back over all their elementary mathematics and see the big picture. For those who had not had previous contact with "the new math," it was particularly revealing.

Chapter 1 describes the abstraction process. In Chapter 2, we talk about the fundamental mathematical concepts of set and function, and also introduce the standard terminology associated with these concepts.

Chapters 3 and 4 include: counting and numeration systems, the connection between whole-number arithmetic and the real world, and computation with whole numbers. The evolution of the familiar (and some not-so-familiar) arithmetic algorithms is traced, and these algorithms are rationalized by relating them to the real world. Chapter 5 discusses the fundamental structural principles of the whole number system. The algorithms are justified again, this time on the basis of structural principles and the conventions of our numeration system.

Chapters 6 and 7 describe the abstraction of the positive rational numbers and the negative integers from the real world, emphasizing the use of these numbers in solving "real" problems. In Chapter 8 the systems of integers and rationals are developed on the basis of assumed structural properties.

Chapter 9, on decimals, provides a transition from the rational numbers to the real numbers, which are discussed more fully in Chapter 10.

Chapter 11 provides a taste of how the mathematician goes about defining the number systems in terms of the basic notion of set.

Chapters 12, 13, and 14 deal with the special topics of number theory, geometry, and probability, respectively. These chapters contain a great many intriguing problems, quite a few of which can be used in the elementary classroom to stimulate interest.

Special features of the book include: a large number of problems ranging in difficulty from routine to challenging; carefully stated and clearly displayed definitions and theorems; informal discussion of logical concepts where they are needed; discussion of the same number systems at several different levels of sophistication (a spiral approach); unifying use of the function concept; emphasis on the essential structural simplicity and similarity of the various number systems.

We wish to express our appreciation to the staff at Addison-Wesley for the care with which they processed the manuscript.

Ann Arbor, Michigan   C. F. B.
August 1968   E. F. K.

contents

1   the abstraction process

1-1   introduction

To be a good mathematics teacher it is necessary but not sufficient to know a substantial amount of mathematics. The elementary teacher must also have a clear understanding of the processes by which a child abstracts from his environment mathematical concepts that are meaningful to him. She presides over this abstraction process and her guidance is decisive in influencing the child's growth in mathematical maturity.

Five identifiable stages of abstraction are described below. The child traverses the first four each time he encounters one of these sets of numbers:

Whole numbers,   Positive rationals,   Integers.

The fifth stage is reached by only a few people. We describe it for the sake of completeness.

1-2   the first stage: the invention of new symbols

The first "mathematical" symbols that a child encounters are *audible* ones: the sounds "one," "two," ... In some manner, not at all well understood, he learns to associate these sounds with sets of objects. As he repeats these sounds he is expected to touch or point to things. Behavior like that indicated below is reprehensible.

"four"   "two"   "five"   "one"   "one"   "two"

But eventually each child, in his own way, relates these new sounds to his environment. Soon he meets *visual* symbols: "1," "2," . . . Because he has already related sounds to certain sets, and because some of the sounds he has heard were themselves chosen to describe the appearance of these visual symbols (compare the sound "twenty-three" with the symbol "23"), he learns to match the written symbols with sets of objects.

1–3   the second stage: the invention of operations on the new symbols

Once a child has firmly associated certain symbols and sets, then, as he watches something *done* to the sets, he can *imagine* doing corresponding things with symbols. A symbolic sentence like "3 + 2 = 5" tells a simple story. *"Three girls were joined by two boys. In the resulting set are five children."* The close relationship between operations on sets and operations on numbers* justifies the inclusion of set-theoretic ideas in teacher-training programs. Children can see (or imagine) sets being manipulated. Manipulations of sets suggest corresponding manipulations of symbols. After much experience of this sort the child begins to associate "answers" with expressions like

$$5 + 5, \quad 9 + 2, \quad 7 - 2$$

without any consideration of sets. He builds on his knowledge of "symbolic" facts and learns to play various games with the symbols of arithmetic *without relating the symbols to the physical world*. The abstraction is beginning to take place. The child thinks of *addition, multiplication, subtraction,* and *division*, not as activity he engages in as he handles sets of physical objects, but as activity he engages in as he thinks about symbols. Operations on *sets* of physical objects are replaced by operations on *sets* of mathematical symbols.

1–4   the third stage: learning to play the symbolic game

This is the skill stage. The vast complexity of the game begins to unfold. Every game has its special terminology: "hit," "bunt," "steal," "plate," "runner," "fly," "grounder," . . . The game of arithmetic has "addend," "minuend," "subtrahend," "unit fraction," "improper fraction," "mixed number." One must do all manner of strange things: "keep decimal points in line," "annex

---

* Note that we have used the word "numbers" instead of the word "symbols." We do not feel that it is sensible to emphasize the distinction between numbers and numerals (symbols for numbers) until Stage 4, and accordingly we shall use the terms interchangeably until then. For a fuller discussion of this point, see pages 7 and 89.

zeros," "move decimal points," "carry 2," "borrow 1," "invert fractions," "change to lower terms," "find common denominators," . . .

The child begins to view arithmetic as a game played according to a vast number of unrelated rules. He has to memorize addition and multiplication tables. Success in the game seems to depend more on memorization than on logical reasoning. There is a danger in this stage that heavy emphasis on skill development will cause students to lose touch with reality. Many students are overwhelmed by the mass of apparently unrelated concepts and lapse into confusion. In most university classes of prospective elementary teachers, there are students who confess that from the time fractions appeared in the arithmetic curriculum they felt engulfed in an intellectual fog.

Traditionally Stage 3 has been the terminal stage of instruction in the elementary grades, and most junior high school teachers have continued work of this type in their classes returning now and then to real world applications. Of course good teachers have always attempted to make arithmetic reasonable by simplifying the rules of the game. This simplification properly belongs to what we call Stage 4 of the abstraction process. This stage characterizes much of the current reform in the teaching of mathematics.

1–5   the fourth stage: analyzing the structure of the game

In this stage we seek to simplify the symbolic game of arithmetic by identifying simple basic principles which underlie the rules of the game. An analogy with other games can be made. In bridge, for example, one first learns the mechanics of sorting one's hand, bidding, and following suit in the play of the hand. Then one begins to learn many rules governing one's behavior in both the bidding and play. This memorization of rules corresponds to our Stage 3 in mathematical abstraction. But nearly all bridge players give mute testimony to the fact that it is very difficult to memorize enough rules to become an excellent player. There are just too many rules. One who wishes to become a really fine player must examine the source of the rules. What fundamental principles justify the rules? Once these principles are understood, relatively few rules are needed. As critical situations arise they can be analyzed in terms of these principles.

And so it is with the game of arithmetic. In relatively recent years mathematicians have carefully analyzed the fundamental principles that underlie the game. These principles are described by such terms as:

Commutative principle,   Associative principle,   Distributive principle, . . .

This new terminology is viewed by some teachers as a nuisance. But it is a terminology well worth learning because it is descriptive of the structure of the game. As the new terminology is introduced, much of the old terminology can be

discarded. The old terminology for the most part describes the appearance of
mathematical symbols and the *physical activity* of manipulating symbols. The
new terminology refers to mathematical *ideas* and the *thought processes* involved
in dealing with those ideas.

The old language	The new language
$\overset{2\ \ 1}{\cancel{3}\ 4}$ $-\ 1\ 6$	$3\ 4$ $-\ 1\ 6$
You can't take 6 from 4. Borrow 1 from the 3 and write it by the 4. Strike out the 3 and write a 2 . . .	Think of 34 as $20 + 14$ . . .
$4\frac{1}{2}$ $\times\ 3$	$4\frac{1}{2}$ $\times\ 3$
First multiply the whole numbers. $3 \times 4 = 12$. Then multiply the numerator of the fraction $\frac{1}{2}$ by 3 and write this . . .	The symbol $4\frac{1}{2}$ means $4 + \frac{1}{2}$. We multiply this sum by 3, using the distributive principle.

The ideas developed in Stage 4 complete the abstraction of arithmetic from
the physical world. Once the few basic principles are isolated and properly
understood, then none of the calculation of arithmetic depends on real-world
interpretations. One can now view arithmetic as a beautifully coherent game
played with "meaningless" symbols. The real world vanishes as did the Cheshire
cat.

These remarks are not to be interpreted as implying that arithmetic should
be isolated from the real world. On the contrary, modern programs in arithmetic
place more stress on important applications than did traditional programs. The
modern point of view is that when a student faces a difficult problem, his recourse
should not be to a bag of tricks, or memorized techniques. From his basic understandings of the *structure* of arithmetic, he should attempt to devise a method for
attacking the problem.

1–6   a fifth stage of abstraction: defining the number systems

Numbers are mysterious entities only to philosophers and mathematicians. It
would never enter a child's head that a definition should be formulated for the
number three. The question, "What is three?" is no more perplexing than the
question, "What is green?" Most people never define green-ness. They know it

intuitively. They say that green-ness is something that grass, dollar bills, and sick children have in common. Three-ness can be viewed similarly as a common property of the bears in Goldilocks, the Musketeers, and the branches of our federal government. So long as we all agree on what things are called green, no problem arises. So long as we agree on what things are called three, there is no difficulty. (Indeed, three-ness is a more satisfying property than green-ness. What you call green someone else may call blue. We are not likely to disagree on three. This is one of the nice characteristics of mathematics.)

Now although there seems no practical reason for defining green, a physicist may choose to do so for the sake of having a well-rounded physical theory. The physicist defines green to be electromagnetic radiation of wavelength 5500 angstrom units. Similarly, the mathematician defines three to be the set

$$\{\varnothing, \{\varnothing\}, \{\varnothing, \{\varnothing\}\}\}.$$

(If you do not now understand this symbol, you will after you read Chapter 11.) The mathematician is motivated, as is the physicist, by his desire to have a beautifully rounded theory. Most people justifiably ignore both the physicist's definition of green and the mathematician's definition of three. It is surely inadvisable to attempt to describe for children the mathematician's definitions of numbers. It is questionable whether or not it should be done for elementary teachers.

In Chapter 11 we shall give a brief account of how the mathematician *defines* numbers and the operations on them in terms of the single concept of (mathematical) set. Insofar as this concept is intuitively meaningful, the mathematician has attained another level of abstraction. He has restored a meaning to the "meaningless" symbols of Stage 4.

2 sets, functions, and relations

2-1 set membership and set inclusion

In everyday life we say that a person "is on a team," "belongs to the country-club set," "is a member of a class." Words like "team," "set," and "class" refer to *collections* of things. Phrases like "is on," "belongs to," and "is a member of" denote *membership* in collections. Many collective nouns have special connotations. The members of an *audience* are listening to the same thing. Anything in a *gaggle* has the property of being a goose. Sets and properties are intimately related. Usually we think first of some property (for example, the property of being tall) and then pass to a set of objects having this property.

The language of mathematics is less colorful than the language of everyday life. The single term *set* is used pretty much to the exclusion of other collective nouns, although sometimes, to break the monotony, a mathematician will substitute *collection, class,* or *family.* Mathematical sets come to our attention in much the same way as physical sets do. We observe a mathematical object with some special property and then are led to think of the set of all objects with that property.

EXERCISES 2-1

1. Name some collective nouns, each of which suggests some special property.
2. Name some collective nouns, none of which suggests a special property.
3. Describe a common property of the four numbers 20, 40, 80, 200. List 5 other elements of the set suggested by this property.
4. For the numbers of Exercise 3 describe two common properties other than the one you noted, and for each property list several elements of the resulting set.

6

Membership in a mathematical set is indicated by terminology much the same as that used for physical sets. One says, "a point is *on* a line," "4 *belongs* to (is a *member* of, is an *element* of) the *set* of even numbers." We use the abbreviations

$$\underbrace{x \in A}_{\downarrow} \qquad\qquad \underbrace{x \notin A}_{\downarrow}$$

x belongs to set *A*   *x* does not belong to *A*

If $x \in A$, we say that *A contains x*.

▶ *Aside.* We have used "$x \in A$" as an abbreviation for "*x* is contained in *A*." When one reads this one may wish to think:

"This means that there is an element, which we are calling *x*, which is a member of a set, which we are calling *A*."

This would correspond to interpreting "Al Kaline is on the Tigers" to mean:

"There is a man, named Al Kaline, who is a member of a set of men, called the Tigers."

On the other hand, one may decide to leave unspoken (as obvious) the distinction between the thing and its name. The first point of view is apparent in a statement such as

"let *n denote* a natural number";

the second in

"let *n be* a natural number."

We shall take both points of view. When we feel that it is important to emphasize the distinction between a thing and a label for a thing, we shall take the first. Otherwise we shall be content with the second.

We take the same fence-straddling position in the number–numeral controversy. At times it is reasonable to make a distinction between numbers (things? sets?) and numerals (symbols for numbers); at other times it is unreasonable. Specifically it seems futile to try to force a subtlety such as this on a child who is not yet beyond the third stage of abstraction. He does not yet conceive of a number as a *thing*. His things are objects in the physical world. "Three" is an adjective, not a noun.

In Stage 4 a number is a thing, though not a very substantial one. (It is an undefined element of an intangible set whose very existence has to be assumed.) In Stage 5 a number is again a thing, this time conceptually somewhat more concrete. In these last two stages it is reasonable, and occasionally important, to distinguish between a number and its labels (numerals). ◀

If every element of set A also belongs to set B, we say that A is a subset of B. We use the symbolism

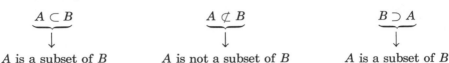

$A \subset B$ $A \not\subset B$ $B \supset A$

A is a subset of B A is not a subset of B A is a subset of B

and the suggestive diagram.

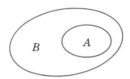

If $A \subset B$ we also say that B *includes* A.

We shall say that a set *contains* its *elements* and *includes* its *subsets*. Some writers use "contains" and "includes" interchangeably. What is important is to remember that the symbol $\in$ denotes set membership while the symbol $\subset$ denotes set inclusion.

Some mathematicians use a more complex symbolism for set inclusion.

$A \subseteq B$ $A \subset B$

A is a subset of B (this is our usage A is a subset of B, and there is at least
of $A \subset B$).   one element in B which is *not* in A.

When $A \subset B$ and B contains an element not in A, we call A a *proper* subset of B.

It is easy to confuse the concepts of set membership and set inclusion. One set can be a *subset* of a second set and, at the same time, an *element* of a third. For example, consider the following sets:

P: The set of American League baseball players.
A: The set of teams that comprise the American League.
D: The Detroit Tiger baseball team.

Explain why $D \in A$ and $D \notin P$; why $D \subset P$ and $D \not\subset A$.

EXERCISES 2–2

1. Describe at least three subsets of the set A which consists of the numbers 0 and 1. Which of these are proper subsets of A?
2. Describe two sets, each of which includes the set A of Exercise 1 as a proper subset.

3. Let B be the set whose elements are the vowels a, e, i, o, u.

    a) Using our definition of set inclusion, is it true that $B \subset B$?

    b) Using the set-inclusion symbols as some other mathematicians are said to do, is it true that $B \subset B$? that $B \subseteq B$?

    c) How many 4-element subsets does B include? 3-element subsets?

4. If you know that $R \subset S$ and $S \subset T$, what can you conclude?

5. Give an example of sets A and B such that $A \not\subset B$ and $B \not\subset A$.

6. In a set G of people, let T be the subset of tall persons, R the subset of red-haired persons, and H the subset of tall redheads. Write down several correct statements of the form $X \subset Y$ for these sets.

2–2   equality

When one is studying a set it is inconvenient to assemble the elements each time one wishes to investigate some question. It is easier to work with a list of labels or symbols for the objects. (For example, I can compute enrollment by counting names in a class book rather than by counting students; I can do the former at home.) A single element, however, may have several different labels. One man may be called Mr. Smith, or John Smith, or J. H. Smith, or John. In order to assert that all these labels designate the same element, we write

John Smith $=$ Mr. Smith;   John $=$ J. H. Smith; . . .

This is how we use the symbol " $=$ "; thus

$A = B$

means that "A" and "B" are names (labels, symbols) for the same thing. (What does $A \neq B$ mean?) If we were being extremely fussy about the use of language, we would use the term *equal* when we were talking about *symbols* and the term *identical* when we were talking about *things named* by these symbols. That is, referring to the statement

$A = B$,

we might assert:

"A" and "B" are equal symbols.
A and B are identical objects.

Note that the use of quotation marks would indicate a reference to symbols.

    Under this interpretation of the equality symbol (the equals sign), it follows that if $A = B$, then in *any* statement that we may make about the thing named by A, we may substitute B for A. This is referred to as the *substitution* property of equality.

If A has 6 toes and $A = B$, then B has 6 toes.
If B is tall and green and $A = B$, then A is tall and green.
If $x \in A$ and $A = B$, then $x \in B$.
If $D \subset B$ and $A = B$, then $D \subset A$.

Equality has other obvious properties. Explain why the following are obvious. Whatever objects are named by A, B, and C,

1) $A = A$.
2) If $A = B$, then $B = A$.
3) If $A = B$ and $B = C$, then $A = C$.

When making proofs it is sometimes convenient to refer to these properties of equality:

Property (1) is called the *reflexive* property (Ref.).
Property (2) is called the *symmetric* property (Sym.).
Property (3) is called the *transitive* property (Tran.).

To say that sets A and B are *equal*,

$$A = B,$$

means, then, that we have actually one set with two names.

EXERCISES 2–3

1. Prove that if A is a set and $A = B$, then $A \subset B$ and $B \subset A$.
2. If $A = B$ and $x \notin A$, what can you conclude?
3. If $R = S$ and $T \not\subset S$, what can you conclude?
4. If $A \not\subset B$, could it be the case that $A = B$?
5. Describe some ways in which you used the properties of equality in school algebra or geometry.
6. Does set inclusion have (a) the reflexive property? (b) the symmetric property? (c) the transitive property?
7. Is set membership (a) reflexive? (b) symmetric? (c) transitive?
8. Let us agree that in space every line is parallel to itself. Which of the properties, Ref., Sym., Tran., does parallelism for lines possess?
9. Which of the Ref., Sym., Tran. properties does perpendicularity for lines have?

Exercise 1 above points out the (obvious) fact that if $A = B$, A and B have the same elements. Suppose now that sets A and B have the same elements. Are A and B the same? A careful examination of this question discloses one of the differences between mathematical set theory and physical set theory. It is easy to give examples of physical sets which have the same members and yet seem to be different. For example, let S and B represent a soccer team and a baseball team, respectively. Assume that the same 15 boys make up each team. Then the sets S and B have the same members. But S has scheduled 8 games, while B has scheduled a season of 16 games. We cannot substitute "S" for "B" in the statement "B has a schedule of 16 games." We have the apparent result

$$B \subset S; \quad S \subset B; \quad \text{but } B \neq S!$$

In mathematical set theory we arbitrarily exclude such a possibility. For mathematical sets we say: *A set is determined by its elements.* In other words:

If sets A and B have the same elements, then $A = B$.

This is one of the basic assumptions that underlies mathematical set theory. Combining this assumption with the result you established in Exercise 1 above, we can say:

$A = B$ if and only if $A \subset B$ and $B \subset A$.

This statement is sometimes presented as a *definition* of equality for sets, but to do so is to abuse the concepts of definition and equality.

The "if and only if" statement above is actually a combination of two statements:

If $A = B$, then $A \subset B$ and $B \subset A$ (which we prove).
If $A \subset B$ and $B \subset A$, then $A = B$ (which we assume).

There are several differences between the theory of mathematical sets and the theory of physical sets. In general your intuitive understanding of relationships between sets of physical objects will be helpful in your mathematical work, but you can anticipate some conflict with your intuition.

One source of confusion resides in the mathematical treatment of sets with very few elements. In the everyday world we might refuse to admit the existence of sets containing only one element (could one bee form a hive?), and we would almost certainly balk at accepting a set with no elements. (Has a professor, lecturing to an empty classroom, an *audience*?) In mathematics such sets are fully as respectable as any others. The set of *even prime* numbers contains the single element 2. One-element sets are called *singletons*. The set of prime numbers between 114 and 126 contains no elements. Such a set is called a *null* or *empty* set. Let us make two observations about mathematical set theory:

1)   A singleton set is not the same as the element it contains. (Example: the *set* of even prime numbers is not the same thing as the *number* 2.)

2)   There is only one empty set. If A and B are both null sets, then $A = B$.

Observation (2) is a logical consequence of our agreement that two sets are the same if they have the same elements. Certainly, if A and B are empty sets, everything in A is in B and vice versa. Because of the uniqueness of the empty set, we denote it by a special symbol:

The empty set $= \emptyset$ (an ancient Nordic symbol).

Observation (1) must be accepted on faith. It is almost a consequence of our agreement that a set is determined by its elements, but not quite. We might attempt to argue:

i)   The number 2 *belongs* to the set of even prime numbers.

ii)   The number 2 *does not belong* to 2.

iii)   Hence the number 2 is not the same thing as the set of even prime numbers.

The trouble with this argument resides in assertion (ii). How do we know that the statement "$2 \in 2$" is false? Since we have not defined the number 2, there is no basis for such an assertion. It happens that conclusion (iii) is true, although we cannot establish its truth here. (It is a consequence of an *axiom* of mathematical set theory called the axiom of regularity. See *Axiomatic Set Theory*, Patrick Suppes, Van Nostrand, Princeton, New Jersey, 1960, pages 53 ff.)

EXERCISES 2–4

1. Show that $\emptyset$ is a subset of every set. Count the total number of subsets included in a 1-element set; a 2-element set; a 3-element set, a 4-element set. Guess a formula for the number of subsets of an n-element set and check it for a 5-element set.

2. A farmer remarks, "I must go milk my herd of cows." Later you learn that his herd consists of a single cow which he duly proceeded to milk.

   a) Did the farmer mislead you?

   b) Did the farmer lie to you?

   c) Does this example suggest that in the case of physical set theory a singleton (in this case the farmer's herd of one cow) can be considered to be identical with the element it contains (in this case the cow), or does it indicate that a distinction should be made between the two concepts?

3. Suggest some differences between physical sets and mathematical sets other than those already noted.

4. Give an example for which there seems to be a difference between a physical object and the 1-element set containing it.

5. Note that forms of the verb "to be" are used in at least three different senses in everyday discourse. Each of these ways is related to one of the mathematical symbols: $=$, $\in$, $\subset$. That is, in everyday speech when we say "X is Y," we might mean any one of the three assertions:

$$X = Y; \qquad X \in Y; \qquad X \subset Y.$$

Distinguish each usage of the verb below.

a) Our king *is* Henry the eighth.

b) Our kings *were* all brave men.

c) Our king *is* dead.

d) Good men *are* hard to find.

e) Her coat *is* red.

f) Mother *is* nice.

g) The murderer *is* John Doe.

h) The line segment *is* 3 inches long.

i) The officers *are* John, Jerry, and Sue.

j) His name *is* Fremont Thurston Smithson the Fifth.

k) His test grade *was* 87%.

l) The weather *is* horrible.

m) She *is* fifth in line.

6. Exercise 5 illustrates one important reason why mathematicians use non-verbal symbols. A single word can have different meanings in different contexts; a mathematical symbol generally has just one meaning.

a) Discuss the following extreme example of the ambiguity of the English language: "The skies are not cloudy all day."

Another reason for using symbols is that one saves time and ink.

b) Translate the following symbolic sentence into English:

"$x^2 - 4 = (x + 2)(x - 2)$."

c) Translate into symbols: "The product of the positive number whose square is seven and the positive number whose square is three is the positive number whose square is the product of three and seven."

2–3   notation for sets

There are many ways to designate sets, but since a set is determined by its elements, no method is satisfactory unless it specifies precisely what elements belong to the set. (We say that a set must be *well-defined*.) In everyday life we may speak of the set of all honest people, but since we lack criteria for sorting out honest folk from the other kind, the phrase "all honest people" does not define a set. On the other hand, we can refer unambiguously to the set of chairs in a particular room. The property of being a chair is more easily recognizable than the property of being honest.

We may simply *enumerate* the elements of a set, writing names of the elements in braces:

$A = \{1, 2, 3, 4, 5\}$;
$B = \{4, 5, 6, 7\}$.

The braces are not essential, but they are traditional. Sometimes *Venn diagrams* are used.

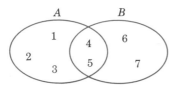

A Venn diagram

The Venn diagram above calls attention to the fact that the numbers 4 and 5 belong to both sets A and B, while none of the other numbers has this property.

The most useful mathematical technique for designating sets, and the one we shall usually employ, is sometimes referred to as *set-builder notation*. With this technique we select in advance some set which contains all the elements we wish to consider. In arithmetic this might be the set of whole numbers. In geometry it might be the set of all points in 3-dimensional space. This large set is referred to as the *universal set* for the discourse. Then as other sets are needed they are described as subsets of this universal set.

As an example of the set-builder notation, let the universal set be the set W of all whole numbers:

$W = \{0, 1, 2, 3, \ldots\}$.

These are the numbers one obtains by beginning with 0 and repeatedly adding 1.

Then in set-builder notation we indicate subsets of W:

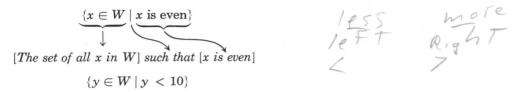

$$\{x \in W \mid x \text{ is even}\}$$

[The set of all x in W] such that [x is even]

$$\{y \in W \mid y < 10\}$$

The set of all y in W such that y is less than 10.

Note the use of variables (the letters x and y) in this set-builder notation. We could read $\{y \in W \mid y < 10\}$ as "The set of *all numbers* in W such that *each number* is less than 10." The variables can be interpreted as convenient abbreviations for phrases like "all elements," "each element," etc. Thus it is immaterial what letter we use for variables $\{x \in W \mid x < 10\} = \{y \in W \mid y < 10\}$.

EXERCISES 2–5

1. Let W be the set of all whole numbers. Enumerate the elements belonging to each of the following sets:

   a) $\{x \in W \mid x < 7\}$

   b) $\{x \in W \mid x > 14 \text{ and } x < 20\}$

   c) $\{x \in W \mid x = 3 \text{ or } x = 7 \text{ or } x = 20\}$

   d) $\{x \in W \mid x + 4 \leq 9\}$ *0, 1, 2, 3, 4, 5*

   e) $\{x \in W \mid 2x + 3 > 16 \text{ and } 3x + 5 < 30\}$

2. Describe in set-builder notation:

   a) The set of all numbers in W less than 100.

   b) The set of all numbers in W greater than 2000.

   c) The set of all numbers in W strictly between 100 and 200.

   d) The set of all numbers in W satisfying the inequality $4x - 7 < 500$.

   e) The set of all multiples of 5 in W which are greater than 27. *5x ∈ w/x > 27*

   f) The set of all odd numbers in W between 100 and 200.

   g) The set of all numbers in W which are either odd and less than 100, or even and greater than 500.

   h) The empty set (a subset of W).

   i) $\{1, 4, 9, 16, 25, 36 \dots\}$ Why is set-builder notation superior to enumeration in this case?

   j) $\{0, 1, 2, 3, 4, 5, 97, 98, 99, 100, 101, 102, 103\}$ *x ∈ w/x < 6 and x > 96 + < 104*

3. Consider the set $A = \{x \in W \mid x > 30 \text{ and } x \text{ is odd}\}$
   a) Is $27 \in A$?   b) Is $50 \in A$?   c) Is $49 \in A$?   d) Is $10 \in A$?

4. Consider the set $B = \{x \in W \mid x < 100 \text{ or } x \text{ is even}\}$
   a) Is $73 \in B$?   b) Is $200 \in B$?   c) Is $64 \in B$?   d) Is $111 \in B$?

5. From a strictly logical point of view, one cannot "well-define" an infinite set by "enumeration." The ellipsis marks are necessarily ambiguous.

   a) What number do you think follows 4 in the "enumeration" $\{1, 2, 4, \ldots\}$? Why?

   b) Give different answers to (a).
   [*Hint:* The population of Truro, Nova Scotia, was 12,421 at the last census.]

   Given that U is a set of people and A is the subset consisting of all people in U with a certain property, it is natural to contemplate the subset of all people in U who do not have the property. These are just the people in U who are *not* in A. We denote this set by A', and call it the *complement* of A.

$A' = \{x \in U \mid x \notin A\}$.

Example $A = \{x \in U \mid x \text{ is a grandfather}\}$
           $A' = \{x \in U \mid x \text{ is not a grandfather}\}$

Because there is no element in both A and A', we say that the two sets are *disjoint*.

EXERCISES 2–6

1. Let A be any subset of a universal set U. Is every element of U in one of the sets A, A'?

2. If U is the set of whole numbers and $A = \{x \in U \mid x \text{ is even}\}$, how do we usually describe the set A'?

3. Interpret the Venn diagrams below. (Imagine more elements not pictured by dots.)

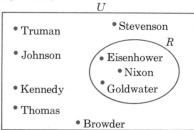
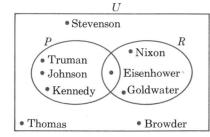

4. The Venn diagram below indicates that two subsets, A and B, can partition U into four subsets.

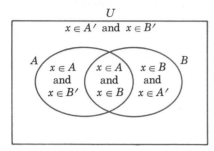

Draw and label similarly a diagram for three subsets A, B, C of a universal set U.

a) Into how many "pieces" can three subsets split U?

b) Into how many such pieces can four subsets A, B, C, D split U?

5. Suppose that in one situation the universal set U is the set of whole numbers $\{0, 1, 2, \ldots\}$, and $A = \{x \in U \mid x \text{ is odd}\}$. Suppose that in another situation the universal set U is the set of integers $\{\ldots -2, -1, 0, 1, 2, \ldots\}$, and $B = \{x \in U \mid x \text{ is odd and } x > 0\}$. Does $A = B$? Does $A' = B'$? Is the importance of agreeing on the universal set clear?

6. Show that if $A \subset B$, then $B' \subset A'$.

2–4   union and intersection of sets

Set-builder notation enables us to form new sets from given sets. If U is any set, then we can pick a property and use set-builder notation to indicate the subset of U consisting of just those elements which possess the property. We can think of *complementation* as an operation we apply to a set A to form the set A'. *Union* and *intersection* can be thought of as operations on pairs of sets. The Venn diagrams below illustrate these operations.

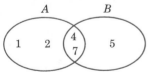

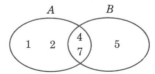

The union of sets
A and B is the set
$\{1, 2, 4, 5, 7\}$

The intersection of
sets A and B is the set
$\{4, 7\}$

We denote the union and the intersection of sets A and B, respectively, by

$A \cup B$ and $A \cap B$.

An element is in the *union* if it is in *at least one* of the sets. An element belongs to the *intersection* if it is in *both* sets. Set-builder notation can be used to define union and intersection. Let U be the universal set for the current discourse, and let A and B be any subsets of U. Then:

$A \cup B = \{x \in U \mid x \in A \text{ or } x \in B\}.$
$A \cap B = \{x \in U \mid x \in A \text{ and } x \in B\}.$

These definitions can be formulated informally as:

To form the *union* of two sets, we combine them.

To form the *intersection* of two sets, we take just those things in both sets.

The expression $x \in A$ *or* $x \in B$, used to define $A \cup B$, is formed by combining the simple *atomic expressions* $x \in A$, $x \in B$. The word "or" links these two expressions to form one expression. If we wish to decide whether $3 \in A \cup B$, we replace x by 3 and examine the statement

$3 \in A$ *or* $3 \in B$.

If this lengthy statement is true, $3 \in A \cup B$; if false, $3 \notin A \cup B$. One of the basic objectives of mathematical logic is to develop agreements and basic techniques that enable one to determine the truth or falsity of complex statements.

EXERCISES 2–7

1. Two brick streets cross. Each street may be considered to be a set of bricks. What is the usual name assigned to the set of bricks common to the two streets?

2. If $A = \{2, 5, 9\}$, $B = \{9, 10, 15\}$, enumerate the elements of $A \cup B$ and $B \cap A$.

3. Give an example of two sets, A and B, containing 3 and 4 elements, respectively, whose union contains 5 elements. How many elements are in $A \cap B$?

4. Set A has m elements. Set B has n elements. If $A \cup B$ has $m + n$ elements, what can you say about the set $A \cap B$?

5. Set A has m elements and set B has n elements. Their union, $A \cup B$, has r elements. If r is less than $m + n$, explain how to determine the number of elements in $A \cap B$.

6. Given that A has 8 elements, $A \cap B$ has 3, and $A \cup B$ has 19, how many has B? *14*

7. Given that A and B have the same number of elements, $A \cup B$ has 20 and $A \cap B$ has 12, how many has A? *16*

8. By now you have probably deduced the two-set "theorem,"

   $$n(A) + n(B) = n(A \cup B) + n(A \cap B)$$

   where $n(X)$ denotes the number of elements in set X. What is the corresponding three-set theorem?

   [*Hint:* Consider the Venn diagram below.]

   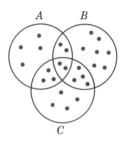

   $$n(A) + n(B) + n(C) = n(A \cup B \cup C) + \ldots$$

9. Let U denote the 50 states of the United States. Let P denote the set of states bordering on the Pacific Ocean. Let C denote the set of states having a common boundary with Canada. Draw an appropriate Venn diagram.

10. Given that A is any subset of a universal set U, what can you say about the set (a) $A \cup A'$? (b) $A \cap A'$?

11. Complete the table below. The second line asserts that if the statement $a \in A$ is true (T) and the statement $a \in B$ is false (F), then the statement, $a \in A$ and $a \in B$, is false, while $a \in A$ or $a \in B$ is true.

$a \in A$	$a \in B$	$a \in A$ and $a \in B$	$a \in A$ or $a \in B$
T	T	T	T
T	F	F	T
F	T	F	T
F	F	F	F

12. Designate each statement below as true or false, where $A = \{0, 2, 4, 6, 8\}$, $B = \{1, 3, 5, 7, 9\}$, $C = \{x \in W \mid x < 10\}$.

   a) $A \subset C$ T   b) $A \in C$ T   c) $A \cup B = C$

   d) $A \cap B = \varnothing$ e) $\{1, 3, 5, 7\} \subset B$ f) $A \cap C = C$

   g) $B \cup C = C$ h) $0 \in A$ i) $\{0\} \in A$

   j) $\{0\} \subset A$ k) $A \cap (B \cup C) = (A \cap B) \cup (A \cap C)$

   l) $A \cup (B \cap C) = (A \cup B) \cap (A \cup C)$

   m) B is the complement of A in C.

The table that you completed in Exercise 11 indicates how the terms *and* and *or* are used in mathematics. The statement

$$x \in A \qquad and \qquad x \in B$$

is true in only the one case, when x is in both sets. This conforms with the every-day usage of "and." The "or" of mathematics is the and/or of legal terminology and is referred to as the *inclusive or*. The statement

$$x \in A \qquad or \qquad x \in B$$

is false in only the one case, when x is in neither A nor B. The "or" of legal terminology (which sometimes occurs in everyday speech) is referred to as the *exclusive or*. The decision:

30 days in jail *or* \$1000 fine

will not result in the infliction of both penalties. An "exclusive-or" statement is true only if exactly one of the two component parts is true. In mathematics the statement

$$x > 10 \qquad or \qquad x < 12$$

is true for every whole number x. (Why?) However, if one interpreted "or" as the "exclusive or," this statement would be false for $x = 11$ and true for every other whole number. (Why?)

2–5   logic and sets

Logic is the tool we use to test the validity of an argument. Applying this test is a matter of determining whether certain statements are true or false. Given a complex statement, we break it into atomic statements, determine the truth or falsity of each "atom," analyze the structure of the complex statement (i.e., how the atomic statements are put together) and finally pass judgment on the original complex statement. This aspect of logic was suggested by Exercise 11 in the exercises of the last section.

In everyday life a statement is a declarative sentence.

"It is hot" is a statement.
"Shut the door" is not.

Statements have the property that they can be classified as true or false.

"6 is a prime number" $\rightarrow$ *false*.
"2 is a prime number" $\rightarrow$ *true*.

In our use of set-builder notation, we designated sets by expressions like

$$A = \{x \in U \mid x < 4\}.$$

Strictly speaking, the expression, $x < 4$ is not a statement. Given that $U = \{1, 2, 3, 4, 5, 6\}$, then we use the expression "$x < 4$" to decide exactly which elements of U belong to set A. We replace the variable x by all names of elements of U. This results in the formation of six statements:

$$1 < 4; \quad 2 < 4; \quad 3 < 4;$$
$$4 < 4; \quad 5 < 4; \quad 6 < 4.$$

Of these statements, the first three are true, the others false. Hence

$$A = \{1, 2, 3\}.$$

Expressions like $x < 4$ are called *open sentences*. When the symbol x is replaced by the name of an object in the universal set, a statement results. In this case we say that the open sentence, $x < 4$,

is *true for* 1, 2, 3 and is *false for* 4, 5, 6.

Each use of set-builder notation is of the type indicated below.

Designation of   Designation of a *property* by means of an open
the universal set.   sentence which is either *true* or *false* for each
                         element of the universal set.

The set described by this notation is the set of all elements of the universal set which render the open sentence true.

All complex statements are constructed from simple ones by the repeated application of a few basic operations. We describe three of these basic operations. We denote arbitrary statements by p and q.

OPERATOR	*EFFECT OF THE OPERATION*	*EXAMPLE*
not	$p \rightarrow$ not p	$3 + 4 = 6 \rightarrow 3 + 4 \neq 6$
and	$p, q \rightarrow p$ and q	It will rain. It will turn cold $\rightarrow$ It will rain *and* it will turn cold.
or	$p, q \rightarrow p$ or q	It will rain. It will turn cold $\rightarrow$ It will rain *or* it will turn cold.

Of course, complex *open* sentences can be constructed from simple ones in the same way.

There is an intimate relationship* between operations on open sentences and operations on sets. To illustrate this, let U be a set of people and P, Q the subsets of popular and quiet people, respectively. We denote the open sentences, x is popular; x is quiet, by p, q, respectively (rather than by the more accurate but clumsier $p(x)$, $q(x)$). Now observe that we can write abbreviated definitions of P, Q, $P \cup Q$, P', ... (Read these definitions aloud.)

$$P = \{x \in U \mid p\}; \quad Q = \{x \in U \mid q\};$$
$$P \cup Q = \{x \in U \mid p \text{ or } q\}; \quad P' = \{x \in U \mid \text{not } p\}.$$

The form of these definitions suggests that it is worth while to note the correspondence below. We say that each set is the *truth set* for its matching open sentence.

1) $P \leftrightarrow p$ 5) $P', Q' \leftrightarrow \text{not } p, \text{not } q$

2) $Q \leftrightarrow q$ 6) $P \cap Q' \leftrightarrow p \text{ and } (\text{not } q)$

3) $P \cup Q \leftrightarrow p \text{ or } q$ 7) $P' \cup Q' \leftrightarrow (\text{not } p) \text{ or } (\text{not } q)$

4) $P \cap Q \leftrightarrow p \text{ and } q$

Lines (1) through (7) are self-explanatory. One interprets (6) as asserting:

The elements in the intersection of P and Q' are precisely those which render the statement, p and (not q), true.

The correspondences (1) through (7) call attention to the fact that if we are given any open sentences p, q, r, ... and the corresponding truth sets P, Q, R, then if we form a new open sentence by applying the *logical* operators "and," "or," "not" to p, q, r, ..., we get the truth set for this new open sentence by properly applying the *set* operators

$\cap$, $\cup$, ' to P, Q, R, ...

exchanging "and" for $\cap$, "or" for $\cup$, and "not" for '.

Example $(p \text{ and not } q) \text{ or } r \leftrightarrow (P \cap Q') \cup R.$

Explain the correspondences below, where:

$p = x$ is popular; $q = x$ is quiet.

1)   There is an $x \in U$ such that $p \leftrightarrow P \neq \varnothing$.

2)   For all $x \in U$, $q \leftrightarrow Q = U$.

3)   For all $x \in U$, *if p then q* $\leftrightarrow P \subset Q$.

4)   For all $x \in U$, *if p then q and if q then p* $\leftrightarrow P = Q$.

---

* This relationship is described more precisely, but in more technical terms, in Exercise 6 of Exercise List 3–11.

The "if . . . then . . ." language of (3) and (4) is the language of *implication*. Sometimes we use an arrow to replace "if-then." We write:

$$x + 4 = 7 \Rightarrow x = 3 \qquad \text{for} \qquad \text{if } x + 4 = 7, \text{ then } x = 3.$$

We may read $x + 4 = 7 \Rightarrow x = 3$ as "$x + 4 = 7$ *implies* that $x = 3$."

The double-arrow notation

$$x + 4 = 7 \Leftrightarrow x = 3$$

is read:

$x + 4 = 7$ implies $x = 3$ *and* $x = 3$ implies $x + 4 = 7$

or

if $x + 4 = 7$ then $x = 3$, and *conversely*, if $x = 3$ then $x + 4 = 7$

or

$x + 4 = 7$ *if and only if* $x = 3$.

Problem   Relate the discussion of implication above to the following statements of two theorems of plane geometry. What must be proved to establish each theorem?

Theorem 1   A triangle is isosceles *if and only if* it has a pair of congruent angles.

Theorem 2   In any triangle, the greater of two sides subtends the greater angle, and *conversely*, the greater of two angles is subtended by the greater side.

EXERCISES 2–8

1. Explain the notations in the Venn diagram below, where P, Q, are sets associated with the open sentences p, q, respectively.

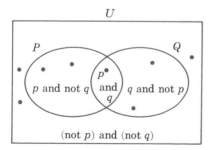

2. Describe each of the four regions pictured in Exercise 1, using P, Q, and the operators $\cup$, $\cap$, $'$.

3. In Exercise 2 you associated each of the four pictured regions with one of the sets

    $P \cap Q'$; $P \cap Q$; $P' \cap Q$; $P' \cap Q'$.

    a) What is the union of all four of these sets?

    b) What can you say about the intersection of any two of these sets?

    c) Express each of the following sets as the union of some of these four sets:

    (1) P (2) Q (3) $P \cup Q$ (4) P' (5) Q' (6) $P' \cup Q'$

4. Each of the six parts of Exercise 3(c) can be translated into an interesting expression involving statements. For example, in (1) we have

    $$P \,=\, (P \cap Q') \cup (P \cap Q),$$

    This statement about sets translates into

    $p \Leftrightarrow (p \text{ and not } q) \text{ or } (p \text{ and } q).$

    This is the assertion that, *whatever statements p and q may be, the complicated statement,* (p *and not* q) *or* (p *and* q), *conveys precisely the same information as does the simple statement* p.
    Make similar interpretations of other parts of Exercise 3(c).

5. The Venn diagram hypothesizes that a certain relationship exists between the set V of all virtuous men and the set H of all honest men. Which statements agree with the diagram?

    a) $H \subset V$

    b) $V \subset H$

    c) $V = H$

    d) If a man is honest, then he is virtuous.

    e) If a man is virtuous, then he is honest.

    f) A man is honest only if he is virtuous.

    g) A man is virtuous only if he is honest.

    h) In order to be virtuous it is necessary to be honest.

    i) In order to be virtuous it is sufficient to be honest.

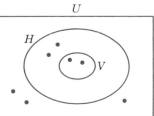

    Which characteristic deserves greater respect: virtue or honesty?

6. a) Draw a Venn diagram for two subsets P, Q of U and shade $(P \cap Q)'$.

    b) Draw a similar Venn diagram and shade $P' \cup Q'$.

    c) Compare (a) and (b) and translate your conclusion into an assertion about the equivalence of certain statements about *popular* and *quiet* people.

    d) Perform the analysis of parts (a) through (c) for $(P \cup Q)'$ and $P' \cap Q'$.

e) Perform the analysis of parts (a) through (c) for $P \cap (Q \cup S)$ and $(P \cap Q) \cup (P \cap S)$ (S denoting the set of studious people).

f) Perform the analysis of parts (a) through (c) for $P \cup (Q \cap S)$ and $(P \cup Q) \cap (P \cup S)$.

We shall now indicate very briefly how the ideas we have developed can be applied. Consider the following "practical" problem:

Jack says: We will win our Friday game *and* we will win our Saturday game.

Jill says: Your statement is false.

Exactly what is Jill asserting?

Jack's statement has the form: p and q.

Jill's statement, the form: not (p and q)

If we pass to set notation,

p and $q \rightarrow P \cap Q$,
not (p and q) $\rightarrow (P \cap Q)'$.

Now inspect a Venn diagram:

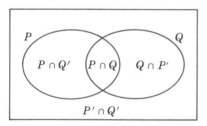

We see that

$$(P \cap Q)' = (P \cap Q') \cup (Q \cap P') \cup (P' \cap Q').$$

We pass back
to statements

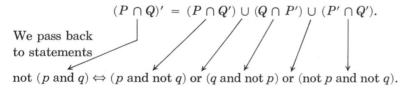

not (p and q) $\Leftrightarrow$ (p and not q) or (q and not p) or (not p and not q).

We see that Jill is saying:

We will win Friday and not win Saturday, *or* win Saturday and not win Friday, *or* will not win either game.

Problem   Show that an acceptable abbreviation of Jill's statement is:

We will not win Friday *or* we will not win Saturday.

EXERCISES 2–9

1. Jill says: "We will go to the dance Saturday night or to the beach Sunday."
   Jack says: "Your statement is false." Precisely what is Jack asserting?

2. Statements which employ *or* can always be rephrased in the if-then
   terminology.

   Examples   You will sit quietly *or* leave the room ⇔ if you do not sit quietly,
   then you will leave the room.

   Translate similarly:

   a) You will wash the supper dishes or stay home from the party.

   b) $x = 2$ or $x = 4$.

   c) Jim is 20 or 21 years old.

   d) p or q.

3. Give if-then statements for 2(b), (c), (d) other than the ones you formulated.

4. Translate the if-then statements below into *or* statements.

   a) If you don't go to bed this minute, then I will whip you.

   b) If I will not pay my rent, then I will be evicted.

   c) If $x \neq 2$, then $x = 4$.

   d) If not p, then q.

   e) If p, then q.

Sometimes we wish to deny (negate) a statement of the type, "All brave men
are honest." Do the statements of (1) below have the same meaning? of (2)?

1)   *Not* all brave men are honest. All brave men are *not* honest.

2)   Not all brave men are honest. There is at least one brave man who is not
     honest.

Use the Venn diagrams below to support your answer.

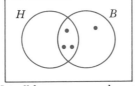
Not all brave men are honest.

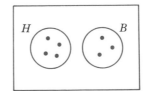
All brave men are dishonest.

Two statements that have the same meaning are said to be *equivalent*.

EXERCISES 2–10

1. Complete the "grammatical" argument begun below that the following statements are not equivalent:

Not all cows are black. All cows are not black.

In the first statement the adverb *not* modifies the adjective *all* . . .

2. Form the negation of each of the following statements:
   a) Every Chinese is short.
   b) Every Frenchman is honest.
   c) One of her cats has no tail.
   d) Someone stole my watch.
   e) All my friends are good and brave.
   f) All his friends are dishonest or stupid.
   g) There exists a number x in A such that $20 < x < 30$.
   h) For all $x \in A$, $20 < x < 30$.

Convenient abbreviations for the phrases "for all" and "there exists" are $\forall$ and $\exists$:

$\forall x \in A, x > 10$ means: For all $x \in A$, $x > 10$.

$\exists x \in A$, such that $x > 10$ means: There exists an $x \in A$ such that $x > 10$.

Symbols $\not\forall$ and $\not\exists$ have the expected meaning:

$\not\forall x \in A, x > 20$ means: It is not true that all elements of A are greater than 20.

$\not\exists x \in A$ such that $x > 20$ means: There is no element of A greater than 20.

EXERCISES 2–11

Translate the following statements into ordinary language.   Decide whether each statement is true or false.

1. U is the set of all lines in the plane. A line is considered to be parallel to itself.
   a) $\forall x, y \in U, x \perp y \Rightarrow y \perp x$.
   b) $\forall x, y, z \in U, x \parallel y$ and $y \parallel z \Rightarrow x \parallel z$.
   c) $\forall x, y, z \in U, x \parallel y$ and $z \perp y \Rightarrow x \perp z$.
   d) $\forall x, y, z \in U, x \parallel y$ and $y \not\parallel z \Rightarrow x \not\parallel z$.

2. *W, E, O* are the sets of whole numbers, even numbers, and odd numbers, respectively.

   a) $\forall x \in W,\ x \in E$ or $x \in O$.

   b) $\exists x \in E$ such that x is a prime number.

   c) $\forall x, y \in E,\ x + y \in E$ and $x \cdot y \in E$.

   d) $\forall x, y \in O,\ x + y \in O$ and $x \cdot y \in O$.

   e) $\forall x \in E,\ \forall y \in O,\ x + y \in O$ and $x \cdot y \in E$.

   f) $\forall x \in O,\ x^2 + x + 1 \in O$.

   g) $\forall x \in E$, if $x > 4$, then $\exists y, z \in O$ such that $x = y + z$ and both y and z are prime numbers.

2–6 functions

The idea of a function is very simple. Functions are mental constructs. Whenever you consider an object and mentally associate it with some second object, you have formed a function. You may associate people with their names, their telephone numbers, or their addresses. In each case you are forming a function. In order to read aloud one must learn a function: the function that associates each written word with a sound. When a secretary takes dictation, she uses this function in reverse, passing back from sounds to written symbols.

If we associate *each* element of a set *X* with *exactly one* element of a set *Y*, then we say that we have constructed a function *from X into Y*. The diagram below pictures a function from a set of children into a set of women. Each child is matched with his mother. Explain the diagram.

Example

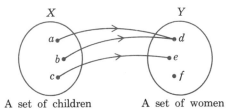

A set of children   A set of women

y is the mother of x

Any such matching is called a *function*.

Problem   Which children are siblings? Which woman has no child in *X*? two children in *X*?

The phrases "each" and "exactly one" are crucial for the function concept. The "each" tells us that set Y contains the mothers of all the children in X (and perhaps other women as well). The "exactly one" reflects the fact that each child has a *unique* mother. In contrast to this example, the diagram below shows that the relationship described by

y is a brother of x

is not a function for the pictured sets.

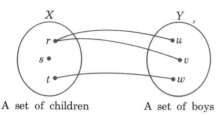

A set of children   A set of boys
            y is a brother of *x*

The *exactly one* breaks down. (Why?) The *each* breaks down also. (Why?)
    Use of *the* in "the mother of" implies uniqueness. Use of *a* in "a brother of" leaves the matter of uniqueness open. In general, phrases of the form

"the . . . of . . ."

refer to functions. Examples are:

the square *of* a number
the union *of* a pair of sets
the ratio *of* a first number to a second
the melting point *of* a solid

    Referring to the example at the beginning of the section, the set X is called the *domain* of the function. The subset of Y consisting of those elements paired with some $x \in X$ is called the *range* of the function.

EXERCISES 2–12

1. What elements are in the domain of the function pictured at the beginning of this section? List the elements in the range of this function.
2. The domain of a function f consists of the numbers 2, 4, 6, 8. The function adds 3 to each number. What elements belong to the range of f?
3. The range of a function g consists of 5, 10, 15, 20, 25. The function multiplies each number in its domain by 5. What numbers are in the domain of g?

4. Domain $f = \{1, 2, 3, 4\}$ and f assigns to each x in its domain the number $2x + 3$. List the elements of the range of f and draw an arrow diagram for this function.

5. The function f assigns to each x in its domain the number $3x - 1$, and the range of $f = \{2, 8, 14, 20\}$. List the elements in the domain of f and draw an arrow diagram.

6. Each phrase below suggests a function f. In each case describe a "reasonable" domain and range for f and call attention to any interesting properties of the function. In some cases it may be impossible to describe the range of f precisely.

   Example   *The* age in years *of* a person.

   It is reasonable to choose for domain f the set of all living persons. Then range f is some subset of W. We can be reasonably sure that the range of f is a subset of $\{x \in W \mid x \leq 130\}$, but even if we knew that the oldest person was 130 we still could not be sure that

   $$\text{range } f = \{x \in W \mid x \leq 130\}. \qquad \text{(Why?)}$$

   a) *The* weight to the nearest ton *of* a whale
   b) *The* cost in cents *of* postage for an air-mail letter in the United States
   c) *The* midpoint *of* a line segment
   d) *The* circle *of* (through) three points
   e) *The* father *of the* mother *of* a man
   f) *The* square *of the* double *of* a number

7. Explain how parts (e) and (f) of Exercise 6 indicate that one function can be constructed from two functions. Draw an arrow diagram for 6(e) to illustrate this concept.

We introduce more abbreviating notation. We write

$$f: A \rightarrow B \qquad \text{or} \qquad A \xrightarrow{f} B$$

and say "f is a function *from* A *into* B" or "f maps A *into* B." Note that this notation does three things.

   i) It establishes a name for the function, namely "f."
   ii) It establishes the domain of f, A.
   iii) It assures us that range $f \subset B$.

We use the language "f of x" just as we say "age of x," "weight of x," "square of x," etc. For example, if $f: W \rightarrow W$ and f is the *doubling* function, then we say

"f of 4 is 8"   and write   "$f(4) = 8$."

Other notation is used:

$$f: 4 \rightarrow 8; \qquad 4 \xrightarrow{f} 8.$$

We also say "*f maps* 4 *upon* 8." Note that if $f: X \to Y$, then for each $x \in X$, $f(x) \in Y$.

Some functions can be described by simple formulas. For example, the two statements:

$f: W \to W;$ $\forall x \in W, f(x) = 2x$ describe the function f completely.

EXERCISES 2–13

1. Let $A = \{1, 2, 3, 4,\}$, $B = W$, $f: A \to B$, $\forall x \in A$, $f(x) = 2x + 1$. Compute $f(1)$, $f(2)$, $f(3)$ and $f(4)$.

2. Let $A = \{1, 2, 3\}$, $B = \{3, 4, 5, 6, 7, 8, 9\}$. Describe, by a formula, a function $f: A \to B$ and list all elements of the range of f.

3. The diagram below suggests a function $f: W \to W$. Suggest a simple formula for $f(x)$.

$$W = \{0, 1, 2, 3, 4, 5, 6, 7, 8, 9, 10, 11, \ldots\}$$
$$f: W = \{0, 1, 2, 3, 4, 5, \ldots\}$$

Using your formula for $f(x)$, compute: (a) $f(10)$, (b) $f(43)$, (c) x, if $f(x) = 67$.

4. The table suggests a function $f: X \to Y$, where X is a set of students and Y a set of whole numbers. Suggest a possible interpretation for $f(x)$.

$f: X \to Y$	
x	$f(x)$
John	72
Joe	71
Mike	70
Tim	69
Pete	72

5. Given a function $f: A \to B$, define the range of f using set-builder notation.

The diagram below presents the same information as the table of Exercise 4. We interpret f as a height function: $f(x)$ = the height of x to the nearest inch.

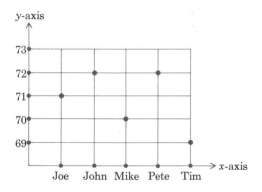

This is the type of diagram most people have in mind when they speak of the *graph* of a function. In general, any kind of a pictorial representation of a function can be called a graph. Sometimes the term "graph" is used in a narrow sense to refer to the points plotted on a diagram such as this one. In this sense the above graph consists of just 5 points.

Because the above representation of functions is so important, we analyze it with some care. Let f be a function from a set X into a set Y: $f\colon X \to Y$. The elements of X = domain f are represented by points on a horizontal line called the X-axis, and those of Y are pictured on a vertical line called the Y-axis. Of course, if we use the notation $f\colon A \to B$, we speak of A-axis and B-axis, but the X, Y notation is traditional.

Now consider the grid consisting of all vertical lines through the X-points and horizontal lines through the Y-points. In our example we have 5 of each. Each intersection point P connects an $x \in X$ and a $y \in Y$ in an obvious manner. Marking a dot at P indicates that this x and y are paired.

▶ *Aside*. It is interesting to note that this single technique for "graphing" a function utilizes 4 separate functions. Our sketch below illustrates this fact.

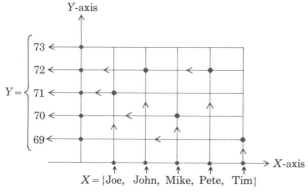

The arrow diagrams describe the four functions that comprise this graphical representation.

1) A function which matches each element of X with a point on the X-axis.
2) A function which matches each X-point with a point at the intersection of two grid lines.
3) A function which matches each of the points obtained in (2) with one of the Y-points.
4) A function which matches each of the Y-points obtained in (3) with an element of set Y.

If you will look back at the earlier graph of this function in which we did not draw the arrows, you will realize that you really use all 4 of these functions. For example, in order to determine Joe's height you *first* locate the point on the X-axis matched with Joe. *Second*, you look up and locate the grid point matched with this point. *Third,* you look over to the X-axis and locate the Y-point matched with this grid point. *Fourth,* you observe the element of Y matched with this Y-point, in this case the whole number 71.

It is amusing that in order to describe one function we rely on four! But this fact only emphasizes the simplicity and pervasiveness of the function concept. You apply these four functions and pull information from the graph in approximately a second. In our society we use function concepts automatically, without being conscious of so doing. When you begin to analyze the ways in which mathematical ideas are abstracted from the real world, you will see the basic role played by function concepts. ◀

We need a bit more terminology. A function from a set X *into* a set Y may also be *onto* Y.

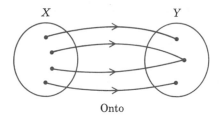   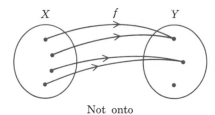

Onto   Not onto

$f: X \xrightarrow{\text{onto}} Y$ means that $\forall y \in Y \exists x \in X$ such that $f(x) = y$.

Less pretentiously, range $f = Y$. Colloquially, we say that every element of Y is "used."

Some functions are one-to-one (1–1).

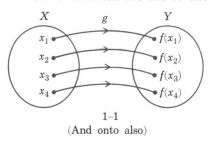   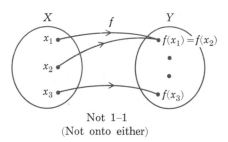

1–1   Not 1–1
(And onto also)   (Not onto either)

$f: X \xrightarrow{1-1} Y$ means that $\forall x_1, x_2 \in X, x_1 \neq x_2 \Rightarrow f(x_1) \neq f(x_2)$.

Colloquially, we say that different elements have different images.

Those functions which are both 1–1 and onto are the most important ones that we shall employ in our analysis of arithmetic. Such functions are called *one-to-one correspondences.*

If $f: X \xrightarrow[\text{onto}]{1-1} Y$, then f is a 1–1 correspondence.

EXERCISES 2–14

1. Sketch an arrow diagram showing:

   a) a function neither 1–1 nor onto   b) a function 1–1 but not onto

   c) a function onto but not 1–1   d) a function 1–1 and onto

2. Without counting, but using the idea of 1–1 correspondence, find out whether you have the same number of fingers on each hand. Bend down one thumb and try the same experiment.

3. A large crowd enters an auditorium. We know neither the number in the crowd nor the number of seats. How can we decide without counting, but using the idea of 1–1 correspondence, whether there are more people than seats?

4. Set X has 10 elements. $f: X \to Y$. What can be said about the number of elements in Y if:

   a) f is 1–1 but not onto   b) f is onto but not 1–1

   c) f is 1–1 and onto   d) f is neither 1–1 nor onto

5. Explain why the function $f: W \to W$ which maps each $x \in W$ upon $x + 3$ is

   a) 1–1   b) not onto.

6. Let E be the set of even whole numbers. $E = \{0, 2, 4, \ldots\}$, $f: W \to E$, $f(x) = 2x$. Explain why

   $$f: W \xrightarrow[\text{onto}]{1-1} E.$$

7. Use the result of Exercise 6 and show that it is reasonable to say that there are *just as many* even numbers as there are whole numbers.

8. The symbol $\sqrt{9}$ exemplifies function notation. Note that:

   a) $\sqrt{}$ names the *square-root function.*

   b) 9 names the *number* that the function $\sqrt{}$ operates on.

   c) $\sqrt{9}$ names the number that results when the function $\sqrt{}$ operates on 9.

   In general, when we use $f(x)$ notation, f names a function; x names an element in the domain of f; $f(x)$ names the element in the range of f which is matched with x. In each example below, identify a symbol that names a function.

   a) $\sqrt[3]{8}, \sqrt[3]{5}$ b) $|-4|, |23|$

   c) $5^2, 3^2$ d) $-(5), -(-4)$

   e) $\log_{10} 100, \log_{10} 1000$ f) $\sin 30^0, \sin 90^0$

9. We use function notation in geometry. For example, let A, B, C name the points pictured at the right. Then you are probably familiar with the use of the symbol $\overleftrightarrow{AB}$ to denote the *line* which contains A and B. Note the following facts.

1) The symbol $\leftrightarrow$ names a function.

2) The symbol AB names the pair of points on which the function operates.

3) The symbol $\overleftrightarrow{AB}$ names the line that the function $\leftrightarrow$ matches with the points A and B.

Explain similarly the function concepts associated with each of the following symbols:

a) $\overline{AB}$ b) $\overrightarrow{AB}$ c) $\angle ABC$ d) $\triangle ABC$

e) $\triangle ACB$ f) $\angle ACB$ g) $\overline{BA}$ h) $\overrightarrow{BA}$

10. The graph presents the population of a country in millions as a function of the time. Read off from the graph the approximate populations in the following years:

   a) 1880   b) 1920   c) 1960.

In each case note that you are actually employing the four functions mentioned earlier.

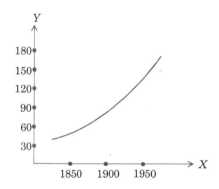

11. Explain why the graph below does not describe a function from X into Y but does describe a function from Y into X.

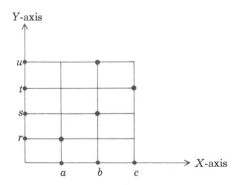

If $f: X \xrightarrow[\text{onto}]{1-1} Y$, then if one reverses the arrows in the arrow diagram for f one has pictured a second function from Y to X which is also 1–1 and onto. For example, let $X = \{1, 2, 3, 4\}$, $Y = \{2, 4, 6, 8\}$ and $f(x) = 2x$.

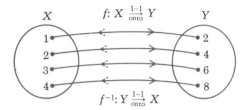

Each of these functions is said to be the *inverse* of the other. We denote the inverse of a function f by f^{-1} (read "f inverse"):

$$\forall x \in X, f(x) = 2x; \qquad \forall y \in Y, f^{-1}(y) = \tfrac{1}{2}y.$$

Note that $(f^{-1})^{-1} = f$.

EXERCISES 2–15

1. You know the numbers of the players on a basketball team. Someone asks you for the number of a particular player. Later he asks which player has a particular number. Identify functions f and f^{-1}.

2. A seating chart assigns a seat to each student. A parent comes to school and asks which is his child's desk. Later you observe a very untidy desk and use the chart to decide who sits at that desk. Identify functions f and f^{-1} which are being used.

3. Counting forward is a function that assigns to each whole number a next number:

   $$0 \xrightarrow{C} 1 \xrightarrow{C} 2 \xrightarrow{C} 3 \xrightarrow{C} 4 \xrightarrow{C} \ldots$$

   Counting backward is the inverse of this function:

   $$0 \xleftarrow{C^{-1}} 1 \xleftarrow{C^{-1}} 2 \xleftarrow{C^{-1}} 3 \xleftarrow{C^{-1}} 4 \xleftarrow{C^{-1}} .$$

   What is the domain of C? of C^{-1}?

4. In an example similar to 3 relate the concept of a function f and its inverse f^{-1} to reciting the alphabet.

5. Each function below has an inverse if set X (domain) and Y (range) are properly chosen. Give a formula for the inverse function:

   a) $f(x) = x + 3$; $f^{-1}(y) =$

   b) $g(x) = 3x$; $g^{-1}(y) =$

   c) $h(x) = 2x + 1$; $h^{-1}(y) =$

d) $F(x) = x^2$; $F^{-1}(y) =$

e) $G(x) = x^2 + 5$; $G^{-1}(y) =$

6. In Exercise 5(a), if one chooses domain $f = W$, then

range f = domain f^{-1} = {3, 4, 5, 6, ...} = $\{y \in W \mid y > 2\}$.

Assuming that for each of the functions g and h in parts (b) and (c) the domain is W, give the domains of g^{-1} and h^{-1}.

Phrases like, "the father of the mother of" and "the double of the square of" show that we often apply functions successively. The following diagrams suggest that you can think of the successive application of two functions as a single function.

$$A \xrightarrow{f} B \xrightarrow{m} C; \qquad A \xrightarrow{m} B \xrightarrow{f} C.$$

$$\underbrace{\phantom{A \xrightarrow{f} B \xrightarrow{m}}}_{g} \qquad \underbrace{\phantom{A \xrightarrow{m} B \xrightarrow{f}}}_{h}$$

If we interpret f as the function which matches each person with his father, m the corresponding mother function, then what common names are assigned to the functions g and h?

We say that g is the *composite* of f and m. Note that this language indicates that we obtain g by first applying f and then m. The composite of m and f, as you have already observed, is an altogether different function. We write the composite of f and m above as $m \circ f$ rather than $f \circ m$, for when we write

$$m \circ f(x)$$

we mean that first the father of x is computed and then the mother of the father of x:

$$m \circ f(x) = m(f(x)).$$

Hence, in the illustration above, we would write g as $m \circ f$ and h as $f \circ m$.

An example of composition of functions is diagrammed below.

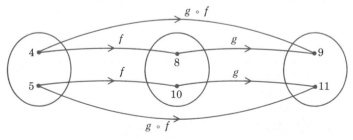

$f(4) = 8; \; g(8) = 9; \; g \circ f(4) = g(f(4)) = 9$

$f(5) = 10; \; g(10) = 11; \; g \circ f(5) = g(f(5)) = 11$

EXERCISES 2–16

1. A teacher plays a game with a third-grade class. She says, "I will name a number. You are to add 3 to the number I give you and then add 7 more and give the answer."

   a) What answers should be given for 2, 3, 5, 7, respectively?

   b) How would some children abbreviate the work by *composing* the two, functions they were asked to use?

   c) Suppose that the rules are changed to: "Double the number and then add 3." What answers should be given for 2, 3, 5, 7?

   d) Reverse the functions of (c), first adding 3 and then doubling. What answers should be given for 2, 3, 5, 7?

2. Solve the problems below, relating them to classroom situations, as in Exercise 1.

   a) $f(x) = 2x; g(x) = 5x; f \circ g(x) = $ _____; $g \circ f(x) = $ _____

   b) $f(x) = x + 8; g(x) = x + 12; f \circ g(x) = $ _____; $g \circ f(x) = $ _____

   c) $f(x) = 2x; g(x) = x + 5; f \circ g(x) = $ _____; $g \circ f(x) = $ _____

3. Let f, g be functions from W into W; $f(x) = 2x + 3; g(x) = 3x + 1$. Compute formulas for $(f \circ g)(x)$ and $(g \circ f)(x)$.

4. Let $A_0, A_1, A_2, \ldots$ denote the functions from W into W which add $0, 1, 2, \ldots$, respectively, and let $M_0, M_1, M_2, \ldots$ be corresponding multiplication functions. Verify the following statements.

   a) $\forall x \in W, (A_2 \circ A_4)(x) = (A_4 \circ A_2)(x) = A_6(x)$

   b) $\forall x \in W, (A_9 \circ M_3)(x) = (M_3 \circ A_3)(x)$

   c) $\forall x, y \in W, (A_y \circ M_1)(x) = (M_1 \circ A_y)(x)$

5. Solve each equation for x.

   a) $A_3(x) = 7$ b) $M_2(x) = 10$ c) $(A_3 \circ M_2)(x) = 13$

   d) $(M_3 \circ A_4)(x) = 21$ e) $(A_2 \circ M_3 \circ A_4 \circ M_2)(x) = 32$

6. Relate Exercise 5(c) to the equation $2x + 3 = 13$. What are the corresponding equations for 5(d) and 5(e)?

7. Write each of the following equations in the style of Exercise 5.

   a) $3x + 6 = 21$ b) $3(x + 6) = 21$

   c) $3(x + 6) + 4 = 24$

8. Explain the symbolism used below and show how each solution of a problem is related to the techniques you used in school algebra. Composition circles are omitted to simplify the notation.

   a) $M_2(x) = 14 \Rightarrow D_2 M_2(x) = D_2(14) \Rightarrow x = 7$

   b) $M_2 A_3(x) = 14 \Rightarrow S_3 D_2 M_2 A_3(x) = S_3 D_2(14) \Rightarrow x = 4$

   c) $M_3 A_4 M_2(x) = 42 \Rightarrow D_2 S_4 D_3 M_3 A_4 M_2(x) = D_2 S_4 D_3(42) \Rightarrow x = 5$

9. Give the inverse of each function.

    a) A_5 b) M_7 c) $A_2 M_5$

    d) $M_5 A_2$ e) $M_2 A_5 M_3$

10. Suppose that $f: S \xrightarrow{1-1} T$ and $g: T \xrightarrow{1-1} U$. Is $g \circ f$ a 1–1 function from S to U?

11. Suppose that the f and g of Exercise 10 are onto. Must $g \circ f$ be onto U?

12. Suppose that f is a 1–1, onto function from a set X to a set Y. Describe the domain, range, and any interesting properties of:

    a) the function $f^{-1} \circ f$ b) the function $f \circ f^{-1}$.

Equivalent sets. If A and B are sets and there is a function $f: A \xrightarrow[\text{onto}]{1-1} B$, then we say that A is *equivalent** to B. When this is the case we say that sets A and B "have the same cardinal number." Note that this is *not* a definition of what a cardinal number is. It only tells us what it means to say that two sets have the *same number*. But we do not yet know what *numbers* are. It is not important that we know. We remind you that you probably do not know what *color* is. What is important is that you be able to tell when two things have the *same color*. (The interested reader can find definitions of ordinal and cardinal numbers in the book, *Naive Set Theory*, Paul Halmos, Van Nostrand, Princeton, New Jersey, 1961.)

    You will think of equivalent sets as sets having the same number of elements, but you should remember that the formal definition of equivalence of sets involves the concept of one-to-one correspondence.

    Observe that equivalence of sets is reflexive, symmetric, and transitive.

Ref.   For every set A, A is equivalent to A. That is, there is a function f such that $f: A \xrightarrow[\text{onto}]{1-1} A$. (Describe such an f.)

Sym.   If A is equivalent to B, then B is equivalent to A. For:

If $f: A \xrightarrow[\text{onto}]{1-1} B$, then $f^{-1}: B \xrightarrow[\text{onto}]{1-1} A$.

Tran.   If A is equivalent to B and B is equivalent to C, then A is equivalent to C. For:

If $f: A \xrightarrow[\text{onto}]{1-1} B$ and $g: B \xrightarrow[\text{onto}]{1-1} C$, then $(g \circ f): A \xrightarrow[\text{onto}]{1-1} C$.

---

* This usage of the word "equivalent" is different from that of page 26. Equivalent is a popular word among mathematicians and will be used in still another sense later (page 46). You will have to rely on context to decide how the word is being used. The term "equipollent" is also used to describe sets connected by a one-to-one, onto function.

EXERCISES 2–17

1. Two 1–1, onto functions from a set A to a set B are pictured below. Give a formula for each function.

   $A = \{1, \quad 2, \quad 3, \quad 4\}$ $A = \{1, \quad 2, \quad 3, \quad 4\}$
   $f: \quad \downarrow \quad \downarrow \quad \downarrow \quad \downarrow$ $g:$
   $B = \{5, \quad 6, \quad 7, \quad 8\}$ $B = \{5, \quad 6, \quad 7, \quad 8\}$

   a) $f(x) =$ _____   b) $g(x) =$ _____

2. $A = \{x \in W \mid 99 < x < 200\}; B = \{x \in W \mid x < 100\}$

   a) Give a formula for $f(x)$ such that $f: A \xrightarrow[\text{onto}]{1\text{-}1} B$.

   b) Give a formula for $g(x)$ such that $g: B \xrightarrow[\text{onto}]{1\text{-}1} A$.

3. A and B are the sets of Exercise 2. $C = \{x \in W \mid x < 200 \text{ and } x \text{ is even}\}$.

   a) Give a formula for $k(x)$ such that $k: B \xrightarrow[\text{onto}]{1\text{-}1} C$

   b) Give a formula for $F(x)$ such that $F: A \xrightarrow[\text{onto}]{1\text{-}1} C$

   c) Give a formula for $G(x)$ such that $G: C \xrightarrow[\text{onto}]{1\text{-}1} B$

   d) Give a formula for $H(x)$ such that $H: C \xrightarrow[\text{onto}]{1\text{-}1} A$

   e) Give a formula for $h(x)$ such that $h: A \xrightarrow[\text{onto}]{1\text{-}1} A$

One final topic remains in our study of functions. Perhaps you have noticed that no formal definition of *function* has been formulated. It is not necessary that a definition be made, but it seems aesthetically pleasing to do so. (See Exercise 8 following.) Functions are defined as special kinds of sets. We are led to the definition by considering a special kind of representation of a function.
   Consider

$$f: A \xrightarrow[\text{onto}]{1\text{-}1} B,$$

where

$$A = \{1, 2, 3, 4\}, \quad B = \{2, 4, 6, 8\}, \quad \text{and} \quad f(x) = 2x, x \in A.$$

The symbol $\{(1, 2), (2, 4), (3, 6), (4, 8)\}$ is a good *name* for f, in the sense that we can extract from this symbol all significant information about f, namely, range f, domain f, and the formula, $f(x) = 2x$. Each of the symbols $(1, 2)$, $(2, 4)$, $(3, 6)$, $(4, 8)$ names an *ordered pair*. The function f is simply considered to be this set of ordered pairs.

$$f = \{(1, 2), (2, 4), (3, 6), (4, 8)\}.$$

Problem   Explain how one extracts from this symbol for f, domain f, range f, and the formula, $f(x) = 2x$.

Note that the ordered pair $(1, 2)$ is not the same as the set $\{1, 2\}$.

$\{1, 2\} = \{2, 1\}$; a set has no *first* element.

$(1, 2) \neq (2, 1)$; 1 is the first *component* of $(1, 2)$ while 2 is the first *component* of $(2, 1)$.

You used ordered pairs in your school algebra in graphing.

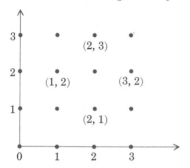

If you have read the above discussion carefully you will have noted that we have given no definition of ordered pairs. A definition can be formulated in terms of the notion of set (Halmos, page 23), but we shall take *ordered pair* as a primitive, undefined concept. All you need to know is that

$(a, b) = (c, d) \Leftrightarrow a = c$ and $b = d$.

The concept of an ordered pair leads us to introduce a new operation on sets, which we call forming the *cartesian product*. If A, B are any sets, then:

The cartesian product of A and B, written $A \times B$, is the set of all ordered pairs (a, b) such that $a \in A$ and $b \in B$.

Example $A = \{1, 2, 3\}$, $B = \{m, n\}$.

$A \times B = \{(1, m), (1, n), (2, m), (2, n), (3, m), (3, n)\}$.

Schematically, we have the following.

	B	
	m	n
1	$(1, m)$	$(1, n)$
A 2	$(2, m)$	$(2, n)$
3	$(3, m)$	$(3, n)$

or

n $(1, n)$ $(2, n)$ $(3, n)$
m $(1, m)$ $(2, m)$ $(3, m)$
　　　1　　　2　　　3

$B \times A = \{(m, 1), (m, 2), (m, 3), (n, 1), (n, 2), (n, 3)\}$.

Note that generally $A \times B \neq B \times A$. There is, however, a "natural" function f such that

$$f: A \times B \xrightarrow[\text{onto}]{\text{1-1}} B \times A.$$

Problem   Give a formula for $f((x, y))$ where $(x, y) \in A \times B$.

You have probably observed that the set operation, union of sets, is connected with the arithmetic operation, addition of numbers. Make a conjecture concerning the cartesian product operation. With what operation of arithmetic might complementation of sets be associated?

EXERCISES 2–18

1. Set A has 5 elements and set B has 6. How many elements has
   a) $A \times A$,   b) $A \times B$,   c) $B \times A$,   d) $B \times B$?

2. $A = \{1, 3, 5\}$, $B = \{1, 2, 4\}$. List elements of
   a) $A \times B$,   b) $B \times A$,   c) $A \times A$,   d) $B \times B$.

3. Let $A = \{1, 2, 3, 4\}$. $f = \{(x, y) \in A \times A \mid y = x + 1\}$.
   a) List elements of f.   b) Show that f is a function.
   c) Give domain f and range f.

4. Give domain f and range f for $f = \{(1, 7), (3, 5), (5, 3), (7, 1)\}$.

5. Prove that the set $\{(1, 2), (2, 3), (1, 3)\}$ is not a function.

6. Explain how to decide whether a given set of ordered pairs is a function. To what visual property of the graph of the set of ordered pairs does this correspond?

7. Each set of ordered pairs below is a function $f: W \rightarrow W$. Suggest a formula for $f(x)$.
   a) $\{(1, 8), (2, 11), (3, 14), (4, 17), \ldots\}$
   b) $\{(1, 2), (2, 3), (3, 5), (4, 7), (5, 11), (6, 13), (7, 17), (8, 19), \ldots\}$
   c) $\{(1, 2), (2, 5), (3, 10), (4, 17), (5, 26), (6, 37), \ldots\}$
   d) $\{(1, 1), (2, 3), (3, 6), (4, 10), (5, 15), (6, 21), \ldots\}$
   e) $\{(1, 1), (2, 2), (3, 6), (4, 24), (5, 120), (6, 720), \ldots\}$
   f) $\{(1, 1), (2, 4), (3, 27), (4, 256), (5, 3125), \ldots\}$

8. Complete the following formal definition: A function f from a set A to a set B is a subset of $A \times B$ such that . . . .

2–7   Relations

The concept of a *relation* is more general than that of a *function*. In order to have
a function *f*, one must associate with *each* element of a set *A* *exactly one* element
of a set *B*. For relations we relax both these requirements. Sometimes we use the
language of functions and speak of a relation from *A* into *B*, but the more usual
language is simply to speak of a relation *in* a set *S*. The following diagram
illustrates this.

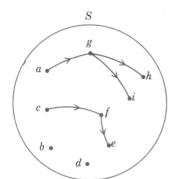

A graph of the *relation* *R*;
y is a child of *x*, *in* the set *S*.

Problem   Describe the relationship between *a* and *h*. Explain how this diagram illustrates that the "each" and "exactly one" conditions are dropped for
relations. We can think of the relation *R* pictured above as a set of ordered
pairs

$$R = \{(a, g), (g, h), (g, i), (c, f), (f, e)\}.$$

The "domain," "range" terminology is used for relations

$$\text{domain } R = \{a, g, c, f\}; \qquad \text{range } R = \{g, h, i, f, e\}.$$

Observe that *R* is a subset of $S \times S$:

$$R = \{(x, y) \in S \times S \mid y \text{ is a child of } x\}.$$

Most relations arise from contemplation of some set. One observes "relationships" between certain elements of a set *S* and is led to contemplate all the
ordered pairs in $S \times S$ that exemplify this relationship. Conversely, we may
begin with any set *S*, form the cartesian product $S \times S$, and then view each
subset of $S \times S$ as a *relation in S*.

The most common graphical representation of a relation utilizes coordinate
axes. The elements of *S* are matched both with points on a horizontal line and
points on a vertical line. One point in the plane of the lines, then, can represent
an ordered pair, and the relation is pictured as an array of dots. For convenience

we still refer to the horizontal axis as the X-axis and the vertical axis as the Y-axis.

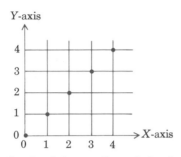

Graph of the equality relation in $\{0, 1, 2, 3, 4\}$, $x = y$. (This relation is a function.)

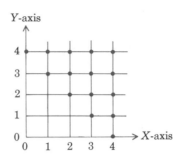

Graph of the "inequality" $x + y > 3$. This is not a function.

EXERCISES 2–19

1. Enumerate the ordered pairs in the relation R, described by

   $R = \{(x, y) \in S \times S \mid x < y\}$, where $S = \{1, 2, 3, 4\}$.

   a) What is domain R?   b) What is range R?

2. Repeat Exercise 1 for the relation defined by $y < x$. Observe that the domain of this relation is not the same as that of the relation of Exercise 1.

3. Graph the relations of Exercises 1 and 2.

4. With S as in Exercise 1, list all elements of the following:

   a) $R_1 = \{(x, y) \in S \times S \mid x = y + 1 \text{ or } y = x + 1\}$

   b) $R_2 = \{(x, y) \in S \times S \mid x = y - 1 \text{ or } y = x - 1\}$

   c) $R_3 = \{(x, y) \in S \times S \mid x = y^2 \text{ or } y = x^2\}$

   d) $R_4 = \{(x, y) \in S \times S \mid y + 3 > x^2 - 1\}$

5. Use the fact that a set of n elements includes 2^n subsets and show that:

   a) there are exactly 16 relations in a 2-element set,

   b) there are exactly 512 relations in a 3-element set,

   c) there are more than 1,000,000 relations in a 5-element set.

As Exercise 5 suggests, there are too many relations in each large set for us to examine them all carefully. We content ourselves with a look at two special categories, *order* relations and *equivalence* relations. One of the crucial attributes of order relations is *transitivity*. A relation is transitive if, whenever a first element is related to a second and the second to a third, the first is related to the third.

If Joe is taller than Bill and Bill is taller than Sue, then Joe is taller than Sue. "Is taller than" is a transitive relation. We do not permit "circularity" in an order relation. In the rock-scissors-paper game rock breaks scissors, scissors cut paper, and paper covers rock. These conditions do *not* describe an order relation in the set {rock, scissors, paper}. It would be difficult to rank three tennis players *a*, *b*, *c*, if *a* won from *b* regularly, *b* from *c*, and *c* from *a*.

Arrow diagrams for the two order relations, "less than" and "less than or equal to" in the set $S = \{1, 2, 3, 4\}$ are pictured below.

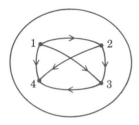   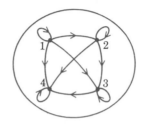

A graph of the order relation

$R_1 = \{(x, y) \in S \times S \mid x < y\}$

R_1 is transitive

R_1 is *not* reflexive

A graph of the order relation

$R_2 = \{(x, y) \in S \times S \mid x \leq y\}$

R_2 is transitive

R_2 is reflexive (as indicated by the loops at all points)

Precise definitions of transitivity and reflexivity are as follows:

A relation R in a set S is

transitive if $\forall x, y, z \in S$, $(x, y) \in R$ and $(y, z) \in R \Rightarrow (x, z) \in R$, and

reflexive if $\forall x \in S$, $(x, x) \in R$.

The relations $<$ and $\leq$ in the set $S = \{1, 2, 3, 4\}$ are examples of *total* order relations in the sense that any two elements of S are related; that is, $\forall x, y \in S$ either (x, y) or $(y, x) \in R$. The use of the word "total" suggests that there may be *partial* order relations. There are. One is pictured here. The dots represent cities on the banks of a navigable river and its tributaries. $S = \{a, b, c, d, e\}$.

$R = \{(x, y) \in S \times S \mid$ one can float on a raft *from x to y*$\}$.

Note that we can find two cities such that it is impossible to float from either city to the other. Only "part" of the pairs of cities are in this relation.

EXERCISES 2–20

1. Let R be the relation of the above example.

   a) Agreeing that for each $x \in S$ we can float from x to x, list the ordered pairs in R.

   b) Is R a transitive relation?

   c) Is R a reflexive relation?

   d) Explain why we call R a *partial* order and say that it is not a *total* order.

2. Give an everyday example of (a) a total order, (b) a partial (not total) order.

3. Explain why the relation "is a brother of" in a family of 2 boys is not transitive. (Use an arrow diagram.)

4. If R is a transitive relation, what can you conclude if you know

   a) $(a, d) \in R$ and $(d, c) \in R$?   b) $(a, d) \in R$ and $(d, a) \in R$?

Each equivalence relation is *reflexive* and *transitive*. It also has the property of *symmetry*.

R is *symmetric* if $(x, y) \in R \Rightarrow (y, x) \in R$.

Problem Show that, in general, in a set of people, the relation of being a sister is not a symmetric relation, but that in any set of girls this relation is symmetric.

Earlier we noted that equality is a reflexive, symmetric, transitive relation. The abbreviation "rst-relation" is often used for equivalence relations. The following arrow diagrams reemphasize the meaning of reflexivity, symmetry, and transitivity.

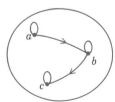   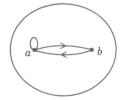

R *is* ref (Why?) R is *not* ref (Why?) R is *not* ref (Why?)
R is *not* tran (Why?) R *is* tran (Why?) R is *not* tran (Why?)
R is *not* sym (Why?) R is *not* sym (Why?) R *is* sym (Why?)

The important characteristic of equivalence relations in a set S is that each relation splits S into mutually disjoint subsets. For example, if we use the word "age" as it is used when we fill out official forms, then in any set S of people, the relation "is the same age as" is an equivalence relation.

$R = \{(x, y) \in S \times S \mid x \text{ is the same age as } y\}.$

We observe, concerning R, that

$\forall x \in S, (x, x) \in R$; ref.
$\forall x, y \in S, (x, y) \in R \Rightarrow (y, x) \in R$; sym.
$\forall x, y, z \in S, (x, y) \in R \text{ and } (y, z) \in R \Rightarrow (x, z) \in R$; tran.

Now it is natural to think of the disjoint sets of people who are 0 years old, 1 year old, 2 years old, ... An important *function* comes to our attention in every situation in which we consider an equivalence relation. We associate with each element $x \in S$ the set of all elements in S that are related to x. (Describe the domain and range of this function.) Traditionally these sets are called *equivalence classes*.

The arrow diagram below pictures how an equivalence relation partitions a set into subsets. Interpret this relation as "x is a friend to y."

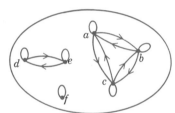

A graph of $R =$
$\{(x, y) \in S \times S \mid x \text{ is a friend to } y\}$

EXERCISES 2–21

1. R is the relation pictured above.
   a) Verify that R is an rst-relation.
   b) How many equivalence classes does R determine?
   c) Denote the equivalence classes associated with $a, b, \ldots$ by $R_a, R_b, \ldots$
   Then

   $R_a = \{y \in S \mid (a, y) \in R\}; \qquad R_b = \{y \in S \mid (b, y) \in R\}; \ldots$

   Verify that

   $R_a = R_b; \qquad R_d = R_e; \qquad R_f \cap R_d = \varnothing.$

2. In the set of whole numbers W, the relation R described by "x has the same remainder when divided by 2 as y has" is an equivalence relation.

   a) How many equivalence classes does R determine?

   b) What common names are assigned to these classes?

   c) What equivalence class does R_3 represent? R_6?

3. In a physical-education class the students count off, "one," "two," "three," ... The instructor directs the *evens* to form one team and the *odds* another. Explain how this illustrates the use of an equivalence relation to partition a set. How could the same technique be used to separate a class into three teams?

4. If any $x \in W$ is divided by 3, one of the remainders 0, 1, 2 is obtained. This suggests the relation

   $R = \{(x, y) \in W \times W \mid x$ has the same remainder when divided by 3 as has $y\}$.

   a) Is R an rst-relation?

   b) List 4 elements for each of the equivalence classes R_5, R_6, R_7.

   c) Show that $R_5 = R_2$, $R_6 = R_0$, $R_7 = R_1$.

5. If we call the equivalence classes determined by the relation of Exercise 2 E and O, respectively, then it is natural to define "addition" and "multiplication" operations on these classes. Tables are given below:

+	E	O		×	E	O
E	E	O		E	E	E
O	O	E		O	E	O

   Explain and justify these tables in the language of "evens and "odds."

6. We have no names in everyday speech for the three subsets of W determined by the relation of Exercise 4. Using R_0, R_1, R_2 for these sets, construct tables analogous to those of Exercise 5.

7. The equivalence relations of Exercises 2 and 4 are generalized as indicated below.

   $\forall x, y \in W$, *x is congruent to y modulo n* if x has the same remainder when divided by n as y has.

The relation *congruence modulo* 2 splits W into the evens and odds. Into how many equivalence classes does each relation *congruence modulo n* split W? Illustrate, for $n = 6$, by listing elements of each class.

8. Let $S = W \times W$.

$S = \{(0, 0), (0, 1), (1, 0), (0, 2), (1, 1), (2, 0), (0, 3), (1, 2), \ldots\}$.

Note that each *relation in S* is a subset of $S \times S$ and so is a set of *ordered pairs* of *ordered pairs!* We define two such relations below.

$R = \{((a, b), (c, d)) \in S \times S \mid a + b = c + d\}$

$R^* = \{((a, b), (c, d)) \in S \times S \mid a + d = b + c\}$

a) Show that R is an equivalence relation in S, that is:

i) $\forall (x, y) \in S,\ ((x, y), (x, y)) \in R$

ii) $\forall (a, b),\ (c, d) \in S,\ ((a, b), (c, d)) \in R \Rightarrow ((c, d), (a, b)) \in R$

iii) $\forall (a, b),\ (c, d),\ (e, f) \in S, \ldots$

b) R partitions S into infinitely many equivalence classes. Only one of these classes contains precisely 6 elements. List all elements of S in this class.

c) Show that R^* is an equivalence relation.

d) List 4 elements in the equivalence class determined by R^* which contains $(2, 5)$.

9. Let W be the set of whole numbers.

$N = \{x \in W \mid x \neq 0\}$

Then

$W \times N = \{(x, y) \in W \times W \mid y \neq 0\}$.

In $W \times N$ we define a relation, denoted by the symbol $\sim$, by agreeing that

$\forall (a, b),\ (c, d) \in W \times N,\ (a, b) \sim (c, d)$ if $ad = bc$.

(Read $\sim$ as "is equivalent to.") As the language suggests, $\sim$ is an equivalence relation. (Verify this.)

a) Show that $(1, 2) \sim (2, 4) \sim (3, 6) \sim (4, 8) \ldots$

b) Show that $(2, 3) \sim (4, 6) \sim (6, 9) \sim \ldots$

c) List 6 elements of the equivalence class which contains $(3, 12)$.

d) The elements of $W \times N$ and the equivalence classes determined by $\sim$ are very important in the arithmetic curriculum of the upper elementary grades. Explain this mysterious remark.

SUMMARY   The following lists call attention to symbols and concepts introduced in this chapter.

SYMBOLS

$x \in A$: x belongs to (is an element of) A. A contains x.

$A \subset B$: A is a subset of B.   (B includes A.)

$A = B$: A is equal to B.

$x \notin A$: x is not an element of A.

$A \not\subset B$: A is not a subset of B.

$A \neq B$: A is not equal to B.

$\varnothing$: The null (empty) set.

$\{1, 2, 3, 4\}$: The set whose elements are 1, 2, 3, 4.

W: The set of whole numbers.

$\{x \in W \mid x < 10\}$: The set of all $x \in W$ such that $x < 10$.

A': The complement of A in some universal set U.

$A \cup B$: The union of A and B.

$A \cap B$: The intersection of A and B.

$n(A)$: The number of elements in set A.

p, q, r: Symbols that represent statements.

$p \Rightarrow q$: p implies q; if p then q; p only if q.

$p \Leftarrow q$: q implies p; if q, then p; q only if p.

$p \Leftrightarrow q$: p if and only if q; if p, then q, and if q, then p; p is equivalent to q.

$\forall$: For all

$\exists$: There exists

$f\colon X \to Y$: f is a function from set X into set Y.

$x \xrightarrow{f} f(x)$: f maps the element x upon f of x.

$f\colon X \xrightarrow[\text{onto}]{1-1} Y$: f is a one-to-one and onto function from X to Y (1–1 correspondence).

domain f: domain of f

range f: range of f

f^{-1}: the inverse of the function f.

$f \circ g$: the composite of g and f.

(a, b): ordered pair a, b.

$A \times B$: the cartesian product of A and B.

CONCEPTS

1. In mathematical set theory, set membership is undefined. However, we define set inclusion in terms of set membership:

$$A \subset B \qquad \text{means} \qquad \forall x \in A, \, x \in B.$$

2. $A = B$ means that the symbols A and B name the same object.

3. By the agreed-upon definition of equality, we know that equality has the properties Ref., Sym., Tran.

4. From the definition of equality, it follows that if $A = B$, then sets A and B have the same elements. We *assume* that if the sets have the same elements they are equal.

5. The set $\varnothing$ is the unique set that has no elements.

6. If a universal set U is designated, then

$$A' = \{x \in U \mid x \notin A\},$$
$$A \cup B = \{x \in U \mid x \in A \text{ or } x \in B\},$$
$$A \cap B = \{x \in U \mid x \in A \text{ and } x \in B\}.$$

7. $n(A \cup B) = n(A) + n(B) - n(A \cap B).$

8. If p, q are any statements, not p, p and q, p or q, $p \Rightarrow q$, $p \Leftrightarrow q$ are statements.

   not p is false when p is true, true when p is false.

   p and q is true in just the one case, p true, q true.

   p or q is false in just the one case, p false, q false.

   $p \Rightarrow q$ is false in just the one case, p true, q false.

   $p \Leftrightarrow q$ is true in just two cases, p, q both true and p, q both false.

   p or $q \Leftrightarrow$ if not p, then $q \Leftrightarrow$ if not q then p.

   That is these three statements are equivalent.

9. Relative to a chosen universal set U, the truth set of an open sentence $p(x)$ is the set $\{x \in U \mid p(x)\}$.

10. If $f: X \xrightarrow[\text{onto}]{\text{1-1}} Y$, then $f^{-1}: Y \xrightarrow[\text{onto}]{\text{1-1}} X$. That is, if f is a one-to-one correspondence from set X to Y then f^{-1} is a 1–1 correspondence from Y to X.

11. If $f: X \xrightarrow[\text{onto}]{\text{1-1}} Y$, $g: Y \xrightarrow[\text{onto}]{\text{1-1}} Z$, then $g \circ f: X \xrightarrow[\text{onto}]{\text{1-1}} Z$.

12. The compositions $f \circ g$ and $g \circ f$ may not be equal to each other. For example,

$$A_2 \circ A_4 = A_6 = A_4 \circ A_2, \text{ but } A_2 \circ M_2 \neq M_2 \circ A_2.$$

13. $(a, b) \neq \{a, b\}$. $(a, b) = (c, d) \Leftrightarrow a = c$ and $b = d$.

14. $A \times B = \{(a, b) \mid a \in A \text{ and } b \in B\}$.

15. A function f may be thought of as a set of ordered pairs. For example, if

$$f = \{(1, 3), (2, 5), (3, 7), (4, 9)\},$$

$$\text{then} \quad \text{domain } f = \{1, 2, 3, 4\} = X$$
$$\text{range } f = \{3, 5, 7, 9\} = Y$$

$f: X \xrightarrow[\text{onto}]{1\text{-}1} Y; f(x) = 2x + 1, \forall x \in X.$

3 abstracting whole-number arithmetic from the real world

3–1 counting

When a small child begins to talk he speaks in one-word exclamations: "hot," "no," "da-da." After he progresses to short phrases and sentences, his proud parents begin to drill him on nursery rhymes, and thus begins his mathematical training. For, once he is able to memorize sequences of (nonsense) words, such as "hey-diddle-diddle, the cat and the fiddle," it is but a short step to learning other sequences of nonsense syllables such as: "ay, bee, see, dee, . . . ," or "one, two, three, four, . . ."

When he attempts to memorize sequences of this latter type, however, his parents interfere. They distract his attention from the business of making the sounds in the correct order by moving his fingers from block to block. This adds to the difficulty of learning to count. He is expected not only to memorize an *ordered* set (a sequence) of nonsense sounds, but also to construct certain 1–1 functions from special subsets of this ordered set (of intangible sounds) *onto* various physical sets. For example, he is expected to construct functions of the following sort:

"one"

"two"

"three"

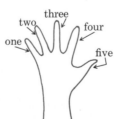
three
two   four
one   five

Naturally he makes mistakes of the following type.

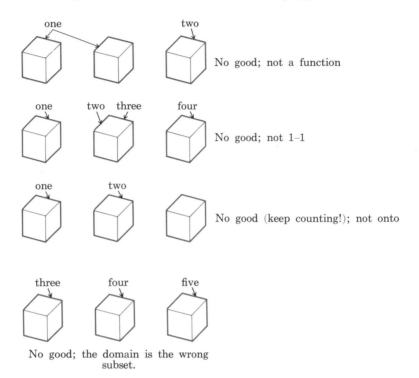

No good; not a function

No good; not 1–1

No good (keep counting!); not onto

No good; the domain is the wrong subset.

It is difficult for the child to grasp the concept that adults don't care which particular 1–1, *onto* function he constructs, that they are really only interested in the *last sound* he makes.

▶ *Aside.* The teaching implications are perhaps too obvious to mention. If he can't *recite* his number sounds in order, then he can't *count* things; and if he can't count, then he can't tell *how many* unless the set involved is very small. The number sound "two" is probably learned before any of the others, in direct response to the question (explicit or implicit), "How many?" Some of the other small-number sounds may also be learned in this way, but it is fairly certain that "six" is first learned as the nonsense sound following "five" in the free-verse nursery rhyme called "number sounds." ◀

It is worth emphasizing that our first several number sounds are historical accidents and not the product of logical planning. The sequence of sounds:

"Little Tommy Tucker sang for his supper"

would serve as well as

"one, two, three, four, five, six, seven,"

and it might even be easier to learn. If we all agreed to use this system, then the child would count his blocks:

and tell you he had "Tucker" of them. You would understand him perfectly.

EXERCISES 3–1

1. Would "hey-diddle-diddle, the cat and the fiddle" be an acceptable sequence for the first eight number sounds?

2. The sound "seven" is an unfortunate choice because it has 2 syllables. What counting difficulty could arise from this? What is the German sound for 7? for 17?

3. The "Tommy Tucker" system is bad, in that the sounds used have other meanings in other contexts. What English number sounds share this feature?

4. The sounds "five" and "nine" are so similar that artillery fire directors use "niner" to avoid misunderstanding. If you were constructing a new language, what properties would you want your number sounds for 0, 1, 2, 3, 4, 5, 6, 7, 8, 9 to have? What are these sounds in Esperanto?

5. Tell why each function pictured below is not a proper counting function.

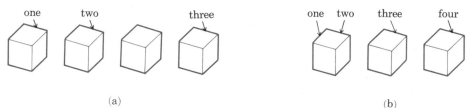

(a)   (b)

3–2   uses of counting functions

We have referred to 1–1 functions from special sets of sounds onto sets of physical objects as *counting functions*. It is convenient to be able to speak of *the* Counting function (capital "*C*") which we picture below.

"one" $\xrightarrow{C}$ "two" $\xrightarrow{C}$ "three" $\xrightarrow{C}$ "four" $\xrightarrow{C}$ "five" $\xrightarrow{C}$ ...

An alternate representation is

$$\{\text{"one," "two," "three," "four," "five," "six," } \ldots\}$$

C:

$$\{\text{"one," "two," "three," "four," "five," "six," } \ldots\}$$

It is this function *C* that a child must understand. (This is just another way of saying that he must know the *ordered* set of number sounds.) If we denote our set of number sounds by *S*, then

$$C\colon S \xrightarrow[\text{into}]{1-1} S.$$

(Why *into* and not *onto*?)
    The child must be able to respond to any $x \in S$ by pronouncing the sound $C(x)$.

"five" $\xrightarrow{C}$ "six;" C ("nine") = "ten"

A child may know quite a bit about the Counting function *C* and yet not understand how adults expect him to use the function.
    A child slightly more than 3 years old could "count." That is, he knew the Counting function all the way to *C*(nine) = ten. He was the proud possessor of several grains of candy corn and he *counted* them, touching each grain in turn as he said: "One, two, three, four, five."

Then he selected two grains and ate them. His fatuous father formulated a problem in his best professorial manner.

"You had *five* grains of candy corn and ate *two*. *How many* are left?"

The child looked puzzled.

"I didn't eat *two*," he said. "I ate *one* and *three*. *Two*, *four* and *five* are left."

    It is clear that, although the child knew the Counting function, his use of it was altogether different from our own. Whereas we use our counting skill to determine how many things are in a particular set, the child was simply using his knowledge of counting to assign names to the elements of a set. Our usage we call *cardinal* usage. The child's usage, which is the same as our usage when we assign numbers to football players in order to distinguish them on the playing field, may be called a *naming* usage. Note that had we counted the grains we might have set up the same function as did the child, matching each grain with a sound.

$$f = \begin{array}{ccccc} \{ \triangledown & \triangledown & \triangledown & \triangledown & \triangledown \} \\ \downarrow & \downarrow & \downarrow & \downarrow & \downarrow \\ \{\text{one} & \text{two} & \text{three} & \text{four} & \text{five}\} \end{array}$$

But having established this function we would draw information from it other than that which the child drew. We would remember the "five" and probably forget which candies were matched with particular sounds.

EXERCISES 3–2

1. A child who has been counting eggs comes running with the information that *four is broken*. Should you correct his grammar?

2. Here is a third type of usage of the Counting function. You have tested five students. On the basis of this test you have ranked them from best to worst. Now you wish to tell someone else about your ranking. You type an alphabetized list of five names as below.

   Joe Andrews   — three
   Andrew Bishop — two
   George Miller — four
   Fred Smith   — one
   Henry Taylor   — five

   This use of counting enables us to tell others how our students compare. This is the *ordinal* usage of counting.

   a) Who is the best student in the group?

   b) Who is the worst?

3. Classify as *cardinal*, *ordinal*, or *naming* usage.

   a) Numbering pages of a book.

   b) Numbering streets in a city.

   c) Numbering players on a basketball team.

   d) Numbering houses on a street.

   e) Numbering people at a party before cutting a cake.

f) Assigning telephone numbers to families.

g) Numbering the days of a month.

h) Numbering customers in a barber shop.

4. Children sometimes count:

a) eighteen, nineteen, tenteen, eleventeen, . . .

b) twenty-nine, twenty-ten, twenty-eleven, . . .

Can you add to this list? What might a child say naturally after 99? After 999?

The cardinal usage of counting, that is, counting with a "how-many" purpose, deserves a bit more analysis. After counting the elements of a set, we produce one special sound and attach it to the set.

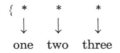

{one, two, three} → three

The operation of "picking off the last sound" from a set of sounds is a function. It is interesting to watch children who are in the process of learning that we want this last sound and don't care about the others. Our predilection for this final sound must seem totally illogical to a child:

{one, two, . . . , seven} → seven.

Only the sound "seven" will satisfy us. The time finally comes when the child, as he counts, associates each sound, not with a single object, but with the subset of *all* objects he has counted up to and including the last.

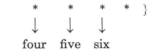

As he counts, the child associates the sound "three" not with the single object, but with the set of all objects he has labeled up to and including this one.

The six, similarly, is viewed as the number of the subset he has counted at this stage.

The special subsets of number sounds {one}, {one, two}, {one, two, three} . . . are sometimes called *standard sets*. Any physical set can be counted by exactly one of these sets. An analog can be drawn between counting and measurement. If you could carry enough measuring rods of various lengths around with you so that for every object you wished to measure you could select a rod of precisely the length of that object, then these measuring rods would play the role of the standard number sets. Carrying the rods would require a considerable amount of physical labor. The standard sets of numbers can be carried effortlessly.

A child who is asked, "How many are three and two?" may respond by counting off a set of three fingers on one hand, two on the other, forming the union of these two sets, and counting. Obviously the child is utilizing many functions. The diagram below dramatizes the role these functions play. Wherever arrows are drawn, some sort of function is being used.

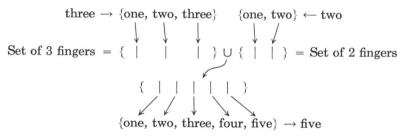

How many are three and two?

As the diagram suggests, the child's solution of this problem involves the utilization of 7 functions! Explain the diagram in detail.

In the process of building on his counting skill and developing facility in mental computation, a child learns to use many new functions. In preparation for subtraction he learns the *counting-backward* function. This is the inverse of C.

$$C: \begin{array}{ccc} \{\text{one, two, three, } \dots\} \\ \downarrow \quad \downarrow \quad \downarrow \\ \{\text{two, three, four, } \dots\} \end{array} \qquad C^{-1}: \begin{array}{ccc} \{\text{one, two, three, } \dots\} \\ \uparrow \quad \uparrow \quad \uparrow \\ \{\text{two, three, four, } \dots\} \end{array}$$

He learns to count by twos. This is the composite function $C \circ C$.

$$\text{two} \xrightarrow{C \circ C} \text{four} \xrightarrow{C \circ C} \text{six} \xrightarrow{C \circ C} \dots$$
$$\text{one} \xrightarrow{C \circ C} \text{three} \xrightarrow{C \circ C} \text{five} \xrightarrow{C \circ C} \dots$$

He learns to count by tens; this is

$$C \circ C \circ \dots \circ C = C^{10}$$
$$\text{ten} \xrightarrow{C^{10}} \text{twenty} \xrightarrow{C^{10}} \text{thirty} \xrightarrow{C^{10}} \dots$$
$$\text{eight} \xrightarrow{C^{10}} \text{eighteen} \xrightarrow{C^{10}} \text{twenty-eight} \xrightarrow{C^{10}} \dots$$

We emphasize that we are describing the processes by which a child acquires mathematical knowledge by working with number sounds. We shall look later at the logical concepts associated with the development of facility in the use of written symbols. The first contacts a child has with mathematical ideas involve forming associations between sets of number sounds and sets of physical objects.

These associations characterize *mental arithmetic*. A child who has little familiarity with our written numerals

0, 1, 2, 3, 4, 5, 6, 7, . . .

and cannot even write them may yet develop remarkable computational skills.

DISCUSSION EXERCISES 3–3

We present below a sequence of steps in which a child of 4 moved in less than a year from basic understandings of the Counting function C to fairly sophisticated computational skill. Analyze the techniques used; show how counting was employed; point out the ideas that the child discovered; observe the growing power of abstraction; watch for uses of set theory and the function concept. Careful examination of the child's thought processes reveals several stages of abstraction.

THE PROBLEM GIVEN THE CHILD

THE CHILD'S SOLUTION

1. How many are three and two?

The child counted off fingers on one hand, "one, two, three," on the other, "one, two." He brought these sets together, counted, "one two, three, four, five," and announced the result: *"Three and two are five."*

(A week later)

2. How many are four and two?

"I already have four. I don't need to count them." (He held up two fingers only.) "Five, *six*."

3. How many are two and four?

The child raised four fingers and counted: "Three, four, five, *six*."

At this stage he computed *eight plus two* by counting, "nine, ten," and *two plus eight* by counting, "three four, five, six, seven, eight nine, ten."
(A month later)

4. How many are two and nine?

The child hesitated momentarily and then commented, "I'll take the nine first. It's bigger. Ten, *eleven*."

(A month later)

5. How many are five and six?

"Five and five is ten. So five and six is one more: *eleven*."

(A month later)

6. Nine plus seven.

"Sixteen! Do you know how I did that so fast? I put one from the seven with nine. That made ten and six and that's what sixteen means."

7. Nineteen and five.

"Nineteen and one is twenty. Four more makes *twenty-four*."

(A month later)

8. Twenty plus thirty.

"Twenty is two tens. Thirty is three tens. Two tens and three tens are five tens: *fifty*."

9. Twenty-two plus thirty-four.

"Two tens plus three tens is fifty. Two plus four is six: *fifty-six*."

(A month later)

10. Sixty-eight plus twenty-seven. (At this point addition is certainly becoming a game that is played by using counting skills. No sets are visualized here. The physical world is ignored.)

"Seventy-eight, eighty-eight. Two more make ninety, and five more make *ninety-five*."

11. Twelve take away three.

"Eleven, ten, *nine*."

12. Forty-two take away twenty.

"Thirty-two, *twenty-two*."

13. One hundred minus fifty-four.

"Fifty, forty-eight, *forty-six*."

14. How much is four sixes?

"Two sixes are twelve. Twelve and twelve is *twenty-four*."

15. How much is eight sevens?

"Fourteen, twenty-eight. That's four sevens. *Fifty-six*."

16. What is eight times ten?

"Eight tens are *eighty*."

17. What is ten times eight?

(Note that the basic principle which assures us that $10 \times 8 = 8 \times 10$ has not yet been recognized.)

"Two eights are sixteen; four are thirty-two; thirty-two and thirty-two is sixty-four. That's eight eights. Two more eights is sixteen more; seventy-four, *eighty*."

The problems above illustrate the gradual abstraction that occurs as a child uses counting effectively in problem-solving. All these solutions were verbal. No symbols were written. Note that in the beginning the child needed to *see* sets of objects before he could count; later he visualized certain sets mentally; finally he seemed to make no effort to visualize sets of objects but relied wholly upon his counting skill and a few memorized number facts. Obviously when he "added" 68 and 27 he thought in terms of

1) counting forward twenty from 68,
2) counting forward seven more.

He could have visualized sets of 68 and 27 objects had he wished to do so, but there was no need. He was beginning, at the age of 5, to view arithmetic as a game which one can play with symbols, in this case, *sounds*. It must be emphasized that he understood *applications* of this symbolic game. He just chose not to think of sets of physical objects as he played the game. Already he was well into the third stage of the abstraction process in which one pays little attention to the real world.

Recall that when we discussed 1–1, onto functions we introduced a definition:

i) Sets A and B have the same *number* if and only if there is a function f such that

$$f\colon A \xrightarrow[\text{onto}]{1-1} B.$$

But now a second definition is implied by our discussion of counting:

ii) Sets A and B have the same number if and only if when we count them we get the *same number sound*.

We shall not define *numbers* until Chapter 11. *Number sounds* are of course already defined. They are really physical "objects," although invisible. Too loud a number sound could rupture your eardrums.

▶ *Aside.* An interesting point of logic arises when we examine definitions (i) and (ii). *We have two different definitions for the same thing.* These two definitions must be reconciled. That is, we must show that whenever one is applicable, so also is the other. For example, suppose that in comparing two sets, A and B, *you* were able to establish a 1–1 correspondence between them. You would use definition (i) and say:

"Sets A and B have the same number."

Suppose, on the other hand, that I counted each set, getting "three hundred ninety-seven" for A and "four hundred one" for B. Then, using definition (ii), I would say:

"A and B do not have the same number."

Assuming that I had counted correctly, and that you had set up a proper 1–1 correspondence between the sets, we would both be right *by our own standards*. In everyday life this sort of thing often happens. Different definitions may lead to different conclusions and so generate arguments.

Of course we shall not tolerate such nonsense in mathematics. As we said, the definitions must be *reconciled*. In the language of logic, we must show that they are equivalent statements. That is, we must *prove* that

(i) $\Rightarrow$ (ii) and (ii) $\Rightarrow$ (i).

Note that (i) says:

A has the same number as *B* if there is a *function* with a certain property.

Note that (ii) says:

A has the same number as *B* if there are *two* functions with certain properties.

We could not possibly prove the equivalence of (i) and (ii) if we did not know quite a bit about functions. Fortunately we do. The diagram below shows how the proof is effected. We must show that *if* two sets have the same number sound, *then* there is a 1–1 correspondence between the sets; and, conversely, *if* there is a 1–1 correspondence between two sets, *then* they have the same number sound.

Proof that (ii) $\Rightarrow$ (i):

$$A = \{\ \ *\quad\quad *\quad\quad *\quad\quad \cdots\quad\quad *\ \ \}$$
$$f:\quad \uparrow\quad\quad \uparrow\quad\quad \uparrow\quad\quad\quad\quad \uparrow$$
$$\{\text{one}\ \ |\ \ \text{two}\ \ |\ \ \text{three}\ \ |\ \ \cdots\quad\quad |\}$$
$$g:\quad \downarrow\quad\quad \downarrow\quad\quad \downarrow\quad\quad\quad\quad \downarrow$$
$$B = \{\ \square\quad\quad \square\quad\quad \square\quad\quad \cdots\quad\quad \square\ \}$$

1) Assume that *A* and *B* have the same number sound and so have the same number according to Definition (ii).

2) Let *f* and *g* be counting functions which determine that sound for each set.

3) Consider the function $g \circ f^{-1}$ represented by the dashed arrows.

$$g \circ f^{-1}\colon A \xrightarrow[\text{onto}]{1-1} B. \qquad \text{(Why?)}$$

4) Hence *A* and *B* have the same number according to Definition (i). (Why?)

The argument that (i) $\Rightarrow$ (ii) is left to the student. One assumes that *h* is a 1–1 correspondence from *A* onto *B*. Then if *f* is any counting function which determines a number for *A*, one considers $h \circ f$.

One more comment is applicable. We have observed that there are many different ways to "count" a set, two ways to count a 2-element set, six ways to count a 3-element set, etc. It would be tragic if different ways led to different number sounds for one set. Our intuition tells us that this cannot happen. Check this out with a child sometime. Have him count a set of nine objects. Mix them up for him and ask him to count them again; and again. Tell him that you think that maybe next time he will get eight or ten instead of nine. The child will probably decide that you are out of your mind. We make no attempt to prove the basic intuitive "fact": that *all* methods of counting *any* set yield the same result. ◄

3–3   numeration systems

In our sequence of number sounds a pattern begins to emerge with "thirteen." This pattern of sounds is a consequence of the pattern devised for our sequence of visual number symbols (numerals).

In this section we shall describe several numeration systems. The chief reason for doing this is to focus attention on the key properties of our own Hindu-Arabic system and to pinpoint the difficulties children face in learning to use such a system.

A numeration system is a collection of visual (as opposed to audible) symbols for numbers. Earliest numeration systems probably employed sets of twigs or stones, one twig or stone for each object in the set being described. Later numeration systems used scratches, still one scratch for each object. With such a system one can keep semipermanent records. Scratches on the wall of a cave, or on a baked clay tablet, can be kept for some time.

Most numeration systems have in common at least the following two properties.

1)   There is a symbol for the number one.

2)   There is a rule by means of which one proceeds from each symbol to the next.

We shall be on the lookout for the rule in each system we study. Note that the invention of numeration systems belongs to Stage 1 of the abstraction process. We are inventing symbols for sets.

The tally system. One of the earliest numeration systems consisted of scratches.

| || ||| |||| ||||| |||||| ||||||| · · ·

The rule was very simple. Make a scratch "|" for the first number; given the symbol (set of scratches) for a number, make an additional scratch to get the symbol for the next number. This delightfully logical numeration system lends itself to some very simple *algorithms* (processes) for adding, subtracting, multiplying, and dividing.

Note that the tally system is solidly based on the concept of 1–1 correspondence. The mathematician of antiquity who recorded the number of sheep in his flock was very conscious of the association between each scratch and a sheep.

A set of sheep: {×   ×   ×   ×   ×}
                                    ↓   ↓   ↓   ↓   ↓
The numeral for the set: {| | | | | }

One must construct a 1–1, onto function as he makes the number symbol.

Why was such a nice system ever abandoned? Obviously large numbers must have presented a problem. Our national budget director is probably much relieved that this system is no longer with us.

Problem Suggest audible symbols for these tally numerals. Use your invention to "read" ‖‖| .

Egyptian numerals. A more economical, but still basically simple, numeration system is the Egyptian system. This system can be thought of as the tally system with abbreviations. The first nine symbols are unchanged. The tenth one is abbreviated.

‖‖‖ ‖‖‖   is replaced by ∧

The numerals following ∧ are

∧| ∧‖   ∧‖‖   ∧‖‖| ∧‖‖‖   ∧‖‖‖| ∧‖‖‖‖   ∧‖‖‖‖| ∧‖‖‖‖‖   ∧∧

This pattern is repeated up to

∧∧∧∧∧ ∧∧∧∧ ‖‖‖‖‖

The next numeral is 𝟵 . The table illustrates the abbreviation system used by the Egyptians.

Familiar Hindu-Arabic numeral	Egyptian numeral
1	| (staff)
10	∧ (heel bone)
100	𝟵 (scroll)
1000	𝕩 (lotus flower)
10,000	∫ (pointing finger)
100,000	⌒ (burbot fish)
1,000,000	𝕩 (astonished man)
2,320,147	𝕩 𝕩 ⌒ ⌒ ⌒ ∫∫ 𝟵 ∧∧∧∧ ‖‖‖‖‖

Observe that an Egyptian numeral does *not* depend on the position of its constituent symbols: ∧∧‖‖‖ and |∧‖|∧ denote the same number. Convention makes the first form preferable, but mathematically there is no ambiguity in using the other form. Contrast this with our Hindu-Arabic numerals.

Problem   a) Convert to Hindu-Arabic numerals:

ꐞꓽꓵꓲ   ꐞ ꐞ ꌇꓲ   ꐞꓵꐞꓵꓵꓵꐞꓵ   ꘊꙠꙠꓵꓵꓵ

b) Convert to Egyptian numerals:

98;   89;   2012;   1,401,026;   999,999;   1,000,000

Problem   Try stating the rule for forming "the next numeral."

Roman numerals.   The Roman-numeral system can also be thought of as an abbreviation of the tally system. Now

||||| is replaced by V.

The Roman "V" was originally a symbol for the human hand. With this background it is natural to invent an abbreviation for VV. (Why natural?)

VV = X (two V's, tip to tip)

And now the process of grouping by *fives* and by *twos* can be repeated. We have the sequence of definitions:

$$
\begin{array}{lll}
||||| = V & CCCCC = D \quad {}^{500} & \overline{XXXXX} = \overline{L} \quad {}^{50000} \\
VV = X & DD = M \quad {}^{1000} & \vdots \\
XXXXX = L \quad {}^{50} & MMMMM = \overline{V} \quad {}^{5000} & \\
LL = C \quad {}^{100} & \overline{V}\,\overline{V} = \overline{X} \quad {}^{10000} &
\end{array}
$$

You can think of the bar placed over a symbol as a multiplying factor of one thousand.

We shall use the old *additive* (as opposed to *subtractive*) notation for Roman numerals, writing IIII in place of IV; VIIII in place of IX; etc. Note that in our notation IV is *six*. Order is not important.

Now we have lost some of the simplicity that made the tally system so attractive. Our rule for passing from any symbol to the next is not quite so simple. Loosely speaking, given any Roman symbol, we make another mark "I" (just as in the tally system), but now if any of the abbreviating definitions are applicable we must employ them. An example:

VIIII → VIIIII = VV = X.

A meticulous description of the technique for writing the next symbol would drone on and on:

1)   Mark another "I."

2)   If there are fewer I's than five, we are done. If not, replace IIIII by V.

3)   If there is now only the one V, we are done. If there are two, replace VV by X.

4) If XXXXX does not now occur, we are done. Otherwise, replace XXXXX by L.

And so on.

This algorithm for constructing the next symbol is not the sort of thing that deserves meticulous description. Anyone who understands the basic definitions knows intuitively how to proceed.

Problem Suggest audible symbols for Roman numerals. "Read" LXXVIII. Count from LXII to LXX. What sounds did the Romans use?

Problem When the modern subtractive notation is used for Roman numerals one sees

IV, IX, XL, XC, . . .

but never

IL, IC, XD, XM, VL, . . .

Find out exactly how the subtractive notation is used and write up a precise description of its use.

Problem a) Convert to Hindu-Arabic numerals:

XXVII, MLXII, LXLXL, IXIIMLV.

b) Convert to Roman numerals:

98; 89; 1,401,026; 999,999; 1,000,000;

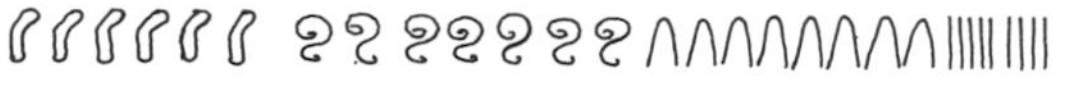

Arabic numerals. Our Arabic system introduces a new idea. Ten basic symbols, or digits (why are they called digits?) are introduced. We refer to this familiar system as a *base ten* system:

0, 1, 2, 3, 4, 5, 6, 7, 8, 9.

Each of these digits except 9 has an "obvious" successor indicated by the order above.

No one knows just how or when these particular symbols were invented. The "1" was lifted from the scratch system. Possibly the original symbols for 2 and 3 were

and someone observed that he could write more rapidly by "dragging" his
marker.

Interestingly, each of 4, 5, 6, 8 can be envisioned as constructed from the
appropriate number of straight line segments:

You can devise your own theory for the origin of 7 and 9. The 9 is a sort of
backward 10 with the "1" on the right.

Each Arabic numeral is a string of these digits. Conventionally, for a symbol
of more than one digit, the first digit on the left is not 0, but there are no other
restrictions. We speak of 1-digit, 2-digit, . . . numbers:

4477 is a 4-digit number.

The rule for passing from one numeral to the next is most easily explained on an
intuitive level by writing and pointing. It is interesting to teach this rule to
children, without attempting any verbal description.

There are two cases.

1)   If the last (rightmost) digit is *not* 9: Replace the last digit by its successor.

2)   If the last digit *is* 9: We consider two cases.

   i)   Not all digits 9: Replace terminal 9's by 0's and replace the first non-9
        digit on the right by its successor.

   ii) All digits 9: Replace all 9's by 0's and annex a 1 on the left.

Our audible symbols for Arabic numerals were not scientifically chosen. We
could do better today, but few people feel that a change would be worth the
temporary inconvenience it would cause one generation. The most efficient
"reading" technique is

$$4 \quad 7 \quad 0 \quad 2$$
$$\downarrow \quad \downarrow \quad \downarrow \quad \downarrow$$

four, seven, oh, two

A few purists reserve "oh" for the big round *O* that comes between *N* and *P* and
insist that the thin 0 be read "zero," but telephone operators don't seem to mind
the sloppy language.

Problem   In using a dial phone which employs both the letter *O* and the digit
0, what confusion could arise?

Other bases. Our Arabic numeral technique for numeration can be generalized by varying the number of basic symbols. For example, if we use only the four symbols

0, 1, 2, 3,

we obtain the rule for passing from each numeral to the next from the rule for Arabic numerals by merely replacing 9 by 3. This 4-symbol system is called a *base four* system.

Problem In this base four system write the numeral following each numeral listed below.

a) 1121   b) 2310   c) 311302   d) 13203   e) 231133
f) 1022333   g) 3033333   h) 3333   i) 3333333333

Explain why the sounds "thirteen" and "twenty-one" are unsatisfactory for base four numerals 13 and 21. Suggest suitable audible symbols.

Problem Describe the rule for numeration in base two which uses only the digits 0, 1. Illustrate the rule by writing the successors of several numerals. What problem would you face in devising a base twelve system?

Other numeration systems. Suppose that we choose to "count" as indicated here:

a, b, c, aa, ab, ac, ba, bb, bc, ca, cb, cc, aaa, . . .

We agree that *a* is matched with sets of a single element: $a \leftrightarrow \{x\}$

    This cursory introduction of a new numeration system exemplifies our faith in your intuition. Without any verbal explanation you are expected to deduce, from the few examples above, the rule for passing from each numeral to the next.

EXERCISES 3–4

1. Give the numeral that follows:
   a) *abba*   b) *babb*   c) *abc*   d) *ccccc*
2. Give the numeral that comes before:
   a) *babac*   b) *cabba*   c) *bcaaaa*
3. Invent audible symbols for these numerals.
4. Would you approve of calling this a base three system? If so, why? If not, why not?
5. Add: a) *c + ab*   b) *ab + ba*   c) *aba + bab*
   Multiply: a) *c × c*   b) *c × bc*   c) *bc × bc*   d) *bbc × bc*

An interesting variant on our base ten system is obtained by dropping off the 0 and replacing it by t for ten. Then we have a base ten system without a zero!

1, 2, 3, 4, 5, 6, 7, 8, 9, t

Now the rule for writing numerals is obtained by replacing 9 by t and 0 by 1 in the rule for writing numerals in the familiar base ten system.

1, 2, 3, . . . , 9, t, 11, 12, . . . , 19, $1t$, 21, . . .

99, $9t$, $t1$, $t2$, . . . , tt, 111, . . .

Are 11 and 12 still our familiar eleven and twelve?

Problem Is 21 still twenty-one? What is $2t$?; $3t$?; $9t$?; tt? Give the numerals that follow: (a) $4t$ (b) $3tt$ (c) $69t$ (d) $9tt$ (e) $ttttt$.

This example somewhat deflates the symbol 0. It doesn't seem necessary after all. In attempting to compute with this system do you anticipate any difficulties because there is no zero? If so, what difficulties?

We promise that, in Chapter 5, we shall say many nice things about zero and restore it to its position of eminence.

3–4   using counting in computation

In Section 3–2 we indicated the way one child built on his understanding of counting and developed skills in mental computation. All children do this to some extent, but one of the weaknesses of early arithmetic teaching is that for most children counting skill is not systematically exploited. The trick is to recognize the child's level of mathematical maturity and ask him the right questions. Parents are notoriously weak at this sort of thing, and so most children receive little direction before entering school. Even in kindergarten and first grade there is a tendency to slight the development of mental computational ability, based on counting, in favor of *writing* numerals. A small child may lack the muscular coordination required to write numerals effortlessly. His fives and sevens may come out as

and yet he may have a mental agility that makes mental computation easy for him. Many youngsters in upper grades seem not to be able to think about a problem of arithmetic unless it is written on paper. This is due primarily to our failure to stress mental computation in the early years.

If, in a first-grade class, you hold up 4 fingers on one hand, most students will be able to say "four" immediately, apparently with no counting. But if you raise

4 on one hand and 1 on the other and ask "How many in all?" then very few students will glance at the one hand, think *four*, and say *five*. With most of them their lips will move as they count

"one, two, three, four, five."

They have not yet learned what the 4-year-old child taught himself, that they can *begin* with the four and count on from there. By setting up the proper situations, teachers can help students learn these basic things.

At some stage children learn that 5 + 5 = 10. This is an "obvious" fact that our hands present clearly. Soon after he learns this the child should be given related problems like

    hoping he will think

5 + 6 → 5 + 5 and 1 *more*

5 + 4 → 1 *less* than 5 + 5

Children learn the doubles quickly and easily.

1 + 1 = 2;   2 + 2 = 4;   3 + 3 = 6; . . .

These "facts" are soon memorized. Other facts should be related to them, as:

3 + 4 = 7 because it is 1 more than 3 + 3.

The ideal way for children to discover these short-cut computational techniques is through the solving of many problems in mental arithmetic. The excellent teacher is highly skilled at encouraging children to "discover" what they should discover.

The main value of the mental computation that utilizes counting skill is that the sounds focus attention on sets. As the child

Says	*He thinks*
thirteen	→ three and ten
twenty-two	→ two tens and two
one hundred thirty-four	→ one hundred, three tens, and four

A first-grade child who has had proper experiences can say

"one hundred and one hundred is two hundred"

with excellent understanding. He may not visualize each hundred as ten sets of ten, but still he knows that each hundred is a large set, and he realizes that he has *two* of them.

The child who has rich opportunities to count and visualize sets of objects as he does mental arithmetic will bring to written arithmetic much more comprehension than his unfortunate classmates who have had few such experiences. As tens and hundreds are mentioned he will visualize them with remarkable clarity.

Problem   In the light of the remarks of this section, examine the ability of some preschool, kindergarten, and first-grade children to use counting effectively.

3–5   from numeration to computation

Our discussion of numeration systems in Section 3–3 was entirely on the Stage 1 level of abstraction. This section deals primarily with Stage 2. Recall that in Stage 2 we settle on some basic manipulative procedures that enable us to use our numerals in problem-solving. In Stage 3 we try to develop a little skill. In this section we shall illustrate ideas of Stage 2 (and some from Stage 3) as we examine a few of the numeration systems described in Section 3–3. We shall not consider computational techniques in our Arabic numeral system. Because of its importance, computation with Arabic numerals will be treated in a separate chapter.

1. Computing in the tally system.   Imagine yourself a cave dweller of 50,000 years ago who has been assigned the task of teaching arithmetic to the children of the tribe. Your tools are sharpened sticks with which you scratch numerals in the dust. The old method of teaching, using sets of twigs instead of sets of scratches, died out over 10,000 years ago, but still some of the oldsters insist that it was a much better system than these newfangled scratches. You could pick up twigs and move them around. If one group of twigs represented a set of girls and another a set of boys, then because you could visualize the boys and girls scurrying together to form one large set, you could scoop the twigs together.

The algorithm for *subtraction* was simple in the twig system.

1. Remove a twig from each set.
2. Repeat step (1) until all twigs are removed from one set.
3. The set of twigs remaining is called the *difference*.

DISCUSSION EXERCISES 3–5

The diagrams below illustrate the computational techniques you teach.

1. Problem   First Step of Solution

$$
\begin{array}{r}
| \, | \, | \, | \\
+ \; | \, | \, | \\
\hline
\end{array}
\qquad
\begin{array}{r}
\not| \, | \, | \, | \\
+ \; | \, | \, | \\
\hline
|
\end{array}
$$

a) The answer to an addition problem must, of course, be written in the proper place, under the line. Copy the problem and complete the solution.

b) Explain how a 1–1 correspondence is used in computing this answer.

c) How might two sticks, one held in each hand, facilitate the computation?

d) If the symbols consisted of twigs instead of scratches, how might the "answer" be put below the line?

2. Problem   First Step of Solution

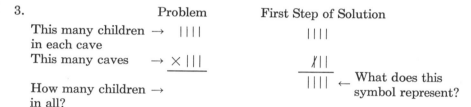

Complete the solution and comment on the technique. Be sure to write the answer where it belongs, below the line. The reason it must be written there is that we havė done it that way for 10,000 years.

3.   Problem   First Step of Solution

This many children → |||| in each cave

This many caves   → ×|||

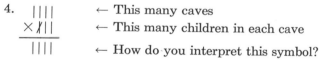

How many children → in all?

What does this symbol represent?

a) Copy and complete the problem. Explain the role of 1–1 correspondence.

b) Can you interpret what you are doing as counting the elements of a set of ordered pairs? Explain.

4. 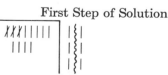   ← This many caves

← This many children in each cave

← How do you interpret this symbol?

5.   Problem

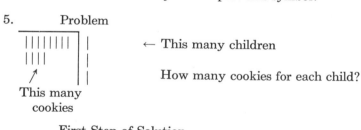   ← This many children

How many cookies for each child?

This many cookies

First Step of Solution

Complete the solution and explain the method.

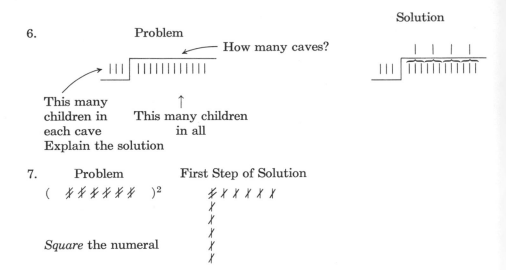

6.   Problem

This many
children in   This many children
each cave   in all
Explain the solution

7.   Problem   First Step of Solution

Square the numeral

Complete the solution. Does this suggest a better technique for multiplying than that suggested in Exercises 3 and 4?

8. Take the square root

Beginning of Solution

Complete the solution.

9. How would you decide whether a scratch numeral is even? odd? a perfect square?

As you see, arithmetic was pretty down-to-earth in those days. A person knew what he was doing. The connection between numerals and the sets they represented was pretty obvious. Actually some of the above techniques are taught in enlightened classrooms today. If children are given bottle caps and asked to solve certain problems, their procedures will be much like those shown above. If a child is given 3 checkers and 12 bottle caps and told to give each child (checker) the same number of cookies (bottle caps), he will probably solve the division problem by the technique of Exercise 5.

2. Computing with Egyptian numerals. You can't get something for nothing. The advantage, in notational economy, of the Egyptian system over the tally system is paid for in more complicated algorithms. The grouping-by-tens conventions must be employed whenever appropriate.

Example

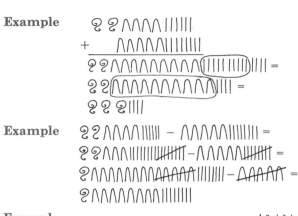

Example

Example

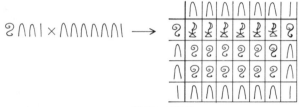

Problem   Compute as in the examples:

a) ΛΛΛΛΛΛΙΙΙΙ + ΛΛΛΛ ΙΙΙΙΙ

b) 𝟿ΙΙΙ + ΙΙΙΙΙΙΙ

c) ΛΛΛΛΛΛΙΙΙΙ − ΛΛΛΛ ΙΙΙΙΙ

d) 𝟿ΙΙΙ − ΙΙΙΙΙΙ

e) 𝟿𝟿ΛΛΛΛΛ × 𝟿𝟿𝟿𝟿ΛΛΙΙ

Check your answers by converting all Egyptian numerals to Hindu-Arabic numerals.

3. Computing with Roman numerals. Perhaps you have heard the comment that calculation with Roman numerals, particularly multiplication and division, is very difficult. With the subtractive notation this is certainly the case, but with the old additive notation the basic operations with Roman numerals are quite simple; certainly simpler than their Hindu-Arabic counterparts.

In the tally system adding is essentially pushing two symbols together. With Roman numerals, as with Egyptian numerals, the procedure is the same. The only new task is that it may be necessary to utilize the basic definitions (abbreviations) to convert an answer to "standard" form.

Example

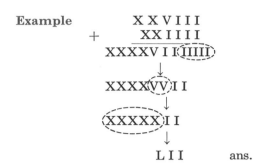

LII   ans.

In subtraction you may need to apply some of the definitions at the beginning of the work.

Example   C I
            − L X VII
                  ↓
            L XXXX V IIIIII
          − L   X V II
                X X X IIII   ans.

Before you try to multiply or divide it is well to construct a multiplication table. This one will serve our purpose.

·	V	X	L	C
V	XXV	L	CCL	D
X	L	C	D	M
L	CCL	D	MMD	$\overline{V}$
C	D	M	$\overline{V}$	$\overline{X}$

As you can see, the task of memorizing such a table would not be difficult. There are only the three "clumsy" products, $V \cdot V$, $V \cdot L = L \cdot V$, and $L \cdot L$.

Example   L X V I
            ×   X V
            ─────────
            D C L X
            CCLLXXVV
            ─────────────
            DCCCLLLXXXVV → DCCCCLXXXX   ans.

Because the Roman system groups by twos and fives it is easy to divide by II, V, X, L, C, etc.

Examples

$$\frac{\text{L V III}}{\text{I I} \ \lfloor\text{C X V I}}$$

$$\frac{\text{XXX IIIII} \ \to \text{XXXV}}{\text{V} \ \lfloor\text{C L X X V}}$$

$$\frac{\text{C L X X VI I I}}{\text{X} \ \lfloor\text{M D C C L X X X}}$$

$$\begin{array}{r} \text{X X I I} \\ \hline \text{XII} \ \lfloor\text{C C L X V} \\ \text{C X X} \\ \hline \text{C X X X X V} \\ \text{C X X} \\ \hline \text{X X V} \\ \text{X I I} \\ \hline \text{X I I I} \\ \text{X I I} \\ \hline \text{I} \end{array}$$

EXERCISES 3–6

1. Find the sums and differences. Give answers in standard form. Use any shortcuts that you wish.

   a) $\quad$ X X X V I
   $+$ X X V I I

   b) $\quad$ D C L X
   $+$ C C C L V

   c) $\quad$ C L X I
   $-$ L X V

   d) M D C + D C L + C L X

   e) M D X I − M C L X V I

2. Explain the following first step in the solution of 1(e):

   $$\cancel{M} D \cancel{X} \cancel{I} - \cancel{M} C L \cancel{X} V \cancel{I} = D - C L V$$

3. Find the products.

   a) $\quad$ X V I I
   $\times$ X V

   b) $\quad$ C L X V I I
   $\times$ L X

4. Find quotient and remainder.

   a) II $\lfloor$ XXVI

   b) X $\lfloor$ LXXXV

   c) L $\lfloor$ $\overline{\text{X}}$MMMDC

   d) V $\lfloor$ LXXVI

   e) VII $\lfloor$ LXXVI

   f) XXV $\lfloor$ DCCLXVI

5. State a brief argument supporting the thesis that it is easier to learn to add, subtract, multiply, and divide with Roman than with Arabic numerals.

6. Try a square-root problem in Roman numerals.

7. What number less than M requires the most Roman numerals for its representation? How many are required? Same question for Egyptian numerals.

8. How would you decide whether a Roman numeral is even? odd? a perfect square?

4. Computing in the base ten system without a zero. This numeration system based on the digits 1, 2, 3, 4, 5, 6, 7, 8, 9, t is enough like our familiar system that we can "almost" handle it, but just enough different to cause some anguish. Re-examine our technique of numeration:

1, 2, ..., 9, t,   11,   ...,   19,   1t,   21,   ...,   99,   9t

            ↓   ↓   ↓   ↓   ↓   ↓   ↓

           ten eleven   nineteen ?? twenty-   ninety- ?

                                   one   nine

t1, ..., tt, 111, ..., ttt, 1111, ...

↓   ↓   ↓   ↓   ↓

?   ?   ?   ?   ?

Problem Explain why you are sure that in this system 21 represents twenty-one and 111 represents one hundred eleven.

If you have thought carefully about the rule of formation for these numerals, you should have convinced yourself that as a result of our rule for forming the successor of a numeral we can interpret a symbol like 4 3 5 2 as

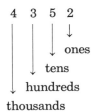

4   3   5   2

               ones

         tens

      hundreds

thousands

EXERCISES 3–7

1. Find the sums (remember, no zeros).

    a) 55   b) 437   c) tt d) ttt

       55   565   47 ttt

2. Find the differences.

a) 8t   b) 84   c) 67   d) 211
   34   3t   27   tt
  ——   ——   ——   ———

3. Show that $1t = (1 \times t) + t = 2 \times t$; $2t = (2 \times t) + t = 3 \times t$;
   $3t = (3 \times t) + t = 4 \times t$.

4. Show that $34 = (3 \times t) + 4$; $57 = (5 \times t) + 7$.

Multiplication embarrasses us. It is not "fair" to write out the solution below, even though we get the correct answer.

```
   32
 × 24
 ————
  128        What is the objection?
   64        Can you modify the work and
 ————        remove this objection?
  768
```

Exercises 3 and 4 call attention to some ideas that are essential for understanding multiplication in this system. Before a child can understand 2-digit multiplication in our Arabic numeral system, he must understand

1) The place-value features of our system

2) How to multiply by ten

We illustrate these ideas by examining the ordinary multiplication of 32 by 24. A child who understands 2-digit multiplication can explain his work as follows:

Step 1   *Explanation*

```
   32               I must multiply 32
 × 24               by 20 and by 4;
 ————               4 × 32 is 128.
  128
```

Step 2   *Explanation*

```
   32               In order to multiply 32 by 20
 × 24               I think that 20 is 2 tens.
 ————               I first multiply 32 by ten.
  128               ——————————————————————
  640               That's 320, and then I multiply
 ————               this by 2: 2 × 320 is 640.
```

Now return to our system without a zero. We know that $24 = 2$ tens $+ 4 = (2 \times t) + 4$. We are faced with the same problem as the child. We must multiply 32 by 4 and then by $(2 \times t)$. If we could multiply 32 by t we could double the answer.

$$\begin{array}{r} 32 \\ 24 \\ \hline 128 \end{array}$$

$$\leftarrow 2 \times t \times 32$$

Our trouble is that we don't know how to multiply 32 by t (ten).

We itch to tack on a zero, because once we memorized a rule that told us to do it that way:

$$t \times 32 = 320.$$

But now such an act is illegal!

The next remark brings us to the crux of the matter: *If we knew how to count by tens then we could multiply by ten.* Observe:

$t,$	$1t,$	$2t,$	$3t, \ldots,$	$9t,$	$tt, \ldots,$	$15t, \ldots,$	$38t, \ldots,$	$425t, \ldots$
$\downarrow$	$\downarrow$	$\downarrow$	$\downarrow$	$\downarrow$	$\downarrow$	$\downarrow$	$\downarrow$	$\downarrow$
one	two	$3 \times t$	$4 \times t$	$t \times t$	$11 \times t$	$16 \times t$	$39 \times t$	$426 \times t$
ten	tens							

Problem   Since $t \times 32 = 32 \times t$, compute this product and complete the multiplication problem properly.

EXERCISES 3–8

1. Multiply 32 by t by computing $(32 \times 5) \times 2$.
2. Give the products:
   - a) $6 \times t$
   - b) $12 \times t$
   - c) $22 \times t$
   - d) $31 \times t$
   - e) $46 \times t \times t$
   - f) $37t \times t \times t$
3. Formulate a rule for multiplying any number by t; by $t \times t$.
4. Compute the products

   a) $\begin{array}{r} 43 \\ \times\ 35 \\ \hline \end{array}$ b) $\begin{array}{r} 43t \\ \times\ 24t \\ \hline \end{array}$

   (Use the facts that $35 = (3 \times t) + 5$ and $24t = (2 \times t \times t) + (4 \times t) + t$.)

The implications for teaching multiplication in our own base ten system are clear. A youngster cannot understand multiplication by two- or three-digit numbers unless he understands multiplication by ten. (To *understand* multiplication by ten does not mean *memorizing* that one must tack on a zero.) If he knows how to multiply by ten he can multiply by 100 by multiplying *twice* by ten. An understanding of multiplication by ten and by 100 can be built on an understanding of counting by tens and hundreds.

10,   20,   30, ..., 170, ..., 4260, ...
↓   ↓   ↓   ↓   ↓
1 ten   2 tens   3 tens   17 tens   426 tens

100,   200,   ..., 1900,   ..., 41200,   ...
↓   ↓   ↓   ↓
1 hundred   2 hundreds   19 hundreds   412 hundreds

Let us now compute a product in our *t*-system, explaining the key steps.

Example

43*t*	43*t* × *t* = 439*t*
354	43*t* × *t* × *t* = 4399*t*

$$\begin{array}{ll} 43t & \\ 354 & \\ \hline 175t & = 4 \times 43t \\ 2199t & = 5 \times t \times 43t \\ 13199t & = 3 \times t \times t \times 43t \\ \hline 15575t & \end{array}$$

$$\begin{array}{l} 43t \times t = 439t \\ 43t \times t \times t = 4399t \end{array}$$

$$\begin{array}{r} 439t \\ 5 \\ \hline 2199t \end{array}$$

$$\begin{array}{r} 4399t \\ 3 \\ \hline 13199t \end{array}$$

3–6   place value

There are two approaches to numeration: one in which we explain how to form numerals successively (the ordinal approach), the other in which grouping is emphasized (the cardinal approach). In the preceding sections we have emphasized the first approach. For example, if we want to determine the Roman numeral for the set below, we proceed as follows:

{×   ×   ×   ×   ×   ×   ×   ×   ×   ×   ×   × }
 ↓   ↓   ↓   ↓   ↓   ↓   ↓   ↓   ↓   ↓   ↓   ↓
 I   II III IIII V   VI VII VIII VIIII X   XI XII

By using the fact that in Roman numeration we group repeatedly, first by fives and then by twos, we obtain the same result in a different way.

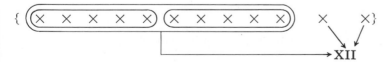

The preceding diagram utilizes the relations

X = VV,   V = IIIII.

This grouping technique enables one to determine the Roman numeral for any set without counting beyond 5.

Example

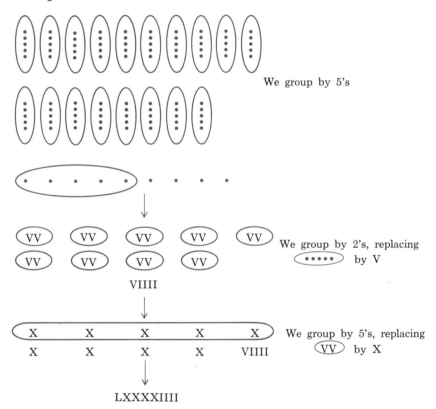

We group by 5's

We group by 2's, replacing
●●●●● by V

VIIII

We group by 5's, replacing
VV by X

LXXXXIIII

Similarly, we can find the Hindu-Arabic numeral for a set either by the ordinal approach,

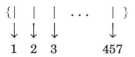

1 2 3   457

or the cardinal approach (in which we need never count beyond ten).

For the preceding set, describe how you would determine the Arabic numeral 457 by repeatedly grouping by tens.

Problem   You are asked to count a very large group of people. They are docile and follow directions well. You tell them to group themselves by tens. They do so. Four singles are left over. How do you continue your directions so as to determine quickly the total number?

In the teaching of arithmetic both approaches to numeration—counting and grouping—must be employed, and students must be given opportunities to relate the two approaches. It is the second approach which brings out the concept of place value most clearly.

Both an odometer and an abacus are excellent devices for bringing together these two approaches to numeration. For example, consider the odometer below, which reports miles. In its initial position we have all zeros.

$$\boxed{0\,|\,0\,|\,0\,|\,0\,|\,0}$$

As one begins to drive, the miles tick off

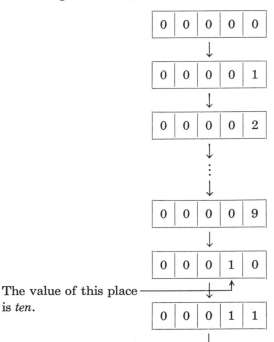

Here is the crucial spot. As the right-hand dial completes one revolution and returns to 0 it nudges the next dial one-tenth of the way around and a 1 shows up. The 1 reflects the fact that ten miles have been driven.

The value of this place is *ten*.

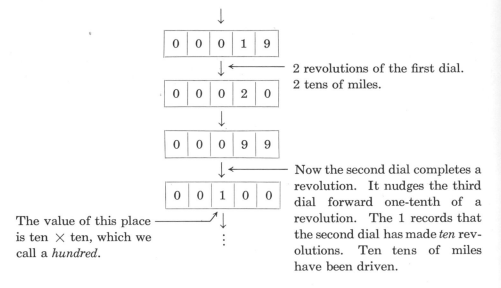

↓

| 0 | 0 | 0 | 1 | 9 |

↓ ←——— 2 revolutions of the first dial.
2 tens of miles.

| 0 | 0 | 0 | 2 | 0 |

↓

| 0 | 0 | 0 | 9 | 9 |

↓ ←——— Now the second dial completes a
revolution. It nudges the third
dial forward one-tenth of a
revolution. The 1 records that

| 0 | 0 | 1 | 0 | 0 |

The value of this place ————↗↓   the second dial has made *ten* rev-
is ten × ten, which we   ⋮   olutions. Ten tens of miles
call a *hundred*.   have been driven.

In ways like this the two approaches to numeration must be reconciled.

EXERCISES 3–9

1. An abacus with 9 beads on each wire can play the same role as an odometer. Counting, 1, 2, . . . , 9, one brings 9 beads forward on the first wire. Describe the next step and explain how place-value ideas unfold.

2. In a base four system, using only the symbols 0, 1, 2, 3, we could demonstrate place value by using an abacus having 3 beads on a wire or by visualizing an odometer for which each dial had only the numerals 0, 1, 2, 3. Obtain such an abacus and show how it describes place value in the base four system.

3. For each base four abacus below, write the base four numeral presented and interpret this number in our ordinary base ten notation.

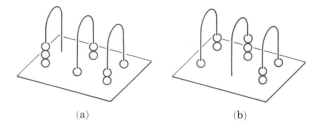

(a)   (b)

4. An abacus for our *t*-system (base ten without a zero) would require 10 beads on each wire. Secure such an abacus and show how to use it to illustrate that this *t*-system is a place-value system.

5. Use an abacus with 3 beads on a wire to show that the strange *abc* system discussed in Section 3–3 is a place-value system. How does use of the abacus reflect the fact that the system has no zero symbol?

Exponential notation can be used to emphasize place-value ideas:

$$325 = 3 \cdot 10^2 + 2 \cdot 10 + 5;$$
$$4038 = 4 \cdot 10^3 + 0 \cdot 10^2 + 3 \cdot 10 + 8.$$

The base four numeral, 23_4, can be expressed in base ten exponential notation as $2 \cdot 4 + 3$. In base four exponential notation, of course,

$$23_4 = 2 \cdot 10_4 + 3.$$

An appearance of symmetry is achieved by writing 10^1 for 10 and 10^0 for 1; 4^1 for 4 and 4^0 for 1; etc.* Thus

The numeral	equals	in base ten exponential notation
5738	=	$5 \cdot 10^3 + 7 \cdot 10^2 + 3 \cdot 10^1 + 8 \cdot 10^0$
321_4	=	$3 \cdot 4^2 + 2 \cdot 4^1 + 1 \cdot 4^0$
3243_5	=	$3 \cdot 5^3 + 2 \cdot 5^2 + 4 \cdot 5^1 + 3 \cdot 5^0$
10110_2	=	$1 \cdot 2^4 + 0 \cdot 2^3 + 1 \cdot 2^2 + 1 \cdot 2^1 + 0 \cdot 2^0$

EXERCISES 3–10

1. Rewrite in base ten exponential notation:
   a) 2376   b) 2376_8 c) 312_6
   d) 2134_5 e) 1021_3 f) 101011_2
   g) $97ET_{12}$ (*T* for ten, *E* for eleven)

2. Translate each number into base ten notation:
   a) 23_5 b) 33_6 c) 47_{11} d) 324_5
   e) 1011_2 f) 1011_3 g) 1011_4 h) 1011_8

---

* We shall give a better reason for these notational conventions in Chapter 5.

3. Translate 64 into:

   a) base 11 notation   b) base 8 notation *100*

   c) base 4 notation   d) base 2 notation

   e) base 5 notation *224₅*   f) base 3 notation

   g) base 64 notation *10*

4. Derive (a) base 6, (b) base 5, (c) base 4, (d) base 3, and (e) base 2 numerals for the following set of dots by repeated grouping. Show that in doing this one need never count beyond 6, 5, 4, 3, and 2, respectively.

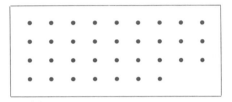

5. Add: a) 21_5 b) 23_5 c) 32_5 d) 44_5 e) 234_5 f) 234_5

            13_5 14_5 41_5 33_5 302_5 341_5

            34₅   *42*   *123*   *132*   *1041*   *1130*

6. Subtract: a) 44_5 b) 41_5 c) 412_5

               21_5 23_5 234_5

               23   *13*   *123*

7. Multiply: a) 32_5 b) 23_5 c) 43_5

                2_5 12_5 34_5 *3 2 2 2*

              114

8. Divide: a) $341_5 \div 13_5$ b) $2230_5 \div 41_5$

9. Decide whether each number below is even or odd.

   a) 2343   b) 2343_5 c) 2343_6 d) 2343_7

10. Fill the blank indicating the number base so that the following statement is true for the dot array: There are 112___ dots in the array.

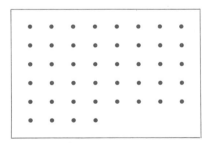

11. Construct base five addition and multiplication tables.

12. Construct base twelve addition and multiplication tables.

13. It is easy to convert Roman numerals to place-value notation. The diagram below indicates how this is done.

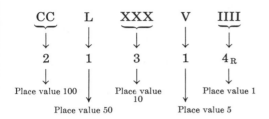

The subscript R indicates that we are using place-value notation for Roman numerals.

a) Express LXXII in this notation.

b) Write the Roman numeral for 1041402_R; the base ten numeral.

c) Note how easily a base-ten numeral is converted to this notation. Explain.

$$
\begin{array}{ccc}
8 & 7 & 6 \\
\downarrow & \downarrow & \downarrow \\
13 & 12 & 11_R
\end{array}
$$

Write the ordinary Roman numeral for 876.

d) Show how to convert 14131214_R quickly to base ten notation.

e) Add: 131412_R f) Subtract: 4021314_R
        101204_R 3130202_R

g) Explain the exponential notation

$$21314_R = 2(2^2 \cdot 5^2) + 1(2 \cdot 5^2) + 3(2 \cdot 5) + 1(5) + 4.$$

Write 13141214_R in exponential notation.

14. Explain the simple method shown below for converting base eight to base two notation, and vice versa.

a)
$$
\begin{array}{ccc}
7 & 6 & 5_8 \\
\downarrow & \downarrow & \downarrow \\
111 & 110 & 101_2
\end{array}
$$
         b)
$$
\begin{array}{ccc}
10 & 110 & 101_2 \\
\downarrow & \downarrow & \downarrow \\
2 & 6 & 5_8
\end{array}
$$

15. On July 14, 1965, the television camera in the Mariner IV spacecraft took the first "fly by" pictures of the planet Mars. These pictures were sent by radio signal some 134 million miles to earth. The earth computer received each picture in the form of binary (base-two) numerals. Each picture consisted of 200 lines. Each line consisted of 200 dots. Each dot was represented by a 6-digit binary numeral. The numeral 000000 represented a

white dot; the numeral 111111 represented a black dot. Numerals between these represented corresponding shades of gray.

a) How many digits had to be sent through space to describe a picture?

b) How many different shades of color could be represented by these numerals?

c) What numeral represented the shade of gray closest to black?

d) What numeral represented the shade of gray closest to white?

e) What two numerals represented shades approximately midway between white and black?

f) Let 11 represent a black square, 00 a white square, 01 light gray, and 10 dark gray. Convert the binary numerals into a picture.

00	11	11	11	11	11	00
00	11	00	01	00	11	00
00	11	01	00	01	11	00
00	11	01	01	01	11	00
00	11	01	00	01	11	00
00	00	01	01	01	00	00
00	10	10	10	10	10	00

$\rightarrow$

16. a) Examine and justify this mechanical procedure for converting a base ten numeral to a base twelve numeral:

$$10{,}267 = (5E37)_{12}$$

because

i) $12\overline{)10267}\ \ \dfrac{855}{}$ with remainder⑦

ii) $12\overline{)855}\ \ \dfrac{71}{}$ with remainder③

iii) $12\overline{)71}\ \ \dfrac{⑤}{}$ with remainder Ⓔ(= 11)

b) Convert 2279 to a base twelve numeral.

c) Convert 1738 to a base twelve numeral.

d) Discover a procedure for converting from base ten to base seven and use it to convert each of the following to base seven: 383, 100, 2800.

3–7   from operations on sets to operations on numbers*

Operations on numbers are suggested by specific physical situations. A child pushes three pencils together with two pencils and counts the resulting set, obtaining five. With three oranges and two oranges he also gets five. From evidence of this sort he decides that when sets of three things and two things are pushed together, a set of five things results.

Thus the union operation on disjoint sets suggests the invention of an "addition" operation on numbers.

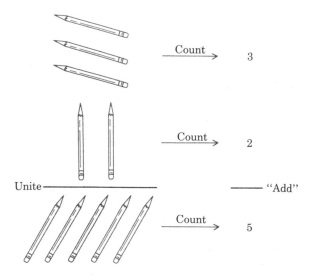

The operation addition is defined so that one will arrive at the same number whether one first unites and then counts or first counts and then adds. More formally,

DEFINITION OF ADDITION OF WHOLE NUMBERS

Given that a, b are whole numbers and that A, B are disjoint sets of a, b elements, respectively, then $a + b =$ the number of elements in $A \cup B$.

---

* We refer to numbers rather than numerals in this section because, even though it is psychologically true that young children add and multiply numerals, still it is better logically to say here that it is numbers that are added and multiplied. We do not intend to explore this logical advantage of numbers over numerals, but you may find the following oversimplification helpful. We avoid the word "numeral" in order to emphasize that what is said in this section does not depend on choosing a particular numeration system; everything remains true in any numeration system at all.

Symbolically, we can picture it this way.

Sets	Counting function n	Whole numbers
A	$\rightarrow$	$n(A) = a$
B	$\rightarrow$	$n(B) = b$
$A \cup B$	$\rightarrow$	$n(A \cup B) = a + b$

That is, addition is defined so that we arrive at the same number whether we first count and then add (go across and then down), or first unite and then count (go down and then across). Briefly:

For disjoint sets A and B,
$n(A \cup B) = n(A) + n(B)$.

A mathematician would describe this relationship between the counting function and the operations of "disjoint union" and addition by saying:

Counting is a *homomorphism* with respect to "disjoint union" and addition.

A child would probably prefer to think of counting as a *bridge* from the "real" world of tangible objects to the "abstract" world of numbers, and a two-way bridge at that. But whether he calls it a homomorphism or a bridge or nothing at all, he exploits its properties with admirable skill to solve seemingly hopeless problems. Let us illustrate.

When a very young child is asked to find the sum of 3 and 2 (a problem in the abstract world), he passes over to the real world by exhibiting disjoint sets of 3 and 2 fingers. He forms their union (a real-world manipulation) and then counts (takes the bridge back to the abstract world).

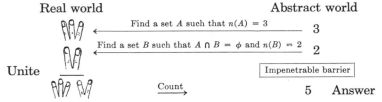

Real world   Abstract world

Find a set A such that $n(A) = 3$ 3

Find a set B such that $A \cap B = \phi$ and $n(B) = 2$ 2

Unite

Impenetrable barrier

Count $\longrightarrow$ 5   Answer

When an older child is asked how many pieces of candy he has eaten in the last two days, he recalls that he ate 4 yesterday and 5 today, adds 4 and 5 in the abstract world, and gives the answer even though it is physically impossible for him to exhibit, unite, and count the sets of (real) objects in question.

Real world		Abstract world
Yesterday's candy	$\xrightarrow{\text{Count}}$	4
Today's candy	$\xrightarrow{\text{Count}}$	5 Add

Impenetrable barrier   ―

$Y \cup T$ (Cannot be exhibited)   9 Answer

It is this latter procedure that is most useful to the child as he progresses in school. He is able to solve all sorts of "practical" problems by first translating them into problems in the world of numbers and then utilizing the techniques and tricks he has devised for use in that world.

The term *homomorphism* is always associated with a function, from one system to another, which translates information obtained by calculation in one system into information about the other.

EXERCISES 3–11

1. A child learning to compute, and relying heavily on his fingers for help, is asked to add 4 and 7. Comment on the problem he faces in securing disjoint sets. How would he be likely to solve his problem?

2. A child in first grade is asked to add 5 and 6. He marches to the blackboard, makes 5 marks, makes 6 more marks, and counts. Explain how he is using the fact that counting is a *homomorphism* relative to disjoint union of sets and addition of numbers.

3. Children in a third-grade classroom are asked to find the total number of children in the two other third-grade classrooms. One child runs off to Miss Brown's room and brings back the number 26. A second child returns from Miss Smith's room with 29. A third child carries out the appropriate calculation on the blackboard. Explain how these children are using the fact that counting is a *homomorphism* relative to disjoint union and addition.

4. The diagram below describes a homomorphism relative to multiplication and addition which you may have used in the past. Explain the diagram. Do you know the technical name of this homomorphism?

$$\times \quad \left(\begin{array}{l} 1000 \to 3 \\ \underline{\quad 100 \to 2} \\ 100{,}000 \to 5 \end{array} \right) \quad +$$

5. Ponder and discuss the diagram.

$$\times \quad \left(\begin{array}{l} 7.41 \quad\;\; \to 2 \\ \underline{12.301 \quad \to 3} \\ 91.15041 \to 5 \end{array} \right) \quad +$$

6. Let U be a set, S be the collection of all subsets of U, and O be a collection of open sentences (cf. page 21). Let t be the function from O to S which assigns to each open sentence its truth set in U; that is the set of all elements in U which, when substituted in the open sentence, yield a true statement.

a) Is t a homomorphism with respect to the operations "or" in O and "union" in S?

b) Is t a homomorphism with respect to the operations "and" in O and "intersection" in S?

7. Some children "peck" when they add. (A generation ago many did this.) To add 8 and 4, when working at the blackboard, they peck on the board with the chalk very quickly—ta, ta, ta, ta—and write "12." Their muscles are trained so that they can look at any of the numerals 1 to 9 and automatically peck the correct number of times. Discuss this shifting back and forth between the real world and the world of mathematics.

8. Some children wriggle their toes as they add. Discuss as in Exercise 7.

9. Some children who have trouble learning their addition table do the following for years. In order to find a sum like $8 + 5$, they whisper to themselves:

"one-nine, two-ten, three-eleven, four-twelve, five-*thirteen*."

Explain.

10. Explain why "disjoint" is an indispensable concept in the definition of addition. Given that $n(A) = 10$ and $n(B) = 8$, what can you say about $n(A \cup B)$ if you don't know whether or not A and B are disjoint.

▶ *Aside.* We have deliberately ignored one crucial point in the preceding discussion. In order to add a and b we choose two sets A and B so that

  i) $n(A) = a$ (the number of set A is a),

  ii) $n(B) = b$,

  iii) $A \cap B = \varnothing$.

Then we agree that

$a + b = n(A \cup B)$.

Suppose that instead of sets A and B we picked other sets C and D satisfying these conditions. That is,

$n(C) = a; \ n(D) = b; \ C \cap D = \varnothing.$

Then would $n(C \cup D) = n(A \cup B)$?

  Unless we have this equality, our definition of addition is ridiculous. Different people would get different answers for the same addition problem. A careful proof that this equality holds would be tedious. We accept this property of sets on the basis of our intuition. In justification of this reliance on intuition, we know of no first-grade child who ever raised this question. ◀

  We observed earlier (recall Exercise 1, page 43) that there is a connection between the *cartesian product* operation on sets and the *multiplication* operation on numbers. The connection is precisely the same as the connection between the union operation on (disjoint) sets and the addition operation on numbers. Let us illustrate with a particular case.

Sets	Counting function	Numbers
$\{a, b\}$	$\rightarrow$	2
$\{r, s, t\}$	$\rightarrow$	3

Form cartesian product   Multiply

$$\{(a, r),\ (b, r),\ (a, s),\ (b, s),\ (a, t),\ (b, t)\} \rightarrow \qquad 6$$

The operation multiplication is defined so that one will arrive at the same number whether one first forms the cartesian product and then counts or first counts and then multiplies. Formally,

DEFINITION OF MULTIPLICATION OF WHOLE NUMBERS

Given that a, b are whole numbers and A, B are sets of a, b elements, respectively, then

$$a \cdot b = \text{the number of elements in } A \times B.$$

Problem. Must we be careful that A and B be disjoint?

Symbolically,

Sets	Counting function n	Whole numbers
A	$\rightarrow$	$n(A) = a$
B	$\rightarrow$	$n(B) = b$
$A \times B$	$\rightarrow$	$n(A \times B) = a \cdot b$

In mathematical terminology:

Counting is a homomorphism with respect to cartesian product and multiplication.

That is:

$$n(A \times B) = n(A) \cdot n(B).$$

Thus if you wish to know the number of elements in the cartesian product of two sets A, B, you can exchange the task of counting $A \times B$ for the triple task of counting A, counting B, and multiplying the resulting numbers. On the other hand, if you don't know how to multiply two numbers a, b, you can exchange this task of multiplication for the quadruple task of counting off an appropriate set A, an appropriate set B, forming $A \times B$, and counting $A \times B$.

To most of us the operation *union of sets* is a very natural operation. We are comfortable with it. But the operation *cartesian product* of sets seems artificial. We just don't perform it very often. Hence the relationship between multiplication and cartesian product tends to be ignored. It is easy to see why the cartesian product fades into the background. By the time multiplication is introduced in the school, children have developed considerable facility with our Hindu-Arabic numeration system. It usually takes a long time to count up the elements of the cartesian product of two sets. It is far easier to exchange this laborious task for the multiplication operation on numbers. Hence when we utilize the fact that counting is a homomorphism relative to cartesian product and multiplication we are always going in the one direction, *away from* the *physical* world and *into* the *abstract* world of mathematics. We almost never count the elements of a cartesian product set.

EXERCISES 3–12

1. In your closet hang the following blouses and skirts with colors White, Red, Green, Yellow.

   Blouses $= \{W, R, Y\}$;   skirts $= \{w, g\}$.

   You wish to know how many choices of outfits are available to you. Will you count the cartesian product set $\{(W, w), (W, g), (R, w), (R, g), (Y, w), (Y, g)\}$ or will you apply the homomorphism as shown below?

   $$\begin{array}{r} \{W, R, Y\} \to 3 \\ \{w, g\} \to 2 \\ \hline 6 \end{array}$$

2. Answer the question of Exercise 1 for a case in which there are (a) 2 blouses and 1 skirt, (b) 6 blouses and 0 skirts, (c) 45 blouses and 57 skirts.

3.

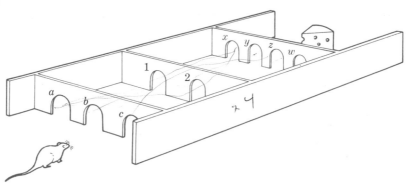

a) How many different paths may the rat follow to get to the cheese?

b) What sort of cartesian product is suggested by this problem? What do its elements look like?

Exercise 2(b) above calls attention to the fact that from our definition of multiplication it follows inexorably that any number times zero is zero. You can make the argument yourself, referring to the diagram below.

$$\left(\begin{matrix} A & \xrightarrow{n} & a \\ \varnothing & \xrightarrow{n} & 0 \end{matrix} \right)$$
$$A \times \varnothing \xrightarrow{n} a \cdot 0$$

$A \times \varnothing = \{(x, y) \mid x \in A \text{ and } y \in \varnothing\}$

Complete the argument.

Although the satisfying theoretical definition of multiplication is the cartesian product definition, the useful classroom definition is phrased in terms of addition.

The "repeated addition" definition of multiplication.   We agree that for any number a

i) $0 \cdot a = 0$

ii) $1 \cdot a = a$

iii) If $b \neq 0$ and $b \neq 1$, then
$$b \cdot a = \underbrace{a + a + \cdots + a}_{b \text{ addends } a}$$

The most interesting thing about this definition is that it is not formulated in terms of operations on sets, but in terms of abstract operations on numbers. This reflects our growing independence from the real world. It also explains why it is more difficult for children to understand when they should use multiplication in problem-solving than it is to recognize when they should use addition. When they apply multiplication they are not quite so close to the real world.

It would be interesting to analyze carefully the "repeated-addition" description of multiplication. If we did this we would be brought back to the cartesian product point of view, but as a practical teaching tool the repeated-addition definition is quite satisfactory. This definition does have the weakness that if it is the only one we know, then when we are faced with a problem that is naturally viewed in terms of the cartesian product (like the 45-blouses, 57-skirts problem), we may not be able to see the applicability of repeated addition, and so not realize that multiplication is the appropriate tool for solving the problem.

EXERCISES 3–13

1. On each of Sunday, Monday, Tuesday, Wednesday I eat three meals, Breakfast, Lunch, Dinner. How many meals do I eat?

   a) Explain how one views this problem from the repeated-addition viewpoint.

   b) Interpret the equation below and explain how it demonstrates applicability of the cartesian product concept to this problem.

$$\{S,\ M,\ T,\ W\} \times \{B,\ L,\ D\} \ = \ \{(S, B),\ (S, L),\ (S, D)$$
$$(M, B),\ (M, L),\ (M, D)$$
$$(T, B),\ (T, L),\ (T, D)$$
$$(W, B),\ (W, L),\ (W, D)\}$$

   c) Whether one views the problem from the repeated-addition or the cartesian product frame of reference, how should he *solve* the problem?

2. Let us return momentarily to the tally numeration system and examine in detail the physical activity required for a meticulous solution of a multiplication problem that leaves nothing to chance. The first four steps of the work are shown below. Complete the computation, explain it in detail, and relate it to the cartesian-product concept.

   Problem

   | | | | ← This many children in each cave
   × | | | ← This many caves
   ─────

   Solution

   Step 1   Step 2   Step 3   Step 4

3. Use the cartesian product definition of multiplication to show that

   i) $\forall a,\ a \cdot 1 = a$

   ii) $\forall a, b,\ a \cdot b = b \cdot a$

   Explain why this illustrates a *theoretical* advantage of the cartesian product definition of multiplication over the repeated-addition definition. With the repeated-addition definition, is it obvious that $a \cdot b = b \cdot a$?

4. We can (and should) describe addition informally in terms of counting. That is, to find the sum of $a + b$, begin at a and count forward b. Then

for $b + a$ we begin at b and count forward a. With this description, is it *obvious* that $a + b = b + a$?

Use the homomorphism that relates addition to disjoint union and prove that $a + b = b + a$.

5. Relate Exercises 3 and 4 to some of the 4-year-old child's thought processes described in Section 3–3.

One nice thing about precise definitions is that they remove the oppressive atmosphere of doubt. We have seen in Exercises 3 and 4 above that by carefully relating addition and multiplication of numbers to operations on sets we make it possible to *prove* certain things about addition and multiplication.

Example

	Since	It follows that
1)	$A \cup B = B \cup A$	$a + b = b + a$
2)	$A \times B$ and $B \times A$ have the same number	$a \cdot b = b \cdot a$
3)	$(B \cup C) \cup A = A \cup (C \cup B)$	$(b + c) + a = a + (c + b)$
4)	$A \times (B \cup C) = (A \times B) \cup (A \times C)$	$\ldots$
5)	$(A \times B) \times C$ has the same number as $A \times (B \times C)$	$\ldots$

Problem Think about (4) and (5) above. Can you convince yourself that these assertions are true for sets? If so, what are the corresponding number statements? Can you suggest other statements of this type that lead to interesting statements about numbers?

Implications for teaching. Counting, and the attendant mental arithmetic, should be heavily emphasized in the early years. It is important that children be given problems (of mental arithmetic) in a logical sequential order so that they are encouraged to invent their own shortcut techniques of problem-solving. Much of mental arithmetic can be done prior to first grade. Mental arithmetic is very difficult to organize in a large classroom with wide degrees of individual differences. Techniques for working with small groups should be developed.

It is desirable that children work with sets of physical objects. Bottle caps can be identified with children, apples, houses . . . For example, two rows of bottle caps can be compared, one representing boys, the other girls, and with the primitive tool of one-to-one correspondence one can show how many more there are in one set than in the other.

As you write number sentences on the board, tell a story:

$6 - 1 = 5.$

"Six children were at the party. One went home . . ."

Stories are particularly important when new algorithms are being introduced:

```
    10
3 | 42    I give each child 10 cookies.
    30    That uses up 30.  12 are
    ‾‾
    12    left
```

```
         4
        10    I can give each child
3 | 42    4 more
    30
    ‾‾
    12
    12
    ‾‾
```

In these early years the children should see the algorithms arise as manipulations of numerals which are identified with manipulations of sets.

Your exposure to the many numeration systems in this chapter should have impressed you with the magnitude of the task that the child faces in learning to handle our Hindu-Arabic system. Computation with Roman numerals and in base five is simple compared with Hindu-Arabic computation.

You should be alert to the role that functions play in the child's organization of arithmetical knowledge. Your understanding of function concepts should increase your insight into the ways that children systematize their knowledge of arithmetic.

It is significant that the child can learn *numeration* quickly and easily. The rule for writing the successor of a numeral is simple. This is an *ordinal* concept. The child should count by 2's, 5's, 10's, etc. It is an easy step from numeration to the consideration of inequalities. Since we recognize that 327 comes *before* 331 in the sequence of numerals, we see that $327 < 331$. But the gap between understanding how to write numerals in sequence and how to compute with these numerals (cardinal usage) is wide. The *abc* system illustrates this gap. You learned the theory of numeration in that system very quickly but undoubtedly found computation quite difficult.

The abacus beautifully relates ordinal and cardinal concepts. As one "counts," place-value concepts (which are cardinal concepts) are graphically portrayed. A 9-bead abacus best brings out place-value concepts. An 18-bead (on each wire) abacus is probably best for explaining "carrying" in addition. (Why?)

The informal description of addition presented to the child should be close to our mathematical definition, involving union of sets. But it appears that the cartesian product definition for multiplication is difficult to present effectively to children. The "sloppy" repeated-addition description seems best. Rectangular arrays of dots present multiplication facts nicely:

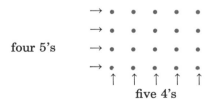

four 5's

five 4's

A game like dominoes encourages students to visualize numbers as arrays of dots. This facilitates the recognition of number relations.

• • •   6 is 4 and 2   • • •

• • •   • • •   9 is three 3's

6 is two 3's   • • •
6 is three 2's   9 is 6 and 3

The ability to count by tens lays a foundation for understanding multiplication by ten and so prepares the child for multiplication by large numbers.

CHAPTER 3 EXERCISES

1. What sound is matched with each set which contains a single element in
   (a) Latin? (b) Greek? (c) French? (d) Russian?
2. Repeat Exercise 1 for the empty set.
3. In Roman numeration:
   a) Count by X's from LXVI to CXVI.
   b) Count backward by C's from MLV to CCCLV.
   c) Begin with 1 and double successively ten times.
   d) Begin with CLXXXXII and halve successively six times.
   e) Begin with I and multiply successively by V five times.
   f) Begin with MD and divide successively by V as many times as possible.
4. In the *abc* system, we have the correspondences below.

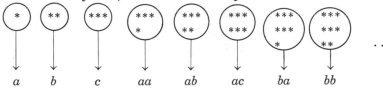

Find each sum below by passing *from* each numeral *to* a set, forming the union of the sets, and determining the numeral of this union.

   a) $c + c$ b) $aa + c$ c) $c + ac$ d) $ab + ba$ e) $ba + bb$

5. For each sum below, "guess" the result, using your intuition, and then verify your guess by counting off the proper sets, forming their union, and counting this union.

   a) $a + a$ b) $aa + aa$ c) $aa + bb$ d) $aaa + aaa$.

6. Find the *abc* numeral for the following set by counting.

7. The numeral for 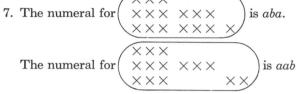 is *aba*.

The numeral for (××× ××× ××× ××× ××) is *aab*.

Get the numeral for the union of these sets by:

a) Using what you have learned about addition in the *abc* system.

b) Counting the union.

8. Counting by *c*'s in the *abc* system runs as below:

c, ac, bc, cc, aac, abc, acc, bac, . . .

If you recognize the pattern, continue counting to *aabc*.

9. Counting by *bc*'s runs:

bc, abc, bbc, cbc, aabc, abbc, . . .

If you recognize the pattern, continue counting to *aabbc*.

10. Use the results of Exercises 8 and 9 to solve the following multiplication problems by a shortcut.

   a) *ac* × *c*   b) *cc* × *c*   c) *babb* × *c*

   d) *bb* × *bc*   e) *cab* × *bc*   f) *abba* × *bc*

11. Relate the "rules" you used in Exercise 10 with our Hindu-Arabic rules for multiplying by 10 and 100.

12. In the base four system count by 10_4's from 10_4 to 1120_4.

13. In the base three system count by 10_3's to 1120_3.

14. In the base four system count by 100_4 to 10200_4.

15. Use a shortcut to get the following products.

   a) $21_4 \times 10_4 = 210$ b) $210_4 \times 10_4 = 2100$ c) $2211_4 \times 10_4 = 22110$

   d) $21_3 \times 10_3 = 210$ e) $210_3 \times 10_3 = 2100$ f) $2211_3 \times 10_3 = 22110$

   g) $21_3 \times 100_3 = $ h) $210_4 \times 100_4 = $ i) $2211_7 \times 1000_7 = $

16. In base four it is easy to multiply by numbers four, sixteen, sixty-four, . . . Explain why.

17. By what numbers can one easily multiply in (a) base three? (b) base seven? (c) base two?

18. A student writes 73_5 in base five notation. Explain his probable error and correct it.

19. A student adds as below in base eight. Correct his error.

$$47_8$$
$$65_8$$
$$\overline{114_8}$$

20. Compute the products below using the indicated notation. Correct the notation in part (l).

a) $4 \times 4 = \underline{\qquad}_7$ b) $4 \times 4 = \underline{\qquad}_6$ c) $4 \times 4 = \underline{\qquad}_5$

d) $4 \times 4 = \underline{\qquad}_8$ e) $12_9 \times 12_9 = \underline{\qquad}_9$ f) $12_8 \times 12_8 = \underline{\qquad}_8$

g) $12_7 \times 12_7 = \underline{\qquad}_7$ h) $12_6 \times 12_6 = \underline{\qquad}_6$ i) $12_5 \times 12_5 = \underline{\qquad}_5$

j) $12_4 \times 12_4 = \underline{\qquad}_4$ k) $12_3 \times 12_3 = \underline{\qquad}_3$ l) $12_2 \times 12_2 = \underline{\qquad}_2!$

SUMMARY

Many different functions are related to counting. We have denoted by C the function which associates each number sound in English with its successor. Of course C has its French, German, etc. counterparts.

Numeration functions associate written symbols with their successors. All one need do to construct a numeration system is to describe such a function, i.e., explain how to pass from one symbol to the next. We make three distinct uses of counting: nominal (naming), ordinal, and cardinal.

To count (verbally) a set is to construct a proper 1–1 onto function from a set of number sounds to the set. We have referred to these functions as counting functions. Each such function has for its domain a standard set, one of

{one},   {one, two},   {one, two, three},   . . .

We associate each standard set with its last number (yet another function!):

{one, two} → two;   {one, two, . . . , nine} → nine.

We have denoted by n the function which associates each set A with its number.

$$A = \{\times, \times, \times\}$$
$$\uparrow \quad \uparrow \quad \uparrow$$
$$\{1, \quad 2, \quad 3\} \rightarrow n(A) = 3$$

It is this function n which is of paramount importance in defining operations on numbers. We define addition and multiplication of numbers so that these operations reflect certain operations on sets. If $A \cap B = \varnothing$ we define $n(A) + n(B)$ to be $n(A \cup B)$. For any sets A, B, disjoint or not, we define $n(A) \cdot n(B)$ to be $n(A \times B)$. We make these definitions to facilitate the analysis of disjoint unions and cartesian products. In technical terminology the "counting" function n is a *homomorphism* relative to the two operations, cartesian product of sets and multiplication of numbers.

The attention given to various numeration systems in this chapter calls attention to the fact that techniques for written and mental computation depend very much on the numeration system that is employed. The child who is skillful at counting can make rapid progress in mental arithmetic. This progress is relatively independent of his ability to write numerals. Simple numeration systems like the tally and Roman lend themselves to simple, easily understood (though often tedious) algorithms. Addition in both the tally and Roman systems is essentially done by forming the union of two disjoint sets of symbols. Multiplication in the tally system is simply a matter of forming a cartesian product set from two sets of marks. The operations on the numerals are very close to the motivating operations on physical sets.

For the more sophisticated numeration systems, like our system of Arabic numerals, the connection between computational techniques and the fundamental set operations on which the techniques are based is not so clear. Accordingly the elementary teacher faces a formidable task as she attempts to help children relate manipulations of numerals to the underlying operations on sets. The *abc* system of numeration dramatizes the difficulty of developing computational skill in a place-value system. Of course it is much simpler than the base ten system we teach, but the reader probably still found it difficult to understand addition, subtraction, and multiplication operations on these symbols.

4   computing with whole numbers

4-1   introduction

Chapter 3 dealt with Stages 1 and 2 of the process by which the arithmetic of the whole number system is abstracted from the physical world. We considered the invention of numerals and the invention of basic operations on numerals. We saw that the physical and mental activity in which we engage, as we use numerals to solve problems, depends very much on the system of numeration chosen. We made no attempt in Chapter 3 to develop great computational skill in any of the numeration systems. In this chapter we shall focus on the Hindu-Arabic system and examine computation in that system. We shall consider the development of algorithms for addition, subtraction, multiplication, and division. Our contact with the physical world will become more tenuous as we proceed. We shall be interested in clever ways of arranging our work, in shortcuts, and in tricks. This is Stage 3 of the abstraction process, *Learning to Play the Game of Arithmetic*. This is a stage that can be made stimulating and exciting to children.

Chapter 5 will also be concerned primarily with computation. But the approach will be altogether different. In Chapter 5 we *Analyze the Structure of the Game*. This is the Stage-4 abstraction. Although in Chapter 4 the physical world directs what we do, in the sense that we can justify our computational techniques by appealing to the physical world, in Chapter 5 the real world is discarded. We look at arithmetic as a game played with symbols according to a few clear-cut rules that need have nothing to do with the outside world. The *theory* of arithmetic will unfold from basic principles (the rules) in Chapter 5, just as the theory of chess unfolds from the rules of the game.

The practical significance of these two chapters should be made clear. Much of Chapter 4 could be taught directly to elementary school students. Chapter 5, on the other hand, is written for the teacher. The exposition is formal so that the fundamental principles of arithmetic will stand out clearly. Elementary school students should be introduced to these principles more gently and informally.

4–2   utilizing counting skill in computation

In Chapter 3 we saw that with the proper attention to mental arithmetic children can develop quite a bit of computational ability. This skill in mental computation flows directly from their ability to count and to visualize sets of objects. Counting is originally an *ordinal* activity, but as soon as the child learns to associate number sounds with sets of objects, *cardinal* concepts enter the picture. The child who adds 45 and 34 by thinking

"45 is 4 tens and 5"
"34 is 3 tens and 4"
"4 tens and 3 tens is 5, 6, 7 tens"
"5 and 4 is 6, 7, 8, *9*"
"So 45 and 34 is 79"

is blending ordinal and cardinal concepts in a singularly useful way.

Ideally, long before children face such addition problems in their workbooks as

3	8	9	12	21	28	200
2	4	7	3	32	34	100

they should have solved many such problems mentally. To add 68 and 30 mentally the child thinks "78, 88, *98*." To subtract 30 from 100, he thinks "90, 80, *70*."

In the remainder of this section we assume that the teacher is dealing with students who have had much practice with mental arithmetic. They count with understanding. We indicate how one may capitalize on this counting ability in the teaching of written arithmetic. Note that, to use the algorithms shown below, a child does not need to know his addition facts. The ability to count suffices.

Naturally the first techniques for writing down answers to problems should reflect the approach that is used in mental computation. This is a "left-to-right" arrangement of the work, as we indicate below.

Written work   The thinking

```
    32
 +  45
 ───────
    72     ←    "32 and 40 is 72"
    77     ←    "72 and 5 is 77"

   247
 + 328
 ───────
   547     ←    "547; I have added 300"
   567     ←    "20 more is 567; I have added 320"
   575     ←    "567 and 8 is 575; I have added 328"
```

Written work   The thinking

$$
\begin{array}{r}
76 \\
-\ 23 \\
\hline
56 \\
53
\end{array}
$$

56   ←   "Taking away 20"
53   ←   "Taking away 3 more"

$$
\begin{array}{r}
300 \\
-\ 149 \\
\hline
200 \\
160 \\
151
\end{array}
$$

200   ←   "Subtracting 100"
160   ←   "Subtracting 40"
151   ←   "Subtracting 9"

It is easy to change to a right-to-left pattern, as the examples below show.

53	349	82	901
+ 48	+ 483	− 26	− 788
61	352	76	893
101	432	56	813
	832		113

A student who can count forward and backward, by 1's, 10's, and 100's, and has used this skill in mental arithmetic should understand these written solutions. Note the absence of borrowing difficulties in subtraction. The above techniques for addition and subtraction illustrate the principle that the first form of any algorithm should be closely related to students' previous computational experiences.

The long algorithms presented above have the advantage of calling clear attention to the ideas that are being used. The problem list below indicates how these algorithms may be abbreviated.

EXERCISES 4–1

1. Beginning with 457:
   a) Count forward 300 by hundreds.
   b) Count forward 60 more by tens.
   c) Count forward 8 more.
   d) Explain how ability to count as in (a), (b), (c) enables one to add 457 and 368.

2. Beginning with 912:
   a) Count backward 400.
   b) Count backward 30 more.
   c) Count backward 3 more.
   d) What problem have you solved?

3. Explain the abbreviation of the left-to-right work shown below. Point out the 763 and 843 in the abbreviated work.

Long method		Abbreviation	
	First step	Second step	Third step
363	363	363	363
+ 482	482	482	482
763	7	74	745
843		8	8
845			

Note that in the "long" solution, we write 9 digits. In the abbreviated solution there are 4 digits and one "stroke." We emphasize that in the abbreviated work we *think* exactly the same as in the long method. We simply *write* less. For example, in the first step we do not rewrite the 63 below the line.

4. Explain the abbreviation of left-to-right work in this subtraction problem:

Long method		Abbreviation	
	First step	Second step	Third step
802	802	802	802
− 456	− 456	− 456	− 456
402	4	45	456
352		3	34
346			

Point out the 402 and 352 in the abbreviated work.
How much writing is saved by the abbreviation?

5. The striking out of digits *below* the line can be avoided by changing to a right-to-left technique. Explain the abbreviation.

Long method		Abbreviation	
	First step	Second step	Third step
567	7	6 7	6 7
+ 458	5 6 7	5 6 7	5 6 7
575	4 5 8	4 5 8	4 5 8
625	5	2 5	1 0 2 5
1025			

How much *writing* is saved? Note that no *thinking* is saved.

6. Explain each step in this abbreviation for right-to-left subtraction:

Long method		Abbreviation	
	First step	Second step	Third step
802	7 9	7 9	7 9
− 456	8 0 2	8 0 2	8 0 2
796	− 4 5 6	− 4 5 6	− 4 5 6
746	6	4 6	3 4 6
346			

How much writing is saved?

7. Working right to left and *remembering* instead of striking out some digits saves more writing. Explain the abbreviations below. Note that here, for the first time, a little *thinking* is saved. Explain how this is accomplished.

An abbreviation of an abbreviation

Step 1	Step 2	Step 3
567	567	567
+ 458	+ 458	+ 458
5	25	1025

Think: 67 + 8 = 75   Think: 57 + 5 = 62   Think: 6 + 4 = 10
Write: 5   Write: 2   Write: 10
Remember: 7   Remember: 6

An ultimate abbreviation

Step 1	Step 2	Step 3
567	567	567
+ 458	+ 458	+ 458
5	25	1025

Write: 5   Write: 2   Write: 10
Think: 7   Think: 6

Comment on the amount of *thinking* saved by this abbreviation.

8. One could argue that in the final abbreviation presented in Exercise 7 one must *think* that 7 + 8 = 15 before *writing* the 5, and that one must *think* 6 + 1 = 7 before thinking 7. With some definitions of "thinking," this view seems correct. What case can be made for writing the 5 without thinking?

9. Explain how to insinuate more abbreviations into the subtraction technique shown in Exercise 5 until one finally "thinks" as shown below.

First step	Second step	Third step
802	802	802
− 456	− 456	− 456
6	46	346

Think: 9   Think: 7

10. Compare the way you "think", as you work the subtraction problem 802 − 456, with the abbreviated technique shown in Exercise 9.

a) Is the algorithm you use more efficient, less efficient, or essentially the same as this algorithm?

b) In moving from a long method for subtraction to an "ultimate" abbreviation, we considered successive abbreviations. Describe corresponding abbreviating steps for the algorithm you use in subtraction. That is, consider the ways of thinking from which your personal subtraction algorithm evolved, and show how step by step your method was shortened.

Exercise 10 is a deliberate attempt to ensnare the reader. Few people have a clear understanding of how the particular shortcut algorithms they employ originated out of a common-sense approach and then were gradually converted to mechanical procedures. It is desirable that each teacher of arithmetic understand the step-by-step shortening process by which algorithms are constructed. Otherwise the teacher may merely stand before her class and chant jargons like the following:

812	You can't take 6 from 2, so borrow 1 from the 1. Put it with the 2.
− 186	That makes 12. 6 from 12 is 6. Write the 6 under the 6. You can't
6	take 8 from 0 . . .

$$3 \overline{)96} \quad \text{(quotient 3)}$$

3 goes into 9 three times. Write the 3 above the 9 . . .

Now that we have looked with some care at the evolution of two algorithms, let us consider briefly the general problem of constructing efficient algorithms in our Hindu-Arabic numeration system. All algorithms are motivated by the recognition that certain basic types of set computations recur again and again.

1. Again and again we must determine the number of elements in the union of two disjoint sets.

2. Repeatedly we must calculate:

   a) How many more elements are in one set than another.

   b) How many elements must be adjoined to a first set to form a set equivalent to a second.

   c) How many elements are left after removal of a subset from a set.

3. Frequently we must know:

   a) How many elements belong to the cartesian product of two sets.

   b) The number of elements in the union of many sets, all equivalent to one another and each disjoint from all the others.

4. We are often faced with a practical problem in which we must:

   a) Partition a set into a given number of equivalent subsets and determine the number of elements in each such subset.

   b) Determine the number of subsets of a given size into which a set can be partitioned.

It is not at all obvious that a single calculating technique can be devised to handle the three types of problems described above in (2), or the two types of (3) and (4). This is one reason that students encounter difficulty with word problems.

The straightforward way to handle any real-world problem of one of the above types is to write numerals which describe the given sets. Now we *think* about these given sets and *visualize* the new set whose number must be computed in order to solve our problem. Because we can "see" how to manipulate the physical sets and form the needed new set, we can "see" how to work with the numerals of the given sets to form the numeral of the desired set. Because of the place-value aspects of our Hindu-Arabic system, we think of each set as partitioned into sets of one, sets of ten, sets of one hundred, . . . As we work with pencil and paper, we direct groups of one thousand each to march here and there, groups of one hundred to split up into ten groups of ten, etc. Eventually we realize that once we recognize the *type* of problem which confronts us we can *forget* the real world and solve the problem by thinking *only* about the numerals.

Soon we begin to examine our work with pencil and paper, asking how we can get answers most quickly and accurately. We devise clever, systematic ways of arranging our work. We learn that much of the *thinking* we do is not necessary. We finally ask ourselves questions like:

"Once I have recorded the numerals for two sets and know that I must *subtract* them to get my answer, what is the "least" amount of thinking and writing I can do to get the answer?"

Questions like these concern us in this chapter. An *algorithm* is essentially a description of *thinking, writing,* and *remembering* activities that enable one to solve some class of problems. Many algorithms seem to "make no sense." They "work," but few persons know why. Our point of view in this chapter is that to the very best of her ability the teacher must help students acquire insight into the evolution of our polished algorithms for the fundamental arithmetic operations.

4–3   the addition table

Of course, a student can develop little *skill* in addition and subtraction until he memorizes the basic addition table. An old theory of learning, now discredited, held that such memorization is best accomplished by repetitious drill. The current point of view is that, wherever ideas are bound together by logical threads, a certain amount of attention should be devoted to the study of the interrelationships between the ideas. It is very difficult to memorize nonsense. For example, suppose that you try to memorize a random string of 200 letters of the alphabet. You can imagine the effort required and the frustration you would experience. But now suppose that you construct a coherent 200 word speech such that the initial letters of the words are, in order, the 200 letters you wish to memorize. With relative ease you can memorize the speech. Now the *function* that detaches the first letter from each word enables you to know the nonsense string of letters. We can describe this type of learning as learning by *association*.

Basically it is an application of the function concept. In no body of knowledge is there greater opportunity to make useful associations between ideas than in mathematics. In mathematics also there are powerful basic principles which we can apply to simplify learning tasks. The ideal teaching technique would be one in which the teacher rarely found it necessary to formulate a principle for a student or to point out some useful association. Stimulated by a cleverly arranged sequence of problems, the student would make associations and recognize key principles. The chief advantage of this sort of teaching is that students so taught become self-reliant and independent. They develop confidence in their abilities to solve new problems. They are not afraid to think. Socrates understood this method of teaching, although at times even he lectured too much.

We are discussing the "discovery" method of teaching. In actual practice, after students have had reasonable opportunity to discover what they should discover, but have failed to do so, the teacher discovers it for them.

Here are some "associations" you can anticipate students making as they learn their addition facts:

$3 + 4 = 7$ because $3 + 3 = 6$
$5 + 6 = 11$ because $5 + 5 = 10$
$8 + 7 = 15$ because $8 + 8 = 16$

The student makes associations like the above because he automatically utilizes certain basic principles of addition which enable him to "take numbers apart" and "change the order of his work," relating in this way things that he doesn't know to things that he knows. We illustrate these principles below.

i) $2 + 9 = 9 + 2$
ii) $9 + 7 = 9 + (1 + 6) = (9 + 1) + 6$
iii) $8 + 7 = (5 + 5) + (3 + 2)$

Example (i) is important to the student who counts. It shows how changing the order of work is helpful.

Counting, "3, 4, 5, 6, 7, 8, 9, 10, 11" is replaced by counting, "10, 11".

The principle which justifies a reversal of order is called the

Commutative principle for addition.

Thinking in terms of sets, the principle is obvious. (Why?) Thinking in terms of counting, it is not so obvious. (Why not?)

Example (ii) illustrates the usefulness of what we call the

Associative principle for addition.

If *three* numbers are to be added without changing the order, we may begin by adding either the first two or the last two. Thinking in terms of sets, the associative principle is obvious. (Why?)

Example (iii) is an application of both the commutative and associative principles.

EXERCISES 4–2

1. Name each principle illustrated:
   a) $3 + 12 = 12 + 3$ commutative
   b) $8 + (2 + 7) = (8 + 2) + 7$ associative
   c) $(5 + 4) + 7 = 7 + (5 + 4)$ comm
   d) $(8 + 4) + (6 + 3) = 8 + [4 + (6 + 3)]$ ass
   e) $(2 + 2) + 2 = 2 + (2 + 2)$ comm

2. Find each sum. Use the indicated grouping. [In (e), for example, you are expected to think: $99 + 75 = 174$.]
   a) $3 + (7 + 8)$ $3 + 15 = 18$
   b) $(3 + 7) + 8$ $10 + 8 = 18$
   c) $19 + (1 + 8)$ $19 + 9 = 28$
   d) $(19 + 1) + 8$ $20 + 8 = 28$
   e) $99 + (74 + 1)$ $99 + 75 = 174$
   f) $(99 + 1) + 74$ $100 + 1 = 174$
   g) $(8 + 7) + (3 + 2)$ $15 + 5 = 20$
   h) $(8 + 2) + (7 + 3)$ $10 + 10 = 20$

3. The commutative and associative principles have been illustrated with Hindu-Arabic numerals. Do these principles hold in all numeration systems? yes Mention some properties peculiar to our Hindu-Arabic system not possessed by all numeration systems.

4. Comment on the following observations:

   a) Because the commutative and associative principles hold for all numeration systems, it seems reasonable to conclude that they must reflect basic properties of the real world which our numerals describe.

   b) The fact that *all* numeration systems have common properties suggests that we invent the concept of a *number system*, some sort of an idealized object which will exist (in our minds) independently of all numeration systems. Then we can think of different numeration systems as different ways of describing this one number system rather than ways of describing the real world.

A close look at the addition table below discloses many patterns. A clever child instinctively recognizes and uses some of these patterns in computation. In the table we interpret $a + b$ as the entry in the a-row and b-column. Note that the first row is the 0-row and the second row is the 1-row.

+	0	1	2	3	4	5	6	7	8	9
0	0	1	2	3	4	5	6	7	8	9
1	1	2	3	4	5	6	7	8	9	10
2	2	3	4	5	6	7	8	9	10	11
3	3	4	5	6	7	8	9	10	11	12
4	4	5	6	7	8	9	10	11	12	13
5	5	6	7	8	9	10	11	12	13	14
6	6	7	8	9	10	11	12	13	14	15
7	7	8	9	10	11	12	13	14	15	16
8	8	9	10	11	12	13	14	15	16	17
9	9	10	11	12	13	14	15	16	17	18

The basic Hindu-Arabic addition table

EXERCISES 4–3

1. Give an explanation of each of the following patterns:

   a) Each row is the same as the corresponding column.

   b) The entries in the 0-row (column) are the same as corresponding entries across the top (side) of the table.

   c) Diagonals up and to the right repeat one number.

   d) Diagonals down and to the right increase by 2.

   e) All diagonals are either made up of even numbers only or odd numbers only.

   f) Each entry in the table which is not on the border is the center of a 3-by-3 square. For example, 14 occurs in the square:

12	13	14
13	14	15
14	15	16

   The 14 is the *average* of any two entries in this square with which it is aligned. It is also the average of all 9 numbers.

2. A student confronted by a sum that he doesn't know (like $5 + 7$) may think of a "near-by" sum which he does know (like $5 + 5$). Explain why

the "long" diagonal 0–2–4–...–18 is strategically located for such use. (This justifies placing early stress on the doubles.)

3. Why is the most valuable diagonal up and to the right the one consisting of 10's? How does a student carry the information embodied in this diagonal on his hands?

4. A student should not need to memorize the 1-row or 1-column. Why not?

5. Explain, using the example below, how one can use properties of our numeration system and get all the results listed in the table by using only the left upper 6-by-6 block.

$8 + 3 = (5 + 3) + 3$ (How was the $5 + 3$ obtained?)
$(5 + 3) + 3 = 5 + (3 + 3) = 5 + 6$ (How was the 6 obtained?)
$5 + 6 = 5 + (5 + 1) = (5 + 5) + 1 = 10 + 1 = 11$

Note that the last computation, $10 + 1 = 11$, is not taken directly from the table. It is based on the place-value aspect of our numeration system. What significance for teaching has this fact that all table entries can be calculated from this smaller block?

6. Using the table *mechanically*, verify the associative property for:

a) $2 + 3 + 4$ b) $3 + 5 + 2$ c) $8 + 1 + 7$

Why can you not similarly verify this principle for $3 + 4 + 7$?

7. The addition table above pictures only a tiny fraction of the addition function $+$.

$$+ : W \times W \xrightarrow{\text{onto}} W$$

$(12, 15) \xrightarrow{+} 27; \qquad +((12, 15)) = 27.$

We write $+(12, 15)$ as an abbreviation for $+((12, 15))$. It is customary to write $a + b$ instead of $+(a, b)$.

a) Compute $+(347, 596)$.

b) Prove that $+$ is not a 1–1 function from $W \times W$ onto W. How many distinct ordered pairs in $W \times W$ are sent to 14 by $+$?

c) Can you look at one row of the table for $+$ and show that $+$ is an onto function? Which row?

d) Is $+(a, b) = +(b, a), \quad \forall a, b \in W$?

e) Use the table mechanically to compute

$+(4 + 5, 3), \qquad +(4, 5 + 3), \qquad$ and $\qquad +(3 + 4, 5)$.

f) How do

$+(a + b, c) \qquad$ and $\qquad +(a, b + c)$

compare?

g) Explain why $+(+(a, b), c) = +(a, +(b, c))$.

4–4   algorithms for addition and subtraction

An old algorithm for addition that runs from left to right and avoids "carrying" is the following. It was called the *scratch* method. Explain its use.

[A]	487	[B]	487
	538		538
	634		634
	396		796
	627		627
	2452		2852
	23		123
	68		308

There are many excellent ways to develop subtraction algorithms. In Section 4–2 we considered one which is based on skill in counting. Other algorithms are incorporated into problems in the next batch of exercises. Let us comment briefly on the relationship between addition and subtraction. This relationship is illustrated by the following simple diagram and the associated "facts."

$$5 + 4 = 9$$
$$9 - 5 = 4$$
$$9 - 4 = 5$$

5 and 4 are called *addends* of 9.
9 is the *sum* of 5 and 4.

Each subtraction problem involves three numbers. One of these three is the *sum* of the other two, which are *addends* of this sum. In each addition problem the addends are known and the sum is required. In each subtraction problem the sum and one addend are known. The other addend is required. One of the distressing situations in present-day classrooms is that many children are inept at solving *word problems*. They do not know *when* to add, *when* to subtract, *when* to multiply, *when* to divide. The principal way to improve student judgment in these areas of decision is to relate the development of algorithms very carefully to the real world and give students many word problems to solve. However, if students are aware of the simple relationship between addition and subtraction described above, the task is easier. Faced with a word problem involving three numbers, they can ask themselves,

"Is one of these the sum of the other two?"

If so, *addition* or *subtraction* is the appropriate operation. The next question is:

"Is the sum known?"

If the sum is not known we *add*. If it is known we *subtract*.

Confusion often arises in the classroom in situations like the following. The teacher asks a student how much more 8 is than 5. The student says 3. The teacher asks, "How did you get this answer?" The student replies, "I added." The teacher becomes upset and the pupil becomes confused. But the student *did add*. He thought

$5 + 3 = 8.$

He does not understand the teacher's question, which is really, "What operation applied to the numbers 8 and 5 produces 3?"

Many readers undoubtedly employ a subtraction algorithm known as the *Austrian* (or additive) method, which is taught in many schools. We shall develop this and other algorithms in the exercises below.

EXERCISES 4–4

1. Use the calculations below to find x and y.

   a)   342   b)   287
              6   4
            ─────   ─────
            348   291
             50   40
            ─────   ─────
            398   331
            200   500
            ─────   ─────
            598   831

         $598 - 342 = x$ $831 - y = 287$

2. Explain the long solution of the subtraction problem below.

   Problem   Work

   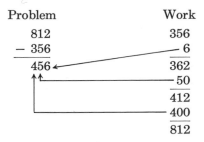

812		356
− 356		6
456		362
		50
		412
		400
		812

3. Explain how each of the steps below is an abbreviation for part of the work of Exercise 2.

Step 1	Step 2	Step 3

$$
\begin{array}{r}
8\ 1\ 2\\
6\\
-\ 3\ 5\ 6\\
\hline
6
\end{array}
\qquad
\begin{array}{r}
8\ 1\ 2\\
4\ 6\\
-\ 3\ 5\ 6\\
\hline
5\ 6
\end{array}
\qquad
\begin{array}{r}
8\ 1\ 2\\
4\ 6\\
-\ 3\ 5\ 6\\
\hline
4\ 5\ 6
\end{array}
$$

4. Explain how the algorithm below is a condensation of the three steps shown in Exercise 3.

$$
\begin{array}{r}
7\ 3\ 2\\
{}^{5}\ {}^{9}\\
-\ \ \not4\ \not8\ 6\\
\hline
2\ 4\ 6
\end{array}
$$

5. Here is how the "striking out" and "replacement" of numerals can be eliminated by mental work:

Instead of

$$
\begin{array}{r}
7\ 3\ 2\\
{}^{9}\\
-\ \ 4\ \not8\ 6\\
\hline
6
\end{array}
$$

Think: $486 + 6 = 492$ $\longrightarrow$

Remember the 9

$$
\begin{array}{r}
732\\
-\ 486\\
\hline
6
\end{array}
$$

Instead of

$$
\begin{array}{r}
7\ 3\ 2\\
{}^{5}\ {}^{9}\\
-\ \ \not4\ \not8\ 6\\
\hline
4\ 6
\end{array}
$$

Think: $492 + 40 = 532$ $\longrightarrow$

Remember the 5

$$
\begin{array}{r}
732\\
-\ 486\\
\hline
46
\end{array}
$$

Work each subtraction below by this abbreviated method.

a) $\begin{array}{r} 87 \\ -\ 32 \\ \hline \end{array}$ b) $\begin{array}{r} 273 \\ -\ 128 \\ \hline \end{array}$ c) $\begin{array}{r} 914 \\ -\ 286 \\ \hline \end{array}$

6. The work of Exercise 5 can be further shortened. Explain.

Step 1	Step 2	Step 3

$$
\begin{array}{r}
732\\
-\ 586\\
\hline
6
\end{array}
\qquad
\begin{array}{r}
732\\
-\ 586\\
\hline
46
\end{array}
\qquad
\begin{array}{r}
732\\
-\ 586\\
\hline
146
\end{array}
$$

Think: $86 + 6 = 92$ Think: $59 + 4 = 63$ Think: $6 + 1 = 7$
Write: 6   Write: 4   Write: 1
Remember: 9   Remember: 6

7. Here is a description of an ultimate algorithm for the Austrian method (that is, a description of what the user of the method actually does):

Step 1	Step 2	Step 3
732	732	732
− 486	− 486	− 486
6	46	246

Think and write: 6   Think and write: 4   Think and write: 2
Think: 9   Think: 5

8. A "chant" to accompany Step 1 of Exercise 7 might be:

"Think 6 + 6 = 12.
Write the 6.
Carry 1 to the 8.
Remember the 9."

Work each problem below by the mechanical method described in Exercise 7. Write out the full chant for (b). Discuss the possibility that the chant really describes *more* than the expert in this method of subtraction actually *thinks*.

a)   357   b)   4018   c)   86253
      − 124   − 1273   − 18194

9. This exercise is an analysis of the most popular algorithm taught for subtraction in the United States, the *decomposition* or *take away-borrow* method.

a) Explain the long method shown below.

$$
\begin{array}{rcl}
532 & \rightarrow & 400 + 120 + 12 \\
- 156 & \rightarrow & 100 + 50 + 6 \\
\hline
376 & \leftarrow & 300 + 70 + 6
\end{array}
$$

b) Work each problem below by the form shown in (a)

1)   73   2)   458   3)   801
      − 25   − 283   − 357

c) Explain the shortcut below for the work in (a).

$$
\begin{array}{r}
\overset{4}{\cancel{5}}\ \overset{12}{\cancel{3}}\ \overset{1}{2} \\
-\ 1\ 5\ 6 \\
\hline
3\ 7\ 6
\end{array}
$$

d) Work each part of (b) above by this shortcut shown in (c).

e) Explain the mechanical final form of this decomposition algorithm:

Step 1	Step 2	Step 3
532	532	532
− 156	− 156	− 156
6	76	376

12 − 6 = 6	12 − 5 = 7	4 − 1 = 3
Subtract 1 from the 3	Subtract 1 from the 5	
Remember the 2	Remember the 4	

The phrase usually used instead of "subtract 1 from the 3" is "borrow 1 from the 3."

f) Work each problem of (b) by the mechanical method shown in (e). Also apply a mechanical method to the following:

$$\begin{array}{r} 500702 \\ - \ 284993 \\ \hline \end{array}$$

g) For the subtraction problem exhibited in part (f), write out the long solution, decomposing each number as shown in (a).

10. Here is an algorithm used by many adults; it is still taught in some schools.

Step 1	Step 2	Step 3
932	932	932
− 547	− 547	− 547
5	85	385

12 − 7 = 5	13 − 5 = 8	9 − 6 = 3
Change the 4 to 5	Change the 5 to 6	

In this method, instead of "borrowing" from top numerals, one "adds on" to bottom numerals. The original long form from which this algorithm is derived is shown below. Explain, and show how this long form is contracted to the final algorithm. This is called the method of *equal additions*.

$$\begin{array}{rcl} 932 & \rightarrow & 900 + 130 + 12 \\ - \ 547 & \rightarrow & 600 + \ 50 + \ 7 \\ \hline 385 & \leftarrow & 300 + \ 80 + \ 5 \end{array}$$

11. Work each problem below by the mechanical algorithm suggested by Exercise 10.

a) $\begin{array}{r} 51 \\ - \ 24 \\ \hline \end{array}$ 　　b) $\begin{array}{r} 321 \\ - \ 134 \\ \hline \end{array}$ 　　c) $\begin{array}{r} 520143 \\ - \ 280975 \\ \hline \end{array}$

12. Explain how a subtraction algorithm can be based on the following ideas. This is the method of subtraction used by a comptometer operator.

    a) $132 - 86 = (132 + 14) - 100$
    b) $821 - 563 = (821 + 437) - 1000$
    c) $3217 - 1859 = (3217 + 8141) - 10{,}000$

13. Explain the following mechanical subtraction procedure, which is suggested by Exercise 12.

Step 1	Step 2	Step 3
862	862	862
−247	−247	−247
5	15	615
$2 + 3 = 5$	$6 + 5 = 11$	$8 + 7 + 1$ (carried) $= 16$
	1 to carry	Drop the 1

14. Find or invent a subtraction technique other than those presented in this text.

No one has ever been able to establish the superiority of one subtraction technique over another, although many abortive attempts have been made to do so. The end result of all methods is a simple mechanical procedure, and clearly there is no reason to prefer one of these mechanical procedures to another. In the past many teachers felt that the only goal in subtraction work is mastery of a mechanical technique. Often not understanding subtraction themselves, they ignored the underlying ideas and taught only the mechanical procedures of a finished algorithm. These teachers are disappearing from the educational scene. More and more teachers are beginning to understand that the primary goal of mathematics instruction is not to develop mechanical skills but rather to encourage the development of students' powers to reason logically. As this primary goal is achieved, mechanical skills can be built on understanding.

4–5 the multiplication table

Just as skill in addition and subtraction rests on memorized addition facts, skill in multiplication and division requires knowing basic multiplication facts. Most children learn their addition facts as a by-product of problem-solving. No great amount of systematic drill is required. If a particular sum is temporarily forgotten it can be quickly computed. The multiplication table is a more formidable array of facts than the addition table. One must exert a considerable systematic effort in order to master it.

The tools needed for efficient memorization of the basic multiplication table are:

i) The ability to add two-digit numbers mentally.

ii) The ability to use the associative, commutative, and distributive principles.

Patterns that show up in the multiplication table help one to memorize it. Examples of utilization of tools (i) and (ii) are given below. Explain:

$$[A] \quad 9 \cdot 2 = 2 \cdot 9$$

$$*\begin{cases} [B] \quad 7 \cdot 6 = 7 \cdot (3 + 3) = 7 \cdot 3 + 7 \cdot 3 = 21 + 21 \\ [C] \quad 7 \cdot 9 = 7 \cdot (5 + 4) = 35 + 28 \\ [D] \quad 7 \cdot 9 = 7 \cdot (6 + 3) = 42 + 21 \end{cases}$$

In the following multiplication table we interpret $a \cdot b$ as the entry in the a-row and b-column. The list of exercises following this table calls attention to some of its interesting properties.

·	0	1	2	3	4	5	6	7	8	9
0	0	0	0	0	0	0	0	0	0	0
1	0	1	2	3	4	5	6	7	8	9
2	0	2	4	6	8	10	12	14	16	18
3	0	3	6	9	12	15	18	21	24	27
4	0	4	8	12	16	20	24	28	32	36
5	0	5	10	15	20	25	30	35	40	45
6	0	6	12	18	24	30	36	42	48	54
7	0	7	14	21	28	35	42	49	56	63
8	0	8	16	24	32	40	48	56	64	72
9	0	9	18	27	36	45	54	63	72	81

The basic Hindu-Arabic multiplication table

EXERCISES 4–5

1. Explain the patterns noted below.

a) Corresponding rows and columns can be interchanged without affecting the table.

b) All entries in the 0-row (column) are 0.

---

* These are illustrations of the *distributive* principle, so called because one factor, in this case 7, is "distributed" over addends of the other factor.

c) The entries in the 1-row (column) are the same as the entries across the top (side) of the table.

d) Diagonals running down and to the right and also up and to the right consist either of all even numbers or of numbers alternately even and odd.

e) The main diagonal running from the upper left corner to the lower right consists of perfect squares. These numbers, 0, 1, 4, 9, 16, . . . increase by 1, 3, 5, 7, 9, 11, 13, . . . , i.e., apparently by consecutive odd numbers.

f) Half the diagonals running up and to the right *intersect* the main diagonal. When an intersection occurs it is at the largest number in this diagonal. (For example, the diagonal with entries 0, 7, 12, . . . intersects the main diagonal at 16, its largest number). When the main diagonal is not intersected, the two numbers on either side of the main diagonal are equal and larger than any others. (For example, the diagonal 18, 24, 28 . . . has for its largest number 30. Two 30's occur consecutively on either side of the main diagonal.

g) Reading down the diagonal just above the main diagonal whose entries are 0, 2, 6, 12, 20, 30, . . . , one finds that consecutive differences are

2, 4, 6, 8, 10, . . .

For the diagonal above this with entries 0, 3, 8, 15, 24, . . . , differences are

3, 5, 7, 9, 11, . . .

These differences seem to be either all consecutive even numbers or all consecutive odd numbers.

h) If we ignore the zero column, the sum of the digits for every entry in the 9-row is 9.

i) If we ignore the zero column, the sum of the digits for entries in the 3-row run 3, 6, 9, 3, 6, 9, . . .

j) If one adds digits repeatedly until a single digit is obtained (for example, $48 \rightarrow 4 + 8 = 12 \rightarrow 1 + 2 = 3$), then in the 8-row (ignoring the first column) one gets the sequence 8, 7, 6, 5, 4, . . . , and in the 5-row 5, 1, 6, 2, 7, 3, . . .

k) In any 3-by-3 or 5-by-5 square, the middle number is the *average* of all numbers in the square.

2. Point out some patterns noted in (1) above which are peculiar to our Arabic numeral system and some others which reflect general properties of all numeration systems.

3. A student should not need to memorize the first two rows or columns. Why?

4. A student who can add should be able to learn the 2-row and column quickly. Why?

5. How is the 4-row easily computed from the 2-row? the 8-row from the 4-row?

6. Using the table mechanically, verify that

    a) $(2 \cdot 3) \cdot 3 = 2 \cdot (3 \cdot 3)$ b) $(3 \cdot 2) \cdot 4 = 3 \cdot (2 \cdot 4)$

    Why cannot one verify by this method that $(3 \cdot 2) \cdot 5 = 3 \cdot (2 \cdot 5)$?

7. When we use the basic principles and the addition operation, we can compute all products in this table by using only the upper left block down to the fact $5 \cdot 5 = 25$. For example:

    $4 \cdot 8 = 4 \cdot 5 + 4 \cdot 3 = 20 + 12 = 32$
    $8 \cdot 7 = 8 \cdot 5 + 8 \cdot 2 = 5 \cdot 5 + 3 \cdot 5 + 5 \cdot 2 + 3 \cdot 2 = 56$

    Illustrate this technique for: (a) $3 \cdot 9$, (b) $7 \cdot 4$, (c) $9 \cdot 9$.

8. Explain the relationship between the geometric diagrams below and the computation in Exercise 7 for $8 \cdot 7$.

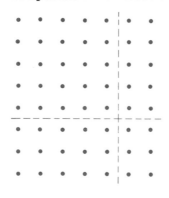
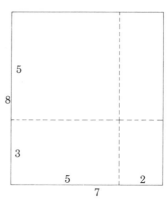

9. Find the products below mentally by visualizing an array of dots as in Exercise 8. In (a) you should visualize a 10×10 block, in (c) a 20×20.

    a) $12 \cdot 13$ b) $13 \cdot 14$ c) $21 \cdot 22$

10. The basic multiplication table pictures only a fragment of the multiplication function

$$\cdot : W \times W \overset{\text{onto}}{\longrightarrow} W$$

    $(12, 15) \overset{\cdot}{\rightarrow} 180;$ $\cdot (12, 15) = 180$

    a) Compute: $\cdot (347, 596)$
    b) Prove that $\cdot$ is not a 1–1 function from $W \times W$ onto W.
    c) What row of the table shows that $\cdot$ is an onto function?
    d) Is $\cdot (a, b) = \cdot (b, a)$, $\forall a, b \in W$?
    e) Use the table mechanically to compute $\cdot (3 \cdot 2, 4)$ and $\cdot (3, 2 \cdot 4)$.
    f) How do $\cdot (a \cdot b, c)$ and $\cdot (a, b \cdot c)$ compare?
    g) Show that $\cdot (\cdot (a, b), c) = \cdot (a, \cdot (b, c))$.

Our preoccupation with the patterns exhibited by the basic multiplication table brings out clearly how our attention is gradually turned from contemplation of the physical world to contemplation of symbols. Certainly many of the patterns we have observed have significance for the physical world, but some do not. (Find an example of each type.) Some of the above patterns are useful aids in memorizing the table. (Indicate several.) Some are not helpful in this way. (Indicate one.)

4–6   multiplication algorithms

All multiplication algorithms in all numeration systems depend on the same basic ideas.

1) One knows certain "facts" about the numeration system.

In the tally system

+	|		·	|
|	||		|	|

In the base-two system

+	0	1		·	0	1
0	0	1		0	0	0
1	1	10		1	0	1

In the base three system

+	0	1	2		·	0	1	2
0	0	1	2		0	0	0	0
1	1	2	10		1	0	1	2
2	2	10	11		2	0	2	11

2) If the product of two numbers is not given by our table of basic facts, then—using the commutative, associative, and distributive principles—we reduce the problem to one which we can handle by means of our basic tables. We break up our numbers, multiply the parts together, and sum up these partial products.

Explain the examples below. How do we use our knowledge of numeration and a basic fact to multiply 20 and 30?

$$
\begin{array}{ll}
23 & \rightarrow \quad 20 + 3 \\
\underline{32} & \rightarrow \quad 30 + 2 \\
& \leftarrow \quad 600 + 90 + 40 + 6
\end{array}
\qquad
\begin{array}{ll}
23_4 & \rightarrow \quad 20_4 + 3_4 \\
\underline{32_4} & \qquad 30_4 + 2_4 \\
& \leftarrow \quad 1200_4 + 210_4 + 100_4 + 12_4
\end{array}
$$

The speed and accuracy with which we compute depends on the effectiveness of our algorithm and the degree of skill we have developed in its use. Every algorithm prescribes how the work is to be done. An algorithm is essentially a string of instructions of three types:

Perform this basic operation.   *Write this.*   *Remember this.*

Machines follow algorithms very obediently. The more one remembers the less he needs to write. The objective is to get answers quickly and accurately. Unfortunately, because of man's poor memory, the quickest algorithms provide more opportunities for man to err, and so compromises are worked out. Obviously what one child can remember easily another cannot, and so one particular algorithm is hardly ever best for all children. There is a tendency in current arithmetic instruction to control our natural urge to pound all pegs through the same square hole and to grant students leeway in their use of algorithms. For example, some students are permitted to divide by a 1-digit divisor, using the long form shown on the left, rather than the abbreviated algorithm on the right, which requires more remembering.

```
      41428
  9 | 372852          9 | 372852
     36                   41428
     --
     12
      9
     --
     38
     36
     --
     25
     18
     --
      72
      72
      --
```

Some children are permitted to continue *striking out* digits in subtraction, *writing* the carried digits in addition, and *tacking on* the zeros in multiplication and division:

```
  9 9 1
  X Ø Ø 0           2 2
  –   4 5 2         7 4 6           472
  ---------         8 5 3           376
      5 4 8         7 9 4          2832
                    9 8 9         33040
         3          -------      141600
        60          3 3 8 2      177472
       300
  12 | 4356
      3600
      ----
       756
       720
       ----
        36
        36
        --
```

The modern point of view is that lengthy, easily understood algorithms should be introduced to students quite early and that pressures to contract these sensible procedures to abbreviated, mechanical forms should be withheld for a period of time which depends on the student's mathematical maturity.

In the next list of exercises we shall consider a number of algorithms for multiplication. All these will be variants of the following basic calculation.

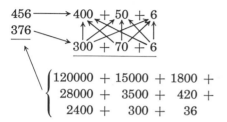

$$\begin{cases} 120000 + 15000 + 1800 + \\ 28000 + 3500 + 420 + \\ 2400 + 300 + 36 \end{cases}$$

In devising an algorithm for the problem above we must decide:

1) In what order we shall perform the 9 multiplications and the additions.

2) How much we shall do mentally.

3) What written record of our work we shall keep.

EXERCISES 4–6

1. Explain the algorithm below and the accompanying abbreviations [A] and [B]. Call attention to the order in which the 9 products are computed, the way they are recorded, the way the additions are performed, and the amount of remembering required.

456	[A]	456	[B]	456
376		376		376
120000		12		125826
15000		15 →		1850
28000		28		2143
1800		18		34
3500		35		23
2400		24		171456
420		42		
300		30		
36		36		
171456		171456		

2. Explain the "lattice" (or grating) method at the top of the next page and show its relationship to the method of Exercise 1.

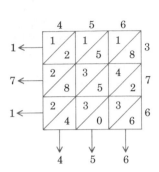 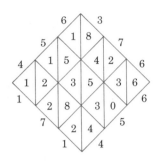

3. The *scratch* method illustrated below was tedious. Explain.

Step 1	Step 2	Step 3	Step 4	Step 5
78	78	78	78	78
97	97	97	97	97
63	632	6̷3̷2	6̷3̷2	6̷3̷2
	7	1̷7̷	1̷7̷	1̷7̷9
		0	70	70
				4

Steps 6, 7, 8

78
97
6̷3̷2̷
1̷7̷9̷
7̷0̷1
4̷
4̷
1̷
5

Steps 9 and 10

78
97
6̷3̷2̷6
1̷7̷9̷
7̷0̷1̷
4̷5̷
4̷6
1̷
5

4. Explain the algorithm below and its two abbreviations. Does it look familiar?

```
    456      [A]      ¹¹
    376              ³⁴
   ----              ³³
     36            ------
    300              456
   2400              376
    420             2736
   3500            31920
  28000           136800
   1800          -------
  15000           171456
 120000
-------
 171456
```

[B]   456
       376
      2736
      3192
      1368

     171456

5. The *cross-multiplication* algorithm enables one to write only the answer. Naturally much mental computation is required.   Explain the order in which the 9 partial products are computed.

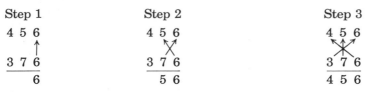

Step 1	Step 2	Step 3
Think: 36	Think:	Think:
Write: 6	$3 + 30 + 42 = 75$	$7 + 24 + 35 + 18 = 84$
Remember: 3	Write: 5	Write: 4
	Remember: 7	Remember: 8

Step 4

$$4\ 5\ 6$$
$$3\ 7\ 6$$
$$1\ 4\ 5\ 6$$

Think: $8 + 28 + 15 = 51$
Write: 1
Remember: 5

Step 5

$$4\ 5\ 6$$
$$3\ 7\ 6$$
$$1\ 7\ 1\ 4\ 5\ 6$$

Think: $5 + 12 = 17$
Write: 17

Multiply 251 and 324 by this method.

6. Many special products can be computed by shortcut techniques.   Our example,

$$376 \times 456$$

is one of these. Explain the following work.

Step 1	Step 2	Step 3
8 ⟌ 456	$3 \cdot 57 = 171$	$171 \rightarrow 171456$
57		
Divide 456 by 8	Multiply by 3	Adjoin "456"

If we ignore special trick techniques, the algorithm of Exercise 5 above is probably the fastest ever devised. However, it would take many hours of practice for the average person to develop significant speed and accuracy in the use of this algorithm. This is an excellent illustration of how compromise is forced on us in the selection of an algorithm. The one we usually teach can be handled by most people without requiring too much practice. Interestingly, during the second world war a Russian-born engineer, Jakow Trachtenberg, devised a modification of this cross-multiplication method that eliminates difficult mental arithmetic.

We can best understand the Trachtenberg technique by relating it to the lattice method described in Exercise 2.

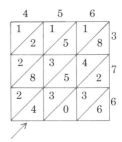

Observe the origin of the digits 4, 3, 5, 4, 8.

4 is the *units* digit of $6 \cdot 4$; 3 is the *tens* digit of $6 \cdot 5$;
5 is the *units* digit of $7 \cdot 5$; 4 is the *tens* digit of $7 \cdot 6$;
8 is the *units* digit of $3 \cdot 6$.

Note that with the lattice method you first write all the partial products row by row and then sum along the diagonals. With the Trachtenberg method you compute the digits *diagonal by diagonal* and sum as you compute.

Study the analysis of the Trachtenberg computation presented below. Compare with the lattice computation above. We shall abbreviate "units digit of $6 \cdot 7$" by $u(6, 7)$ and "tens digit of $6 \cdot 7$" by $t(6, 7)$. This is function notation.

Step 1

```
4 5 6
      )
3 7 6
─────
    6
```

Think: 6 (Do not think 36)

$\downarrow$

$\quad u(6, 6)$

Write: 6

Step 2

```
  ͡ ͡
4 5 6
  ⋎ ↗
3 7 6
─────
  5 6
```

Think: $0 + 3 + 2 = 5$

$u(6, 5)\quad t(6, 6)\quad u(7, 6)$

Write: 5

Step 3

```
͡ ͡ ͡
4 5 6
↖↑↗
 ✖
3 7 6
─────
4 5 6
```

Think: $4 + 3 + 5 + 4 + 8 = 24$

$u(6, 4)\ t(6, 5)\ u(7, 5)\ t(7, 6)\ u(3, 8)$

Write: 4
Remember: 2

Step 4

```
͡ ͡ ͡
4 5 6
↖↑ ↗
 ✖
3 7 6
───────
1 4 5 6
```

Think: 2 (remembered) $+ 2 +$
$\quad\quad 8 + 3 + 5 + 1 = 21$

Write: 1
Remember: 2

Step 5

~~
4 5 6
↑ ↑
∨
3 7 6
_____
7 1 4 5 6

Think: 2 + 2 + 2 + 1 = 7

Write: 7

Step 6

4 5 6

3 7 6
_____
1 7 1 4 5 6

Think: 1

Write: 1

Note that the mental calculations are easy, and there is little to remember. What consumes time is learning the mechanical arrangement of the work and developing the ability to think of units and tens digits separately. During the last years of his life Trachtenberg conducted an institute in Zurich, Switzerland, where his computational methods were taught to children and adults. The institute is no longer in existence, but a few Swiss teachers still give instruction in his methods.

Problem   Compute as many of the products below as you can, using both the cross-multiplication technique and the Trachtenberg technique.

    a) 32   b) 98   c) 231   d) 769
        24   79   324   897

    e) 3214   f) 7986   g) 678649
        2132   6879   897387

4–7   division algorithms

Division and multiplication algorithms are closely related. The algorithm usually taught for division is a "reversal" of the popular multiplication algorithm. Consider the example below.

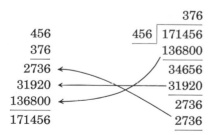

                           376
    456   456 | 171456
    376   136800
   2736   34656
 31920   31920
136800   2736
171456   2736

     There are two distinct points of view that one can take when solving a division problem. We illustrate these in the examples below.

EXAMPLE [A]

102 children are to ride in 3 buses. How many children should we put in each bus? ५ ५|

EXAMPLE [B]

We have 102 hamburgers.   Each child will eat 3. How many children can we feed?   ३ ५

Explain each step in the calculations. Steps are numbered at left.

	[A]		[B]

					We have enough
4)	4 → Load 4 more on each bus	4 ⤴	for 4 more children
1)	30 ↘ ⎰Put 30 children	30 → ⎰We can feed at
	3⟌102 ⎱on each bus	3⟌102 ⎱least 30 children
2)	90 → 3 thirties = 90	90 → 30 threes = 90
3)	12 → 12 children are left	12 → 12 hamburgers are left
5)	12 → 3 fours = 12	12 → 4 threes = 12
6)	0 ↘ ⎰All are loaded	0 ↘ ⎰All hamburgers
	⎱on the buses	⎱are eaten

In [A] the set of 102 objects is partitioned into 3 equivalent sets. We determine the number of objects in one set. In [B] we decide how many sets of 3 the set of 102 can be partitioned into. The language in which problems [A] and [B] are formulated suggests the type of reasoning used to solve each division problem.

The rationale for the division algorithm usually taught is developed along the lines of Example [B]. Multiples of the divisor are subtracted from the dividend in some systematic fashion in a series of repeated subtractions.

EXERCISES 4–7

1. Explain the algorithm employed in each division problem below.

```
                                                                          8
                                                                         40
              4                  13              111                    500
a)  12⟌48       b)  32⟌416       c)  5772⟌52     d)  78⟌42763
        12  1            320  10          2600  50           39000
        36                96              3172               3763
        12  1            64   2            520  10           3120
        24                32              2652                643
        12  1            32   1           2600  50           624
        12                 0  13            52                 19
        12  1                               52   1
         0   4                               0 111
```

2. Explain how Exercise 1(d) is abbreviated to the algorithm usually taught.

3. Explain the advantages and disadvantages of the technique used below.

$$\begin{array}{r} 683\ldots \\ 7483\ \overline{\smash{\big)}\ 5113874\ldots} \\ 44898 \\ \hline 62407 \\ 59864 \\ \hline 25434 \\ 22449 \\ \hline \end{array}$$

Preliminary work

7483	(1)
14966	(2)
22449	(3)
29932	(4)
37415	(5)
44898	(6)
52381	(7)
59864	(8)
67347	(9)

4. Each addition problem below suggests both a multiplication and a division problem. Give problems and answers.

a) 24700
   2470
     247

   27417

b) 21300
   4260
     639

   26199

c)   76800
   38400
     6144

   121344

An algorithm taught in several European schools, but rarely seen in the United States, eliminates the writing of the partial products. The Austrian (additive) method of subtraction is employed. We illustrate the technique with an example below.

Step 1

$$23\ \overline{\smash{\big)}\ 81\!\!\!\nearrow^{3}63}$$
$$2$$

Think: Three 23's in 81 ·
Write: 3 above the 1
Think: $3 \times 3 = 9; 9 + \underline{2} = \underline{11}$
Write: 2 below the 1
Remember: 1

Copy

Gean

Druce

Bart

him

Ron

Step 2

$$23\ \overline{\smash{\big)}\ 81\,\fbox{6}\,3}^{\,3\,5}$$
$$\,\fbox{12}$$

Think: $3 \times 2 = 6; 6 + 1$ (remembered) $= 7; 7 + \underline{1} = 8$

*Write: 1 below the 8
Think: Five 23's in 126
Write: 5

---
* At this stage one has computed: $81 - (3 \times 23) = 12$.

Step 3

$$\begin{array}{r} 35 \\ 23\,\overline{)\,8163} \\ 121 \\ 1 \end{array}$$

Think: $5 \times 3 = 15$;
$15 + 1 = 16$
Write 1:
Remember: 1
Think: $5 \times 2 = 10$;
  $10 + 1 = 11;\ 11 + 1 = 12$
Write: 1

Step 4

$$\begin{array}{r} 3\ 5\ 4 \\ 23\,\overline{)\,81\ 6\,3} \\ 12\,1\,1 \\ 1\,2 \end{array}$$

Think: Four 23's in 113
Write: 4
Think: $4 \times 3 = 12;\ 12 + 1 = 13$
Write: 1
Remember: 1
Think: $4 \times 2 = 8;\ 8 + 1 = 9$;
  $9 + 2 = 11$
Write: 2

Quotient 354, remainder 21

We describe below a division algorithm based on the cross-multiplication method of multiplying.

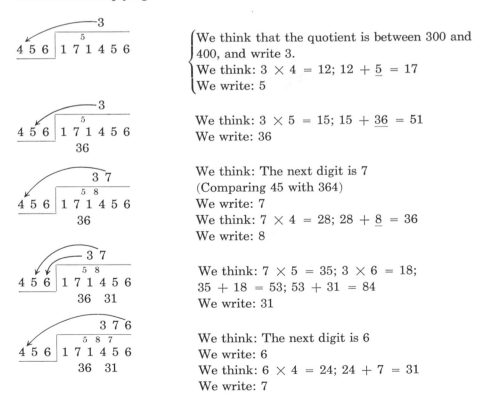

We think that the quotient is between 300 and 400, and write 3.
We think: $3 \times 4 = 12;\ 12 + 5 = 17$
We write: 5

We think: $3 \times 5 = 15;\ 15 + 36 = 51$
We write: 36

We think: The next digit is 7
(Comparing 45 with 364)
We write: 7
We think: $7 \times 4 = 28;\ 28 + 8 = 36$
We write: 8

We think: $7 \times 5 = 35;\ 3 \times 6 = 18$;
$35 + 18 = 53;\ 53 + 31 = 84$
We write: 31

We think: The next digit is 6
We write: 6
We think: $6 \times 4 = 24;\ 24 + 7 = 31$
We write: 7

$$
\begin{array}{r}
\overset{\displaystyle 3\ 7\ 6}{} \\
\overset{5\ \ 8\ \ 7}{} \\
456\,\overline{\,1\ 7\ 1\ 4\ 5\ 6} \\
36\ \ \ 31\ \ 3
\end{array}
$$

We think: $6 \times 5 = 30;\ 7 \times 6 = 42;$
$30 + 42 = 72;\ 72 + 3 = 75$
We write: 3

$$
\begin{array}{r}
\overset{\displaystyle 3\ 7\ 6}{} \\
\overset{5\ \ 8\ \ 7}{} \\
456\,\overline{\,1\ 7\ 1\ 4\ 5\ 6} \\
36\ \ \ 31\ \ 3\ \ 0
\end{array}
$$

We think: $6 \times 6 = 36;\ 36 + 0 = 36$
The remainder is 0
We write: 0

Quotient 376, remainder 0

Note that only 12 digits are written in this solution. It is easy to remember the 5, 8, and 7, instead of writing them. It is possible to remember even the 36, 31, and 3, but this is impractical. If no work is recorded it is more difficult to recover from the error that sometimes occurs of selecting an incorrect quotient digit.

Problem   Work each problem below by the two algorithms described above
a) $43\,\overline{\,2786}$ b) $853\,\overline{\,217946}$

4–8   shortcut techniques

In a computerized society it becomes less and less important that man be able to compute with great speed and accuracy. A man cannot match a machine, and so the sensible procedure is to turn over to machines all possible calculations. Man's chief responsibility in computation becomes one of programming machines, planning the computation, and giving the machines instructions. But for many years to come our schools will stress accuracy and "reasonable" speed in whole-number arithmetic. There will always be children and teachers who will delight in mental arithmetic and who will give thought to shortcut techniques. This interest reflects Stage 3 of our abstraction process, in which arithmetic is clearly a game. In this section we give several suggestions for increasing speed and accuracy in computation, and we describe a variety of shortcuts.

Nearly anyone can improve the speed with which he adds by using opportunities to group by tens. For example, one can compute

$$8 + 7 + 2 + 3 + 6 + 9 + 4 \qquad \text{as} \qquad 15, 17, 20, 26, 35, 39,$$

or he can observe the tens indicated below and "see" the sum at a glance:

$$8 + 7 + 2 + 3 + 6 + 9 + 4 \rightarrow 39.$$

One can even tuck away in his memory the knowledge that certain sums of *three* numbers make 20:

$8 + 7 + 5 = 20;$ $9 + 9 + 2 = 20;$ $8 + 8 + 4 = 20; \ldots$

$8 + 7 + 4 + 5 \rightarrow 24$

$9 + 6 + 9 + 2 \rightarrow 26$

And the enthusiast will observe facts like:

$6 + 7 + 8 + 9 = 30;$ $8 + 7 + 7 + 8 = 30$

$6 + 8 + 9 + 7 + 9 \rightarrow 39$

$8 + 7 + 6 + 7 + 8 \rightarrow 36$

EXERCISES 4–8

Give sums by "glancing" at the problems and grouping by tens.

1) $4 + 6 + 7 + 3 + 8 + 2 + 5$
2) $9 + 1 + 7 + 3 + 5 + 5 + 8$
3) $8 + 5 + 2 + 5 + 4 + 6 + 3$
4) $9 + 4 + 1 + 6 + 8 + 7 + 2$
5) $9 + 8 + 7 + 1 + 2 + 3 + 4$
6) $6 + 3 + 3 + 7 + 4 + 6 + 7$
7) $9 + 9 + 2 + 2 + 9 + 9 + 3$
8) $8 + 7 + 5 + 9 + 9 + 2 + 6$
9) $6 + 7 + 8 + 9 + 4 + 4$
10) $7 + 9 + 8 + 3 + 6 + 7 + 5$

The development of speed and accuracy in computation depends greatly on training your mind to do many things automatically. For example, you should know the multiplication table so well that when you are multiplying you are never conscious of making any effort to compute a basic multiplication fact. It is there for your use when you need it. For example, at the stage indicated below in the multiplication problem you do not have to *think* to produce the 54. Your mental energy goes into the computation of 54 + 7.

$$\begin{array}{r} 368 \\ \times\ 49 \\ \hline 2 \end{array}$$

The fact $54 + 7 = 61$ may not be one that your mind automatically produces, and so at this point in the computation there is a momentary hesitation while you *consciously* think and compute.

If you separate tens and units digits (in a manner reminiscent of Trachtenberg), the multiplication task can be made an even more automatic procedure. We illustrate below. Explain the steps.

[A]   7869
          7
    ————
          3

Think: 3

[B]   7869
          7
    ————
        83

Think: $2 + 6 = 8$

[C]   7869
          7
    ————
      083

Think: $6 + 4 = 10$

[D]   7869
          7
    ————
    55083

Think: $49 + 6 = 55$

At stage [B], how *do* you think when you multiply? Is it $42 + 6 = 48$, or $2 + 6 = 8$? The first requires more time and effort. It is quite probable that many persons make this separation of tens and units digits in multiplying without realizing that they do so.

This separation of tens and units digits can be applied to addition. Consider the sum below

$8 + 7 + 9 + 2 + 4 + 3 + 8 + 6 + 5$
1–5, 2–4, 2–6, 3–0, 3–3, 4–1, 4–7, 5–2

One must do two things as he adds a string of digits: keep track of the sequence of tens digits, in this case

1, 2, 2, 3, 3, 4, 4, 5,

and the units digits, in this case

5, 4, 6, 0, 3, 1, 7, 2.

A little thought will convince you that much more effort goes into the determination of the units digit of the sum than the tens digit.

Keeping track of the tens is the sort of thing that can be made mechanical and turned over to the "unconscious" machinery of the mind (or to the fingers). Explain how this is illustrated by the following computation:

$7 + 4 + 2 + 3 + 2 + 8 + 3 + 7 + 2 + 7$
1–1,   3,   6,   8, 2–6,   9, 3–6,   8, 4–5

EXERCISES 4–8

1. For each problem below compute as quickly as possible *the units digit only* of the sum. Do not compute the tens digit. Use combinations of ten.

   Example: $8 + 7 + 3 + 2 + 9 + 6 + 1 + 3 + 4 \rightarrow 3$

5	7	6	8	4	9	8	7	3	8	3	7	1
5	4	3	2	2	9	8	5	6 (9)	7 (5)	2 (5)	7	4
7	3	3	1	7	2	4	4	7 (6)	9 (4)	6 (1)	5	9
6	6	7	4	6	4	5	6	2 (8)	4 (8)	8 (9)	7	5
4	5	7	9	1	3	6	9	5 (23)	4 (32)	4 (3)	6	8

6	4	6	1	2	6	7	9	8	6	9	5	1
3	6	4	4	4	4	4	2	2	4	6	7	7
5	8	3	7	6	7	2	9	7	7	7	6	3
2	3	7	9	8	2	8	8	6	2	7	8	8
7	2	2	6	5	8	6	7	9	5	9	4	3
1	7	5	2	7	5	5	5	5	8	4	9	7
9	5	8	3	3	9	3	4	3	4	8	8	8

3	7	1	3	7	9	3	7	6	7	6	2
7	2	4	8	5	6	7	2	5	1	5	5
5	5	7	7	4	5	5	5	3	4	3	8
2	4	3	5	2	8	4	4	7	9	7	3
4	3	6	4	3	4	2	3	4	5	8	1
3	8	2	2	1	7	8	6	8	8	2	7
5	6	8	6	6	3	1	8	2	7	1	4
8	5	9	3	2	5	3	9	3	2	9	2
6	2	7	8	4	2	5	4	5	3	6	6
5	7	4	1	7	6	7	2	6	4	4	6

2. Compute sums as quickly as possible for the problems of Exercise 1. Ask yourself whether, by focusing attention on units digits, you have increased your speed or accuracy in addition.

The following exercise list presents a variety of shortcuts. These are not explained in detail. Use the shortcuts to work some of the suggested problems and decide, if possible, why the shortcuts work.

EXERCISES 4–9

1. To multiply by 50 and 25 annex two 0's and divide by 2 and 4, respectively.

   Examples: $684 \times 50 = 34200;$ $684 \times 25 = 17100$

   Compute (a) 8884×25, and (b) 64834×50.

2. The diagram presents a shortcut for multiplying by 11.

$$\overgroup{4\ 2\ 6\ 3}$$
$$\underline{\quad\quad 1\ 1}$$
$$4\ 6\ 8\ 9\ 3$$

$$4 + 2 \longleftarrow\!\!\rfloor \quad \downarrow \quad \lfloor\!\!\longrightarrow 6 + 3$$
$$2 + 6$$

Compute (a) 53241 × 11, and (b) 864977 × 11.

3. Here is a shortcut for multiplying by 111.

$$4\ 3\ 8\ 2\ 1\ 4$$
$$\underline{\quad\quad\quad 1\ 1\ 1}$$
$$4\ 8\ 6\ 4\ 1\ 7\ 5\ 4$$

$$4 + 3 + 1 \longleftarrow\!\!\rfloor \quad\quad \lfloor\!\!\longrightarrow 1 + 4$$
$$4 + 3 + 8 + 1 \ (1\ \text{to carry}) \longleftarrow\!\!\rfloor \quad \lfloor\!\!\longrightarrow 2 + 1 + 4$$
$$3 + 8 + 2 + 1 \ (1\ \text{to carry}) \longleftarrow\!\!\rfloor \quad \lfloor\!\!\longrightarrow 8 + 2 + 1 \ (1\ \text{to carry})$$

Compute (a) 341234 × 111, and (b) 632146 × 111.

4. Devise a shortcut and multiply 123231 by 1111.

5. Note that 82 × 101 = 8282; 243 × 1001 = 243243.   Give products mentally.

   a) 76 × 101   b) 92 × 101   c) 814 × 1001

   d) 722 × 101   e) 69 × 1001   f) 43 × 102

6. Explain why 83 × 99 = 8300 − 83 = 8217. Do all work mentally.

   a) 9200 − 92   b) 6800 − 68   c) 93 × 99

   d) 74 × 99   e) 432000 − 432   f) 867000 − 867

   g) 524 × 999   h) 423 × 998   i) 9999 × 9999

7. Explain the computation below.

   $$125 \times 4824 \rightarrow 8\,\big|\,\underline{4824000}$$
   $$603000$$

   Find all products mentally.

   a) 888 × 125   b) 488 × 125   c) 4088 × 125   d) 8408 × 125

8. Compute the following mentally.

   a) 48 × 25 $^{48 \div 4}_{12 \cdot 0}$ b) 48 × 26 $^{48 \div 4 + 48}_{12 48}$ c) 484 × 250 $^{484 \div 40}_{121000}$

   d) 484 × 251 $^{484 \div 40 + 484}$ e) 48 × 24 $^{48 \div 4 - 48}_{1152}$ f) 484 × 249 $^{484 \div 40 - 484}_{120616}$
   ^{121484}

9. Use the fact that 375 = 3 × 125 and compute mentally:

   a) 888 × 375   b) 4808 × 375   c) 248 × 375

   d) 4088 × 375   e) 824 × 376   f) 648 × 376

   g) 824 × 374   h) 648 × 374

10. Guess the pattern suggested by the examples below and square the indicated numbers mentally.

    $25^2 = \underline{6}25$; $45^2 = \underline{20}25$; $65^2 = \underline{42}25$; $105^2 = \underline{11025}$

    a) 35^2 *1425* b) 75^2 *5625* c) 85^2 *7225* d) 95^2 *9025* e) 115^2 *13225* f) 205^2 *42...*

    g) 245^2 *60025* h) 405^2 *164025* i) 995^2 *990025* j) 495^2 *245025* k) 999995^2

11. Guess the pattern and give the products.

    $4^2 = 16$; $34^2 = 1156$; $334^2 = 111556$

    a) 3334^2 b) 33334^2 c) 33333334^2
    11115556   *1111155556*   *11111115555556*

12. Guess the pattern. $7^2 = 49$; $67^2 = 4489$

    a) 6667^2 b) 66667^2 c) 66666667^2
    44448889   *4444488889*   *44444448888889*

13. Guess the pattern. $13^2 = 169$; $133^2 = 17689$

    a) 13333^2 b) 133333^2 c) 13333333^2
    177768889   *1777768888889*   *17777776888888889*

14. Guess the pattern. $16^2 = 256$.   Compute: 16666666^2

15. Study the example   643
                                               427
                                              ─────
                    7×643 ←   4501
            $(60 \times 7) \times 643$ ←   27006
                                              ─────
                                              274561

    Explain each shortcut below.

    a)   756   b)   4732   c)   6354
          963   567   792
        ─────   ──────   ───────
         6804   33124   5083200
        47628   264992   − 50832
        ──────   ──────   ───────
        728028   2683044   5032368

    d)   5937   e)   8648   f) 7448
             873   3375   5625
         ───────   ─────   ────
         5343300   25944   3724
       − 160299   3243   463
         ───────   ─────   ────
         5183001   29187000   4187000

16. Explain the computation below.

    Step 1   Step 2   Step 3
    1 2 1 2   1 2 1 2   1 2 1 2

    1 2 1 2   1 2 1 2   1 2 1 2
    ───── 4 4   ───── 8 9 4 4   ──── 1 4 6 8 9 4 4
    1 to carry   2 to carry

17. Use the fact that $365 \times 365 = 133225$ to explain the computation below.

Step 1	Step 2	Step 3
365365	365365	365365
365365	365365	365365
225	583225	133491583225

    133 to carry   266 to carry

18. Many years ago a "lightning calculator" attracted attention by squaring 365365365 mentally in a few seconds. He undoubtedly used the method of Exercise 17. See how quickly you can work this problem.

19. The mathematician Gauss as a child used the technique below to "add" the whole numbers from 1 to 100.

$$1 + 2 + 3 + \cdots + 98 + 99 + 100$$

He recognized that the sum was 50×101. Compute similarly the sums below.

a) $1 + 2 + 3 + \cdots + 198 + 199 + 200$

b) $1 + 2 + \cdots + 999 + 1000$

c) $5 + 10 + 15 + \cdots + 90 + 95 + 100$

d) $8 + 16 + 24 + \cdots + 984 + 992 + 1000$

d) $7 + 14 + 21 + \cdots + 693 + 700 + 707$

4–9   implications for teaching

Many of the ideas presented in this chapter have clear-cut teaching implications. We list some of these below.

1) If students can count meaningfully, then that counting skill can be exploited in the first approaches to written addition and subtraction.

2) Algorithms should first be put before students in sensible forms and then gradually contracted to the desired final forms.

3) Many basic addition and multiplication facts that must be memorized are learned as a by-product of mental computation. The amount of formal drill required is sharply reduced if students see connections between basic facts and learn to devise their own methods for quickly computing forgotten facts. Skill in 2-digit mental addition is helpful in learning the multiplication table.

4) Odd bits of information tossed out at the proper time can imprint themselves on the minds of students. Here are examples:

    a) A student has computed 8×8 as 63. You remark, "Haven't you ever noticed that the *only* time you get an odd product is when both factors are odd?"

b) A student is having difficulty with large products, $7 \times 7, 7 \times 8, 8 \times 7$, ... You point out that for any of these products one can

i) get the tens digit by *adding* the numbers and *discarding* 10;

ii) get the units digit by *subtracting* each number from 10 and multiplying.

Examples: $7 \times 7 \rightarrow 7 + 7 = 14 \rightarrow 4$ (tens digit)

$\qquad\qquad 7 \times 7 \rightarrow 3 \times 3 = 9$ (units digit)

$\qquad\qquad 9 \times 8 \rightarrow 9 + 8 = 17 \rightarrow 7$ (tens digit)

$\qquad\qquad 9 \times 8 \rightarrow 1 \times 2 = 2$ (units digit)

c) Note that the method of (b) will work also for 6×8 and 6×9. For 6×7 it works with the modification below.

$$\begin{cases} 6 \times 7 \rightarrow 6 + 7 = 13 \rightarrow 3 \rightarrow 30 \\ 6 \times 7 \rightarrow 4 \times 3 = 12 \qquad \rightarrow \underline{12} \\ \qquad\qquad\qquad\qquad\qquad\qquad\quad 42 \end{cases}$$

One adds the 3 tens and 12 units.

SUMMARY

Chapter 3 dealt with Stages 1 and 2 of the abstraction process, the invention of symbols and operations on symbols. Chapter 4 has dealt with Stage 3, the development of the abstract symbolic game of whole-number arithmetic. After one has memorized enough facts, one can play this game without considering its applicability to the real world.

Emphasis on the evolution of algorithms reflects educational opinion that children should first work problems by methods they understand and then move by easy stages to shortcuts. Current teaching procedures in the development of addition and subtraction algorithms probably fail to utilize effectively the ability of students to count. Section 4–2 indicates the way this ability might be exploited. Addition is viewed as counting forward, subtraction as counting backward.

The classification of problem types on page 108 focuses attention on a basic educational problem. Many children have difficulty deciding which operations of arithmetic to use in problem-solving. This is not surprising when we realize that, as the classification shows, problems of several different types are solved by the same symbolic operation. Three types of subtraction problems are described. This sort of situation is characteristic of mathematics. One operation on mathematical symbols may be applicable to a wide variety of physical problems.

The old approach to the addition and multiplication tables was to commit them to memory. As Sections 4–3 and 4–5 suggest, there are more effective ways to master these tables. Of course all approaches involve a considerable, repetitive effort, but students should be encouraged to develop their own ways of relating difficult addition and multiplication facts to easy ones.

A variety of algorithms for addition, subtraction, multiplication, and division have been presented. You should understand a logical sequence of abbreviating steps by which the algorithms you yourself use for addition, subtraction, multiplication, and division can be developed. Besides these algorithms, you should be familiar with at least one other algorithm for each operation.

Much of the chapter is recreational in nature: cross multiplication, Trachtenberg, rapid addition by grouping tens and twenties, shortcuts, etc. The teacher who knows some of these interesting facets of the game of arithmetic can do much to stimulate student interest.

5   basic principles for whole-number arithmetic

5-1   introduction

We have studied the child's progress through the first three stages of the abstraction process, from the invention of numerals, through the birth of operations on numbers, to the game with symbols. At the third stage the child ignores (physical) sets, the process of counting a set, and the operations of forming the union and the cartesian product of sets. He concentrates instead on numbers and the operations, $+$ and $\cdot$, defined on them.

By the end of the third stage he has learned his addition and multiplication "facts" and the mystic chants which produce answers to addition, subtraction, multiplication, and division problems. He has learned them because they are fun. He vies with his classmates for supremacy in speed and accuracy. When he says, "eight and seven is fifteen," he probably does not think of a union of two sets. When he rattles off, "nine times seven is sixty-three," he almost certainly does not visualize a cartesian product. He may find it extremely difficult to do "word problems" such as the skirt-blouse or rat-cheese problem. The game is the thing.

As do other games, such as bridge, arithmetic has its special terminology, its tricks, and its shibboleths. You deal with addends, sums, subtrahends, differences, minuends, factors, terms, products, . . .   You learn to carry, borrow, cancel, bring down, indent, cast out nines, . . .   You are wary about canceling and you would no sooner divide by zero than you would trump your partner's ace.

It is not an easy game to play, and only the strong survive. The weak are overwhelmed by its complexity; even the strong often emerge with only a certain computational facility and a profound bewilderment as to why the computational procedures (chants, algorithms) work.

This third stage, with all of its unsatisfactory aspects, was the final level of sophistication attained by children taught in the traditional manner. Then came the New Math. The New Math, as we have all heard, is dedicated to explaining *why*, to having children *learn with understanding*. In our terminology the purpose of the New Math is to raise the student to the fourth level of mathematical sophistication, the level at which he perceives the basic structure of the game.

To the fourth stage of the abstraction process we have given the title, Analyzing the Structure of the Game. Our immediate aim in this analysis is (1) to draw out of the mass of available arithmetic facts a short list of the most obvious and simple ones, which we'll call the fundamental principles; (2) to show how the more esoteric machinations, which we've called the algorithms, really amount to just repeated applications of these simple fundamental principles. A longer-range aim is to see what sort of assumptions are reasonable to make about the larger number systems (integers, rationals, reals) which we'll study in following chapters.

▶ *Aside.* In this and succeeding chapters you will encounter occasional *theorems* and *proofs*. Here is a bit of advice for those of you who may be frightened by the very words. When you see the label "theorem" affixed to a statement about numbers, simply think to yourself: "They are claiming that this statement is true, not because it seems to be or because it would be nice if it were, but because it *has* to be. They maintain that it is an inevitable consequence of earlier definitions, assumptions, and theorems." When you see the word "proof," think to yourself: "Now they're about to explain why the statement has to be true. I had better check that their argument is logical and uses nothing but earlier definitions, assumptions, and theorems." ◀

5–2   binary operations and substitution

Before we can begin listing the simple properties of the whole numbers under addition and multiplication, we first have to discuss the "binary operations" of addition and multiplication themselves, and then explain the difficult "substitution principle."

Addition (multiplication) is called a *binary* operation on W because it assigns to each ordered *pair* of elements of W a unique element of W. For example, addition assigns to the ordered pair of whole numbers $(5, 8)$ the (unique) whole number $5 + 8$ (or 13). Multiplication assigns to the ordered pair $(5, 8)$ the (unique) whole number $5 \cdot 8$ (or 40). In general, a binary operation, $*$, on a set S assigns to each ordered pair of elements of S a unique element of S. If the pair is denoted by (s, t), then the element assigned to it by $*$ is denoted by $s * t$. (Note that we followed this convention earlier when we discussed the binary operations on sets: $\cup$, $\cap$, $\times$.)

▶ *Aside.* It is evident then that a binary operation $*$ on a set S is really a function from $S \times S$ into S and that $s * t$ is just neater notation than the usual functional notation, $* ((s, t))$. The pervasiveness of the function concept is illustrated again. ◀

In much of what we do from here on we shall employ the principle of "substitution." We already know, by the transitive property of $=$, that if $a = b$ and if $b = c$, then $a = c$. This is a kind of substitution, but we shall continue to justify such assertions with the word "transitivity." The sort of substitution we are concerned with here, however, is exemplified in the following statement: "Assuming that $14 = 10 + 4$, it follows that $14 + 3 = (10 + 4) + 3$." We shall justify such an assertion with the single word "substitution" (and often omit even that), but one ought to realize that this word conceals a lengthier explanation. Many mathematicians would consider the following brief statement to be adequate justification: "Addition is an operation on elements, not symbols for elements, and the sum of two elements is unique." Others would feel more secure pointing out all the notational conventions and fine distinctions between elements and symbols for elements which are involved. Consider the following example.

STATEMENTS	*REASONS*
1. $14 = 10 + 4$	1. Assumed
2. 14 and $10 + 4$ are two names for a single number.	2. By statement 1 and our convention that when we write $a = b$ we mean that a and b are two symbols for the same element of some underlying set
3. $(14, 3)$ and $(10 + 4, 3)$ are two names for a single ordered pair of numbers.	3. By our convention on naming ordered pairs: If a names an element of set A and b names an element of set B, then (a, b) names the ordered pair whose first component is the element of A named by a and whose second component is the element of B named by b
4. The image of a single ordered pair of numbers under addition is a single number.	4. Addition is a binary operation.

5. $14 + 3$ names the image under addition of the ordered pair named by $(14, 3)$; $(10 + 4) + 3$ names the image under addition of the ordered pair named by $(10 + 4, 3)$.

5. Our convention for denoting images under a binary operation: the image under $*$ of the pair named by (s, t) will be named $s * t$.

6. $14 + 3$ and $(10 + 4) + 3$ name a single number.

6. Statements 3, 4, 5

7. $14 + 3 = (10 + 4) + 3$

7. Our convention about $=$ (recall reason 2)

Similar short and long arguments apply to replacing a symbol by an equal* symbol when the binary operation involved is multiplication or when both binary operations appear.

EXERCISES 5–1

1. Which of the following rules for combination are binary operations on the given set?

a) Set: people in your classroom
   $*$: $a * b = $ the taller of a and b (if $a \neq b$)
   $a * b = a$ (if $a = b$)

b) Set: as in (a)
   $*$: $a * b = a$'s mother

c) Set: as in (a)
   $*$: $a * b = a$

d) Set: points of plane
   $*$: $a * b = $ midpoint of segment joining a to b
   $a * b = a$ (if $a = b$)

d) Set: points of plane
   $*$: $a * b = $ segment joining a to b

f) Set: $N = \{x \in W \mid x \neq 0\}$
   $*$: $a * b = a^b$

g) Set: W
   $*$: $a * b = 2a + 3b$

h) Set: all two-letter "words" $\{aa, ab, ac, \ldots, az, ba, bb, \ldots, \ldots, za, zb, \ldots, zz\}$
   $*$ (sample): $rs̸ * t̸u = ru$

i) Set: as in (h)
   $*$ (sample): $r̸s * t̸u̸ = st$

---

* Recall that to say that two symbols are *equal* is to assert that they name the same object.

2. Justify (in whichever way convinces you) the following assertions:
   a) "Assuming that $5 \cdot 4 = 20$, it follows that $3 \cdot (5 \cdot 4) = 3 \cdot 20$."
   b) "Assuming that $5 + 4 = 9$, it follows that $3 \cdot (5 + 4) = 3 \cdot 9$."

3. a) Prove the following.
   General Substitution Theorem
   If $*$ is a binary operation on a set S, then

   i) $s_1 = s_2 \Rightarrow s_1 * t = s_2 * t$
   ii) $t_1 = t_2 \Rightarrow s * t_1 = s * t_2$
   iii) $s_1 = s_2$ and $t_1 = t_2 \Rightarrow s_1 * t_1 = s_2 * t_2$

   [*Hint:* (iii) is a consequence of (i) and (ii).]

   b) Comment on the liturgy: "If equals be added to (multiplied by) equals their sums (products) are equal."

4. Using function notation, we write $4 + 3$ as $+((4, 3))$ and $4 \cdot 3$ as $\cdot ((4, 3))$
   a) Compute $+((7, 2))$
   b) Compute $\cdot ((8, 9))$
   c) Does $+((a, b)) = +((b, a))$ for all a and b?

5. a) Begin a systematic listing of the set $W \times W$ and begin an arrow diagram for the function $+: W \times W \to W$.
   b) Repeat part (a) for the function $\cdot : W \times W \to W$.

6. Assign to each operation in the left-hand column all sets in the right-hand column on which it is a binary operation. That is, decide which sets are "closed" with respect to each operation.

OPERATIONS	SETS
$+$	a) $\{0\}$
$-$	b) $\{1\}$
$\times$	c) $\{-1, 1\}$
$\div$	d) $\{-1, 0, 1\}$
	e) $N = \{1, 2, 3, \ldots\}$
	f) $W = \{0, 1, 2, \ldots\}$
	g) $I = \{\ldots - 2, -1, 0, 1, 2, \ldots\}$
	h) $I - \{0\}$
	i) Q (the rationals)
	j) Q^+ (the positive rationals)
	k) Q^- (the negative rationals)
	l) $Q - \{0\}$

7. State in words these two important instances of substitution.
   a) $b = c \Rightarrow b + a = c + a$,
   b) $b = c \Rightarrow ba = ca$.

5–3   the laws of addition and multiplication

We are now in a position to partially describe the structure of the game of arithmetic. The game is played with a set

$$W = \{0, 1, 2, 3, \ldots\},$$

and two binary operations, $+$ and $\cdot$, which behave according to the "laws" which follow.

▶ *Aside.* We call them "laws" for two reasons. First, it is traditional to do so. Second, it is not safe to call them either theorems or assumptions (axioms). For example, at the set-counting (second) level of abstraction they are obviously true, while at the fourth level, where nothing is obvious, they must be assumed.
   An implicit assumption about W is that no two of $0, 1, 2, 3, \ldots$ are equal. ◀

The associative law of addition. Addition, as a *binary* operation, assigns to each (ordered) *pair* of whole numbers a whole number called their sum. Frequently, however, we want to add three numbers. The associative law of addition assures us that it makes no difference whether we add the first two and then add their sum to the third or whether we add the last two and then add the first to their sum. For example,

$$(2 + 5) + 4 = 2 + (5 + 4).$$

That is,

$$7 + 4 = 2 + 9.$$

The figure below makes this law plausible.

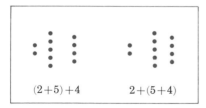

(2+5)+4   2+(5+4)

The general statement of the associative law is

$$a + (b + c) = (a + b) + c, \qquad \forall a, b, c \in W.$$

You may think of this in mechanical terms as allowing you to slide a pair of parentheses one notch left or right.

Warning. The a, b, c in this statement (as in the statements of the other laws we'll be coming to) need not be benign symbols like 2, 5, and 4; they can be complicated expressions. For example,

$(2^3 + 17 \cdot 3)^2 + \{5(6 + 3 \cdot 4) + (16 \cdot 7 + 3)\}$
$= \{(2^3 + 17 \cdot 3)^2 + 5(6 + 3 \cdot 4)\} + (16 \cdot 7 + 3),$

by the associative law of addition.

You should concentrate on learning the *forms* of these statements. It was with great reluctance that we decided against stating this law in the form

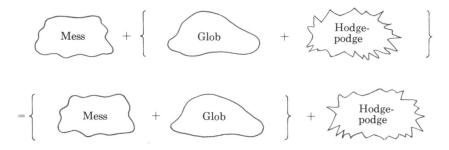

It is natural to ask whether it makes any difference how we associate the terms if we wish to add four numbers. The answer is that it makes no difference. For example,

(*) $[7 + (1 + 4)] + 3 = (7 + 1) + (4 + 3).$

Now note that we can *prove* (*) on the basis of the associative law (for 3 terms).

Proof   (Boldface numbers indicate step numbers.)

1. $[7 + (1 + 4)] + 3 = 7 + [(1 + 4) + 3]$
                    by the associative law (slide [ ] one notch right).
2. But $[(1 + 4) + 3] = [1 + (4 + 3)]$
                    by the associative law (slide ( ) one notch right).
3. Thus $7 + [(1 + 4) + 3] = 7 + [1 + (4 + 3)]$
                    by substitution.
4. But $7 + [1 + (4 + 3)] = [7 + 1] + (4 + 3)$
                    by the associative law (slide [ ] one notch left).

5. Thus $[7 + (1 + 4)] + 3 = [7 + 1] + (4 + 3)$
                              by transitivity of $=$ and steps 1, 3, 4.

It should be clear that this same proof would establish

$$[a + (b + c)] + d = (a + b) + (c + d), \qquad \forall a, b, c, d \in W.$$

Perhaps somewhat less clear, but certainly plausible, is the generalized associative law of addition which states that, given any number of terms to be added, it makes no difference how you associate them, you will still get the same sum.

In the sequel we shall use the abbreviation "Assoc $+$" to refer to both the associative law of addition (for 3 terms) and the generalized associative law of addition (4 or more terms). We shall not distinguish between them any longer.

EXERCISES 5–2

1. Choose x such that
   a) $(8 + 6) + 4 = x + (6 + 4)$
   b) $x + (1 + 9) = (7 + 1) + 9$
   c) $(3 + x) + 4 = 3 + (3 + 4)$

2. a) Insert (in a sensible fashion) parentheses into the expression

   $$9 + 7 + 3 + 6$$

   in at least four ways. Compute and compare the sums.
   b) Why is it permissible to simply omit all parentheses from sums of several numbers? In how many ways can one insert parentheses when there are 4 numbers to be added? 5 numbers? 6 numbers?

3. Decide, for the binary operations (page 145), which ones are associative. [*Note:* You will first have to define what you mean by saying "the binary operation $*$ on the set S is associative."]

4. Prove that

   $$a + [b + (c + d)] = [(a + b) + c] + d$$

   without using the *generalized* associative law.

5. Answer the following objection: "You assumed associativity for 3 terms and then made a big deal about how generalized associativity (4 or more terms) is a consequence of it. And you never gave a proof of it; you just hinted at one by looking at special cases. Why didn't you simply assume generalized associativity in the first place?" [*Hint:* Recall Exercise 3 above.]

The associative law of multiplication. This is exactly analogous to the associative law of addition. An example is $(2 \cdot 5) \cdot 4 = 2 \cdot (5 \cdot 4)$. See the figure.

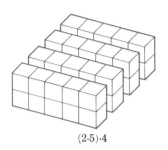   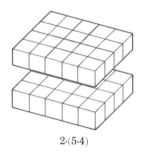

       (2·5)·4   2·(5·4)

The general statement is:

$$(a \cdot b) \cdot c = a \cdot (b \cdot c), \qquad \forall a, b, c \in W.$$

Again there is a generalized associative law of multiplication which allows us to move around or omit all parentheses in a product of several factors.

Hereafter we shall use the abbreviation "Assoc ·" to refer to both the associative law of multiplication and the generalized associative law of multiplication.

EXERCISES 5–3

1. Insert parentheses into the expression

    $9 \cdot 7 \cdot 3 \cdot 6$

    in at least four ways. Compute and compare the products. Why is it legitimate to omit parentheses?

2. Which of the two groupings do you find more pleasant? Why?

    a) $2 \cdot (5 \cdot 7)$ or $(2 \cdot 5) \cdot 7$

    b) $6 + (4 + 9)$ or $(6 + 4) + 9$

    c) $[(9 \cdot 8) \cdot 15] \cdot 0$ or $9 \cdot [8 \cdot (15 \cdot 0)]$

3. Prove that $[a(bc)]d = (ab)(cd)$ without using the generalized associative law.

4. At Stage 2, a person proves that addition is associative by noting that set union is associative. Is cartesian product an associative binary operation on sets? Recalling that multiplication is described in terms of cartesian products, what are some implications of your answer?

The commutative law of addition. This is perhaps the most obvious property of addition (at Stage 2). It is illustrated by the equations:

$$5 + 6 = 6 + 5, \qquad 3 + 7 = 7 + 3.$$

See the figure.

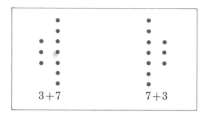

$3+7$ $7+3$

Sometimes it is difficult to see that this law says anything. It may appear more substantial if you think of it as saying that the binary operation, $+$, sends the different ordered pairs, $(3, 7)$ and $(7, 3)$, to the same number.

The general statement of the commutative law of addition is:

$$a + b = b + a, \qquad \forall a, b \in W.$$

When we combine the commutative law with the associative law we get a generalized commutative–associative law, which says that we can mix up the terms of a sum in any manner we please. For example,

$$1 + 7 + 8 + 3 + 2 = 7 + 3 + 8 + 2 + 1.$$

(Which would you rather compute?) We can only hint at a proof of this very general theorem by proving one special case,

$$a + b + c + d = a + d + c + b.$$

Proof (Boldface numbers indicate step numbers.)

1. $a + b + c + d = a + [(b + c) + d]$.

By the generalized associative law of addition we can insert parentheses in any manner we please.

2. $b + c = c + b$ — Comm $+$

3. $(b + c) + d = (c + b) + d$ — Substitution

4. $(c + b) + d = d + (c + b)$ — Comm $+$

5. $(b + c) + d = d + (c + b)$ — Transitivity 3, 4

6. $a + [(b + c) + d] = a + [d + (c + b)]$

Substitution

7. $a + [d + (c + b)] = a + d + c + b$.

By the generalized associative law of addition we can omit parentheses.

8. $a + b + c + d = a + d + c + b$ — Transitivity 1, 6, 7

We shall use the abbreviation "Comm $+$" whenever we rearrange the terms of a sum, be it a two-term sum or a many-term sum.

EXERCISES 5–4

1. Rearrange the terms of this expression in 6 different ways. Compute all the sums and compare.

   $3 + 6 + 8$

2. Decide which of the binary operations (page 145) are commutative. [*Note:* You will first have to *define* what you mean by saying "the binary operation $*$ on the set S is commutative."]

3. Prove, without using any generalized laws, that

   $(a + b) + (c + d) = (d + a) + (b + c).$

The commutative law of multiplication. This is exactly analogous to the commutative law of addition. An example is

$2 \cdot 5 = 5 \cdot 2$

See the figure.

$$2 \cdot 5 \qquad\qquad 5 \cdot 2$$

The general statement is

$a \cdot b = b \cdot a, \qquad \forall a, b \in W.$

Again there is a general commutative–associative law of multiplication that says you can mix up the factors of a product to your heart's content.

We shall refer to this general result and to the simple commutative law of multiplication by the same abbreviation, "Comm $\cdot$ ".

EXERCISES 5–5

1. Rearrange the factors of this expression in 6 different ways. Compute all the products and compare.

   $3 \cdot 6 \cdot 8$

2. Which of the two orderings do you find more pleasant? Why?

   a) $8 \cdot 6 \cdot 5$ or $5 \cdot 8 \cdot 6$

   b) $8 + 9 + 2$ or $8 + 2 + 9$

3. Prove $(ab)(cd) = (da)(bc)$ without using any generalized laws. [*Hint:* Compare with Exercise 3 in Exercise Section 5–4.]

4. At Stage 2, one proves that addition is commutative by noting that set union is commutative. Discuss the situation for cartesian product.

The additive property of 0. The additive property of 0, exemplified by the equation $5 + 0 = 5$, does not lend itself to graphic interpretation. At the set-counting stage of abstraction, it is an obvious consequence of the set equation.

$$A \cup \varnothing = A.$$

If you form the union of a set of 5 elements with the empty set, you end up with a set of 5 elements, namely the original set of 5 elements.

The general statement of the additive property of 0 is

$$a + 0 = a, \qquad \forall a \in W.$$

This property of 0 is often expressed in other terminology: (1) "0 is the neutral element with respect to the binary operation $+$." (2) "0 is the additive identity." Both these expressions mean exactly this: Adding 0 to any number doesn't change that number.

An immediate consequence of the commutative law of addition is that

$$0 + a = a, \qquad \forall a \in W.$$

We shall justify any equation of the form

$$0 + a = a \qquad \text{or} \qquad a + 0 = a$$

with the abbreviation, "Add 0," even though, strictly speaking, one of them involves commutativity of $+$ as well as the additive property of 0.

EXERCISES 5–6

1. If $*$ is a binary operation on a set S and $e \in S$, then we say that e is a neutral element with respect to $*$ if $e * a = a * e = a$ for all $a \in S$. Exhibit neutral elements for those binary operations (page 145) which have them.

2. We spoke of 0 as *the* neutral element with respect to $+$ and as *the* additive identity. Prove that 0 is the *only* whole number which is neutral with respect to $+$. [*Hint:* Suppose that e denotes a whole number which is neutral with respect to $+$. Consider $0 + e$.]

The multiplicative property of 1. The number 1 is neutral with respect to multiplication in the same sense that 0 is neutral with respect to addition: Multiplying any number by 1 doesn't change that number. This property of 1 is also frequently expressed as "1 is the multiplicative identity." The formal statement of the multiplicative property of 1 is:

$$a \cdot 1 = a, \qquad \forall a \in W.$$

Again it is a consequence of the commutative law (this time of multiplication) that

$$1 \cdot a = a, \qquad \forall a \in W.$$

We shall use the abbreviation "Mult 1" as justification for any equation of the above two types.

   At the set-counting stage of abstraction, this property of 1 is a consequence of the fact that if A is any set and B is a set with a single element, then A and $A \times B$ have the same number of elements. [Note that A and $A \times B$ are *not* identical.] For example, if $A = \{a, b, c, d, e\}$ and $B = \{f\}$, then

$$A \times B = \{(a, f), (b, f), (c, f), (d, f), (e, f)\}.$$

Problem   Prove that 1 is the *only* whole number which is neutral with respect to multiplication.

The cancellation law of addition. Suppose we know that there is a whole number x such that $x + 3 = 17$.   One way of determining this whole number is to rewrite 17 as $14 + 3$,

$$x + 3 = 14 + 3,$$

and cancel the 3's:

$$x = 14.$$

The cancellation law of addition says that this procedure is legitimate.   The precise statement of the cancellation law of addition is:

If $b + a = c + a$, then $b = c$, $\forall a, b, c \in W.$

   This is perhaps the least obvious of our laws at Stage 2. The figure below may be somewhat suggestive of the set situation wherein if $A \cup B$ (A, B disjoint) can be put in 1–1 correspondence with $A \cup C$ (A, C disjoint), then B can be put in 1–1 correspondence with C.

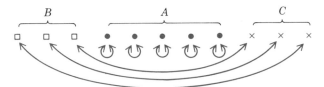

   You can certainly object to our including the cancellation law of addition in our list of fundamental principles. We admit frankly that it is not particularly simple. It is, however, fundamental. You will gain a greater appreciation of its importance as you progress through this book. [Perhaps you have already detected in our first example and in the preceding figure the way that the cancellation law of addition permits us to do "subtraction" problems without ever having to define "subtraction."   When we get to the system of integers

(Chapter 8) and are able to satisfactorily define subtraction as a binary operation, the cancellation law of addition will gracefully fade away.]

  There are many instances of legitimate cancellation implied by this cancellation law and the earlier associative and commutative laws of addition.
Two are:

  1. If $a + b = a + c$, then $b = c$ (cancel on left).
  2. If $a + b + c = d + b + e$, then $a + c = d + e$.

We shall justify all such instances of cancellation with the single abbreviation,
"Cancel +."

EXERCISES 5–7

  1. Using cancellation laws, find a whole number x such that
     a) $5 + x = 8$ $8 = 5 + 3$ $5 + 3 = 5 + 3$ b) $x + 2 = 10$
                                     $x = 3$
     c) $3 + x + 7 = 10 + 8$ d) $6 + x + 2 = 20$
  2. Prove the following, using only the first form of the cancellation law and
     earlier laws.
     a) $a + b = a + c \Rightarrow b = c$ b) $b + a = a + c \Rightarrow b = c$
     c) $a + b + c = b + e \Rightarrow a + c = e$
  3. Suppose that $*$ is a binary operation on a set S. We say that $*$ satisfies the
     cancellation law if ($\forall a, b, c \in S$)

     $b * a = c * a \Rightarrow b = c$.

     Which of the binary operations (page 145) satisfy the cancellation law?
  4. Prove that if there are two numbers a and b such that $a + b = a$, then
     $b = 0$. Compare and contrast with Exercise 2, page 153.
  5. Prove that there is at most one solution to the equation $a + x = b$.
  6. Explain the connection between the cancellation law and the following
     geometrical problems.

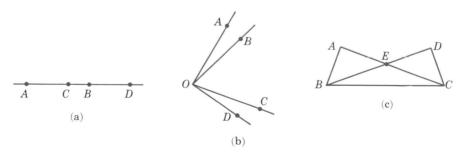

     (a)   (b)   (c)

  7. Compare Cancel + with Exercise 7, page 147.

The cancellation law of multiplication. We would like a law for multiplication analogous to the cancellation law for addition. The first guess that comes to mind is: (?) $ba = ca \Rightarrow b = c$ (?). But anyone at Stage 2 can tell you that $17 \cdot 0 = 3 \cdot 0$, whereas $17 \neq 3$; that is, you can't go about canceling 0's. (We'll shortly prove that, as a consequence of our other laws, 0 times any number is 0.) What we really want as our careful formulation of the cancellation law of multiplication is:

If $ba = ca$ and $a \neq 0$, then $b = c$.

Again this is not the most obvious of properties at Stage 2, although the figure below might be helpful. How do you interpret $B \times A$? $C \times A$?

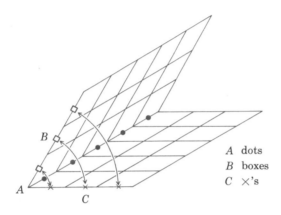

A dots
B boxes
C ×'s

Again the reason we list this law is that it is basic. It is intimately connected with division and will slip from sight when we get to the system of rational numbers and are able to define division satisfactorily.

We'll justify by the abbreviation "Cancel $\cdot$" all assertions of the following sort:

$ba = ac$ and $a \neq 0 \Rightarrow b = c$,
$abc = db$ and $b \neq 0 \Rightarrow ac = d$.

EXERCISES 5–8

1. Using cancellation laws, find a whole number x such that
   a) $2x = 6$ b) $x \cdot 8 = 32$ c) $2 \cdot x \cdot 3 = 24$

2. Prove, using only the first form of the cancellation law of $\cdot$ and earlier laws, that
   a) $ab = ac$ and $a \neq 0 \Rightarrow b = c$ b) $abc = dbe$ and $b \neq 0 \Rightarrow ac = de$

3. Prove that if $a \neq 0$ then $ab = a \Rightarrow b = 1$.   Compare and contrast with the problem on page 154.

4. a) Does $a \neq b$ imply that $ac \neq bc$?

   b) Does $a \neq b$ imply that $a + c \neq b + c$?

5. Prove that if $a \neq 0$, there is at most one solution to $ax = b$.

6. Compare Cancel · with Exercise 7, page 147.

The distributive law. We have now listed four fundamental properties of $+$ and four parallel properties of $\cdot$, but we have stated no property relating the two operations. It is the distributive law which does this. An illustration of the distributive law is

$$5 \cdot (4 + 2) = 5 \cdot 4 + 5 \cdot 2.*$$

See the figure, which can be viewed as

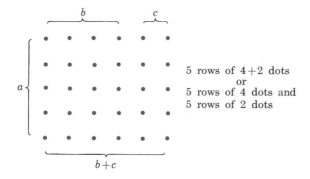

5 rows of $4+2$ dots
or
5 rows of 4 dots and
5 rows of 2 dots

The general statement of the distributive law is:

$$a(b + c) = ab + ac, \qquad \forall a, b, c \in W.$$

There are all sorts of distributive laws. For example,

$$(a + b)c = ac + bc,$$
$$a(b + c + d) = ab + ac + ad,$$
$$(a + b + c)(d + e) = ad + ae + bd + be + cd + ce.$$

We shall refer to all these varieties by the abbreviation "Dist."

---

* Here and throughout we employ the usual convention that, in the absence of parentheses, multiplication takes precedence over addition. That is, $5 \cdot 4 + 2 = (5 \cdot 4) + 2$; $5 \cdot 4 + 2 \neq 5 \cdot (4 + 2)$.

EXERCISES 5–9

1. Compute and compare:
   a) $6 \cdot (10 + 3)$ and $6 \cdot 10 + 6 \cdot 3$
   b) $(12 + 1) \cdot 12$ and $12 \cdot 12 + 1 \cdot 12$
   c) $(7 + 2) \cdot 7$ and $7 \cdot 7 + 2 \cdot 7$
   d) $9 \cdot (9 + 2)$ and $9 \cdot 9 + 9 \cdot 2$
   e) $7 \cdot 10 + 2 \cdot 10$ and $(7 + 2) \cdot 10$
   f) $9 \cdot 7 + 1 \cdot 7$ and $(9 + 1) \cdot 7$

   Which form, first or second, do you prefer to work with in each of parts (a) through (f)?

2. Prove, using only the first form of the distributive law and the earlier laws:
   a) $(a + b)c = ac + bc$
   b) $(a + b)(c + d) = ac + bc + ad + bd$
   c) $(a + b)(a + b) = aa + ab + ab + bb$
   d) A diagram for the equation in (c) is:

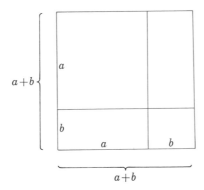

   Which parts of this diagram correspond to aa, ab, bb?
   e) Draw diagrams for the equations in (a) and (b). Give appropriate labels to the parts of each diagram.

3. The property, $a \cdot (b + c) = a \cdot b + a \cdot c$, is often referred to as the distributivity of $\cdot$ over $+$.
   a) Is $+$ distributive over $\cdot$? That is, does $a + (b \cdot c) = (a + b) \cdot (a + c)$?

   Now let S be the set of all subsets of some universal set U. Let $\cup$ and $\cap$ denote the usual binary operations on S of union and intersection.
   b) What would it mean to say that $\cap$ is distributive over $\cup$?

c) Is ∩ distributive over ∪? [*Hint:* Draw and shade some Venn diagrams.]

d) What would it mean if we were to say that ∪ is distributive over ∩?

e) Is ∪ distributive over ∩? [*Hint:* Same as in (c).]

We have now a complete list of the laws of addition and multiplication.

1. Assoc +	4. Comm ·	7. Cancel +
2. Assoc ·	5. Add 0	8. Cancel ·
3. Comm +	6. Mult 1	9. Dist

You should know not only a precise statement of each law but also the general *form* that the statement takes.

EXERCISES 5–10

1. The general form of the distributive law is

$$\square \cdot \left(\triangle + \heartsuit \right) = \square \cdot \triangle + \square \cdot \heartsuit$$

Give the general forms of the other 8 laws.

2. Each equation below can be justified by one of the 9 laws. Pick the right one.

a) $2 \cdot 5 = 5 \cdot 2$

b) If $ab + a = ac + a$, then $ab = ac$

c) $3 + (4 + 7) = (3 + 4) + 7$

d) $(a + b)(c + d) = a\,(c + d) + b(c + d)$

e) $5a + 0 = 5a$

f) $(a + b) + c = c + (a + b)$

g) $1 \cdot a + 1 \cdot a = (1 + 1) \cdot a$

h) $m(n + k) = (n + k)m$

i) $1 \cdot 1 = 1$

j) $ab(c + d) + (ab + 1) = [ab(c + d) + ab] + 1$

k) $2 \cdot (5 \cdot 7) = (2 \cdot 5) \cdot 7$

l) If $5x = 5 \cdot 0$, then $x = 0$

m) $0 + 0 = 0$

n) $x^2 + 2x = (x + 2)x$

o) $[19(1 + 1)]5 = 19[(1 + 1) \cdot 5]$

p) $5a(b + 6) + 5 \cdot 4 = 5[a(b + 6) + 4]$

3. Prove carefully, using only the 9 laws, substitution, and transitivity of $=$.

   a) $ab + (ac + 4) = a(b + c) + 4$

   b) If $a + a = a$, then $a = 0$

   c) If $a^2 = a$, then either $a = 0$ or $a = 1$

   d) (Assuming $1 + 1 = 2$) $(x + y)^2 = x^2 + 2xy + y^2$

   e) (Assuming $2 + 1 = 3$) $(x + y)^3 = x^3 + 3x^2y + 3xy^2 + y^3$

5–4   the laws as axioms; the need for more axioms; elementary facts

The nine laws in Section 5–3 were all more or less obvious when addition and multiplication were viewed as closely tied to counting and the set operations of union and cartesian product. If, however, we want to divorce the game of arithmetic from its physical origins (as the child does at Stage 3), then these laws (now assumptions or axioms) provide most of the moves needed to play the game.

As an example, let us divest the elements of W of all ordinal and cardinal connotations and treat them as meaningless symbols. Let us view $+$ and $\cdot$ simply as binary operations on W (no union or cartesian-product connotations). We attribute to W, $+$, and $\cdot$ no properties other than those stated in the nine laws. Now let's see the sort of things we can and cannot do.

We can prove this important theorem.

Multiplicative Property of 0: $0 \cdot a = 0,$ $\forall a \in W$.

Proof   (Boldface numbers indicate step numbers.)

1. $0 + 0 \cdot a = 0 \cdot a$ Add 0

2. $0 \cdot a = (0 + 0) \cdot a$ Add 0, Subst

3. $(0 + 0) \cdot a = 0 \cdot a + 0 \cdot a$ Dist

4. $0 + 0 \cdot a = 0 \cdot a + 0 \cdot a$ Tran $=$

5. $0 = 0 \cdot a$ Cancel $+$

We repeat. This is an obvious property when W, $+$, $\cdot$ have their physical set connotations. It remains true, however, even when these intuitive notions are stripped away and only the nine laws are assumed. The reasons, of course, are entirely different.

We can also prove the following key theorem.

There are no proper divisors of zero: $ab = 0 \Rightarrow a = 0$ or $b = 0$.

Proof If $a = 0$ we're done, so suppose that $a \neq 0$. (Boldface numbers indicate step numbers.)

1. $0 = a \cdot 0$ Previous theorem, Comm

2. $0 = a \cdot b$ Given

3. $a \cdot b = a \cdot 0$ Tran $=$

4. $b = 0$ Cancel $\cdot$, $a \neq 0$

And now we're really done.

     The nine laws are not all-powerful. A sample of something we cannot prove using only these laws is $1 + 1 = 2$. This is a rather serious deficiency. There are two ways to correct it. The first way is theoretically more satisfactory, but leads us into deep foundational problems. The second, though logically less pleasing, is nevertheless a reasonable compromise between absolute rigor and full reliance on physical interpretation. It is also accessible to the elementary school child.

▶ *Aside.* The first remedy, briefly, is this. We assume that we have an infinite set W containing two special (and distinct) elements called 0 and 1. We assume that we have two binary operations, $+$ and $\cdot$, on W satisfying the nine "laws" (now axioms). We further assume that every element of W (except 0 and 1) can be obtained by adding 1 to itself sufficiently many times. (People who have had an advanced math course may recognize this as a sloppy statement of the Axiom of Induction.) We then successively (recursively) define the symbols 2, 3, 4, . . . by

$2 = 1 + 1$
$3 = 2 + 1 = (1 + 1) + 1$
$4 = 3 + 1 = [(1 + 1) + 1] + 1$
$\vdots$

(By our added assumption, every element of W is in the list: 0, 1, 2, 3, 4, . . .) Behold, we have defined away our unprovable theorem: $1 + 1 = 2$! We can, however, *prove* a lot of other familiar results.

Theorem $2 + 2 = 4$

Proof   (Boldface numbers indicate step numbers.)

1. $2 = 1 + 1$ Defn of 2

2. $2 + 2 = (1 + 1) + (1 + 1)$ Subst

3. $(1 + 1) + (1 + 1) = [(1 + 1) + 1] + 1$ Assoc $+$

4. $[(1 + 1) + 1] + 1 = 4$ Defn of 4

5. $2 + 2 = 4$ Steps 2, 3, 4 and Tran $=$

Theorem $2 \cdot 2 = 4$

Proof   (Boldface numbers indicate step numbers.)

1. $2 = 1 + 1$

2. $2 \cdot 2 = 2 \cdot (1 + 1)$ Subst

3. $2 \cdot (1 + 1) = 2 \cdot 1 + 2 \cdot 1$ Dist

4. $2 \cdot 1 = 2$ Mult 1

5. $2 \cdot (1 + 1) = 2 + 2$ Subst

6. $2 + 2 = 4$ Previous theorem

7. $2 \cdot 2 = 4$ Steps 2, 5, 6 and Tran =

[*Note:* The words "infinite," "sufficiently many," and "successively" mask a number of very deep and difficult foundational problems, problems far beyond the scope of this book.]

Problem   Prove that $2 + 3 = 5$, $3 + 3 = 6$, $2 \cdot 3 = 6$ using the 9 laws and the recursive definitions of $2, 3, 4, \ldots$.

Problem (hard)   Using the assumption that $0 \neq 1$, prove that $2 \neq 1$. Then prove that $2 \neq 3$. Then prove that $K \neq K + 1$. Does this imply that all of $0, 1, 2, \ldots$ are distinct? How would you use the assumption that W is infinite to prove that they are all distinct? Why do we know that $2 \neq 0$? ◀

The second remedy is to assume, in addition to the nine laws, the "elementary addition and multiplication facts."

The elementary addition facts are:

+	0	1	2	3	4	5	6	7	8	9
0	0	1	2	3	4	5	6	7	8	9
1	1	2	3	4	5	6	7	8	9	10
2	2	3	4	5	6	7	8	9	10	11
3	3	4	5	6	7	8	9	10	11	12
4	4	5	6	7	8	9	10	11	12	13
5	5	6	7	8	9	10	11	12	13	14
6	6	7	8	9	10	11	12	13	14	15
7	7	8	9	10	11	12	13	14	15	16
8	8	9	10	11	12	13	14	15	16	17
9	9	10	11	12	13	14	15	16	17	18

The elementary multiplication facts are:

·	1	2	3	4	5	6	7	8	9
1	1	2	3	4	5	6	7	8	9
2	2	4	6	8	10	12	14	16	18
3	3	6	9	12	15	18	21	24	27
4	4	8	12	16	20	24	28	32	36
5	5	10	15	20	25	30	35	40	45
6	6	12	18	24	30	36	42	48	54
7	7	14	21	28	35	42	49	56	63
8	8	16	24	32	40	48	56	64	72
9	9	18	27	36	45	54	63	72	81

To repeat once more: The information contained in these tables is all *obvious* when the elements of W and $+$ and $\cdot$ have their set-counting connotations. When these connotations are stripped away, however, and the symbols 0, 1, 2, . . . are without meaning, then these "facts" are clearly *not* derivable from the nine laws. They must be assumed.

The two tables, together with our 9 laws, allow us to compute certain sums and products which at first glance seem inaccessible.

Example 1 $12 + 18 = 30$

Proof

$$12 + 18 = 2 \cdot 6 + 3 \cdot 6 \qquad \text{Elem mult facts, subst}$$
$$= (2 + 3)6 \qquad \text{Dist}$$
$$= 5 \cdot 6 \qquad \text{Elem + fact, subst}$$
$$= 30 \qquad \text{Elem mult fact}$$

Therefore $12 + 18 = 30$ Tran $=$

Example 2 $10 \cdot 4 = 40$

Proof

$$10 \cdot 4 = (5 \cdot 2) \cdot 4 \qquad \text{Mult fact, subst}$$
$$= 5 \cdot (2 \cdot 4) \qquad \text{Assoc} \cdot$$
$$= 5 \cdot 8 \qquad \text{Mult fact, subst}$$
$$= 40 \qquad \text{Mult fact}$$

Therefore $10 \cdot 4 = 40$ Tran $=$

EXERCISES 5-11

1. Using only the elementary facts and the nine laws compute the following.
   a) $5 + 7$ b) $12 + 2$ c) $12 + 4$ d) $12 + 6$
   e) $4 \cdot 3$ f) $12 \cdot 2$ g) $12 \cdot 6$

   h) Is it possible to compute $2 \cdot 11$?
   i) Is it possible to prove that $19 = 1 \cdot 10 + 9$?

2. What patterns do the tables of facts display as a result of the following?
   a) Comm $+$, Comm $\cdot$
   b) Add 0, Mult 1
   c) Cancel $+$, Cancel $\cdot$

3. Prove carefully that $10 + 10 = 20$.

4. Find, ponder, and discuss patterns in the tables.

5. a) If $a \neq 0$ and $b \neq 0$, does it follow that $ab \neq 0$?
   b) If $abc = 0$, then either $a = 0$ or $b = 0$ or $c = 0$. Prove this, then generalize.

6. Find all whole numbers x such that:
   a) $x(x - 2) = 0$ b) $x^2 - 3x + 2 = 0$
   c) $x^2 + 3x + 2 = 0$ d) $(x - 1)(x)(x + 1) = 0$

7. Using only the elementary facts and the nine laws, find x such that
   a) $(2x) \cdot 3 = 24$ b) $(x + 5) + 7 = 8 + 12$
   c) $x \cdot 1 = 7$ d) $4x = 20$
   e) $3x + 3 = 12$ f) $2(x + 4) = 14$
   g) $x + 0 = 7$ h) $9 + x = 3 + 15$

5-5   exponents, expanded form, and a law of exponents

Let us try to establish one more simple result. In trying to do so, we'll be forced to make some additional assumptions. These will complete our list in the sense that we'll have enough laws, facts, principles, and conventions to analyze the algorithms.

Let us try to prove that $19 \cdot 8 = 152$. A reasonable first step would be: $19 = 10 + 9$. Already we have no reason. $10 + 9 = 19$ is not an "elementary addition fact." We wrote $19 = 10 + 9$ because this was the expanded form for the decimal numeral. But the notion of expanded form was developed in the set-counting framework from which we are trying to free ourselves.

Thus we have to add another assumption. Sample:

A multiple-digit numeral such as 24136 stands for
$2 \cdot 10^4 + 4 \cdot 10^3 + 1 \cdot 10^2 + 3 \cdot 10 + 6.$

This is a *notational convention*. In what follows we shall refer to it by the suggestive term, "expanded form." Hence our proof begins (the boldface numbers indicate step numbers):

1. $19 \cdot 8 = (10 + 9) \cdot 8$ Expanded form, Subst

2. $(10 + 9) \cdot 8 = 10 \cdot 8 + 9 \cdot 8$ Dist

3. $10 \cdot 8 + 9 \cdot 8 = 8 \cdot 10 + 72$ Comm $\cdot$, Elem mult fact, Subst

4. $8 \cdot 10 + 72 = 8 \cdot 10 + (7 \cdot 10 + 2)$ Expanded form, Subst

5. $8 \cdot 10 + (7 \cdot 10 + 2) = (8 \cdot 10 + 7 \cdot 10) + 2$
                                    Assoc $+$

6. $(8 \cdot 10 + 7 \cdot 10) + 2 = (8 + 7) \cdot 10 + 2$ Dist, Subst

7. $(8 + 7) \cdot 10 + 2 = 15 \cdot 10 + 2$ Elem addn fact, Subst

8. $15 \cdot 10 + 2 = (1 \cdot 10 + 5)10 + 2$ Expanded form, Subst

9. $(1 \cdot 10 + 5)10 + 2 = [(1 \cdot 10)10 + 5 \cdot 10] + 2$
                                    Dist, Subst

10. $[(1 \cdot 10)10 + 5 \cdot 10] + 2 = 1 \cdot (10 \cdot 10) + 5 \cdot 10 + 2$
                                Assoc $\cdot$, Assoc $+$, Subst

11. $1 \cdot (10 \cdot 10) + 5 \cdot 10 + 2 = 1 \cdot 10^2 + 5 \cdot 10 + 2$
                                    ?

We pause again. What reason should be given for the statement, $10 \cdot 10 = 10^2$? The reason here is the definition of exponent: 10^2 means $10 \cdot 10$. In fact:

Definition   (For any natural number a)

$a^1 = a$

$a^2 = a \cdot a$

$a^3 = a \cdot a \cdot a$ (parentheses unnecessary due to generalized associative law of multiplication)
$\vdots$

(Again the ellipsis marks mask the problem of recursive definition, which must be faced in a completely rigorous approach.)

In more complicated instances, however, we shall need to justify statements such as

$10^2 \cdot 10^3 = 10^5.$

The reason we shall give in all such cases is "law of exponents." That will signify that we are employing either the definition or the following theorem.

Theorem

$a^m \cdot a^n = a^{m+n}$.   (For example, $2^7 \cdot 2^9 = 2^{16}$.)

A careful general proof requires induction based on the recursive definition of exponents, but anyone can see that in a special case such as $10^2 \cdot 10^3 = 10^5$ it is simply a matter of applying the (generalized) associative law of multiplication and the definitions $10^2 = 10 \cdot 10$, $10^3 = 10 \cdot 10 \cdot 10$, $10^5 = 10 \cdot 10 \cdot 10 \cdot 10 \cdot 10$.

Getting back to our proof, the reasons for Step 11 are: Law of Exponents, Subst.

12. $1 \cdot 10^2 + 5 \cdot 10 + 2 = 152$ Expanded form

13. $19 \cdot 8 = 152$ (Steps 1–12 and) Tran =

EXERCISES 5–12

1. Verify that (a) $3^2 \cdot 3^2 = 3^4$, (b) $2^4 \cdot 2^6 = 2^{10}$.

2. a) We would like to define the zeroth power of a number so that our law of exponents continues to hold. How must 3^0 be defined if

   $3^0 \cdot 3^2$ is to equal 3^{0+2}?

   b) If we define $a^0 = 1$, is it true that $a^m \cdot a^n = a^{m+n}$ for all whole numbers m and n?

3. The second law of exponents states that

   $(a^m)^n = a^{mn}$

   for every natural number a and for all whole numbers m and n.
   a) Verify this law in the special case: $a = 2$, $m = 3$, $n = 4$.
   b) Verify this law in the special case: $a = 3$, $m = 0$, $n = 7$.

5–6   the fundamental principles of whole-number arithmetic

The proof is complete. So is our list of reasons required to justify the algorithms. We list them all below for completeness. And we repeat once again: These are all obvious at Stage 2 of the abstraction process, the set-counting context. In later stages, when the game of arithmetic is played without these connotations, most of these principles must be assumed.

FUNDAMENTAL PRINCIPLES OF WHOLE-NUMBER ARITHMETIC

  1. Assoc +   2. Assoc ·
  3. Comm +   4. Comm ·
  5. Add 0   6. Mult 1
  7. Cancel +   8. Cancel ·
            9. Dist
 10. Elem. addn and mult facts
* 11. Expanded form
 12. Law of exponents
* 13. Tran = (reflexivity and symmetry as well)
* 14. Subst

Some additional rather special facts appear later, but these are all the rules you'll need to know to play the basic game of whole-number arithmetic.

Critique Before we begin dissecting algorithms, let us explore a possible difficulty connected with our list of principles: the matter of interaction of the assumptions. Consider this simple example. We assumed that $2 + 3 = 5$. We assumed the distributive law. In particular then,

$$3 \cdot 2 + 3 \cdot 3 = 3(2 + 3) = 3 \cdot 5.$$

We further assumed that $3 \cdot 2 = 6$, $3 \cdot 3 = 9$, and $6 + 9 = 15$. Thus

$$15 = 6 + 9 = 3 \cdot 2 + 3 \cdot 3 = 3(2 + 3) = 3 \cdot 5.$$

Hence our elementary multiplication "fact," $3 \cdot 5 = 15$, is no assumption at all. It is an inexorable consequence of other assumptions. Fortunately we didn't assume that $3 \cdot 5 = 16$, or we'd have a self-contradictory set of assumptions.

   We feel confident that our assumptions are not contradictory, however, because they are all "obvious facts" at the set-counting level of abstraction. We rely on the consistency of that model.

   One goal of the rigorous axiomatic approach is to minimize the number of assumptions, to pare down the list to the point at which there is no interaction and hence no possible inconsistency.

EXERCISES 5–13

  1. Express as a decimal numeral:
       a) $7 \cdot 10^3 + 1 \cdot 10^2 + 6 \cdot 10 + 4$ b) $9 + 4 \cdot 10^3 + 6 \cdot 10 + 8 \cdot 10^2$
       c) $10^3 + 5 \cdot 10^2 + 2 \cdot 10 + 3$ d) $10^3 + 6 \cdot 10$ e) $5 + 10^2$

---

* Rules 11, 13, and 14 are consequences of notational conventions. They have nothing to do with the *structure* of arithmetic.

2. Write in expanded form:

   a) 5280   b) 1969   c) 12,003   d) 8,704,321   e) 18

   f) 8^3 g) 2^8 h) $2^3 \cdot 2^5$ i) $3^3 \cdot 3$ j) 10

3. a) Write 365 in expanded form.

   b) Multiply the expanded form of 365 by 10 and bring it back to expanded form, using the distributive law and the law of exponents.

   c) Convert the answer in (b) to a decimal numeral and compare with (a).

4. Prove the following:

   a) $(ab)^3 = a^3 b^3$

   b) $(x + 3)(x + 4) = x^2 + 7x + 12$

   c) $(a + 2)^2 = a^2 + 4a + 4$

   d) If $(a + b)^2 = a^2 + b^2$, then either a or b must equal 0.

5. a) Supply a reason or reasons (from the list of fundamental principles) for each step in the following proof that $18 + 7 = 25$:

   1. $18 + 7 = (1 \cdot 10 + 8) + 7$ _____

   2. $(1 \cdot 10 + 8) + 7 = 1 \cdot 10 + (8 + 7)$ _____

   3. $1 \cdot 10 + (8 + 7) = 1 \cdot 10 + 15$ _____

   4. $1 \cdot 10 + 15 = 1 \cdot 10 + (1 \cdot 10 + 5)$ _____

   5. $1 \cdot 10 + (1 \cdot 10 + 5) = (1 \cdot 10 + 1 \cdot 10) + 5$ _____

   6. $(1 \cdot 10 + 1 \cdot 10) + 5 = (1 + 1) \cdot 10 + 5$ _____

   7. $(1 + 1) \cdot 10 + 5 = 2 \cdot 10 + 5$ _____

   8. $2 \cdot 10 + 5 = 25$ _____

   9. Therefore $18 + 7 = 25$ _____

   b) How many times did you use the reason "Substitution"?

   c) The above proof is often abbreviated as follows:

   1. $18 + 7 = (1 \cdot 10 + 8) + 7$ _____

   2. $= 1 \cdot 10 + (8 + 7)$ _____

   3. $= 1 \cdot 10 + 15$ _____

   . . .

   Write down, explicitly, the convention about omissions. Why is each expression equal to every expression preceding it?

6. Show that each of the following is a consequence of other assumptions embedded in the addition and multiplication tables (and our basic laws for $+$ and $\cdot$).

   a) $4 \cdot 6 = 24$ b) $2 \cdot 8 = 16$ c) $3 \cdot 3 = 9$

   d) $4 \cdot 9 = 36$ e) $7 + 5 = 12$ f) $8 + 6 = 14$

7. Explain why we ask children to learn their multiplication facts only up through $9 \cdot 9$ (rather than through $12 \cdot 12$ or $15 \cdot 15$, as some people think would be nice).

5–7 the addition algorithm analyzed

There is a well-known chant which tells one how to write the sum of two decimal numerals. We'll now see why it "works" by studying the specific addition problem: $148 + 79$.

WHAT IS REALLY GOING ON		*THE CHANT*
Statements	*Reasons**	
$148 + 79$		
$= (1 \cdot 10^2 + 4 \cdot 10 + 8) + (7 \cdot 10 + 9)$	Expanded form	
$= 1 \cdot 10^2 + 4 \cdot 10 + 7 \cdot 10 + 8 + 9$	Assoc $+$, Comm $+$	8 and 9 is 17.
$= 1 \cdot 10^2 + 4 \cdot 10 + 7 \cdot 10 + 17$	Elem addn fact	Write down
$= 1 \cdot 10^2 + 4 \cdot 10 + 7 \cdot 10 + 1 \cdot 10 + 7$	Expanded form	the 7 and
$= 1 \cdot 10^2 + 1 \cdot 10 + 4 \cdot 10 + 7 \cdot 10 + 7$	Comm $+$	carry the 1.
$= 1 \cdot 10^2 + (1 + 4 + 7) \cdot 10 + 7$	Dist	1 and 4 is 5
$= 1 \cdot 10^2 + (5 + 7) \cdot 10 + 7$	Elem addn fact	and 7 is 12.
$= 1 \cdot 10^2 + 12 \cdot 10 + 7$	Elem addn fact	
$= 1 \cdot 10^2 + (1 \cdot 10 + 2) \cdot 10 + 7$	Expanded form	Write down
$= 1 \cdot 10^2 + 1 \cdot 10 \cdot 10 + 2 \cdot 10 + 7$	Dist	the 2 and
$= 1 \cdot 10^2 + 1 \cdot 10^2 + 2 \cdot 10 + 7$	Law of exponents	carry the 1.
$= (1 + 1)10^2 + 2 \cdot 10 + 7$	Dist	1 and 1 is 2.
$= 2 \cdot 10^2 + 2 \cdot 10 + 7$	Elem addn fact	
$= 227$	Expanded form	
Therefore $148 + 79 = 227$	Tran $=$	Answer: 227

* We shall henceforth omit the reason "Substitution," which is involved in virtually every step. (Recall Exercise 5 in Exercise Section 5–13.)

There is also a traditional arrangement of the work

$$
\begin{array}{r}
1\,1 \\
148 \\
+\ \ 79 \\
\hline
227
\end{array}
$$

Observe that "lining up the places" (writing the 9 directly below the 8 and the 7 directly below the 4) amounts to the rearrangement of terms

$1 \cdot 10^2 + 4 \cdot 10 + 7 \cdot 10 + 8 + 9.$

Some people like to exhibit more of the inner workings of the algorithm by writing out the partial sums and then adding them:

$$
\begin{array}{r}
148 \\
+\;\;79 \\
\hline
17 \\
+\,110 \\
+\,100 \\
\hline
227
\end{array}
$$

    $(8 + 9 \text{ or } 8 \cdot 1 + 9 \cdot 1)$
    $(40 + 70 \text{ or } 4 \cdot 10 + 7 \cdot 10)$
    $(100 + 0 \text{ or } 1 \cdot 10^2 + 0 \cdot 10^2)$

This amounts to an arrangement of the computations that is somewhat different from the one that we have given (the 4 and 7 were added before the carried 1 was added). In this example, writing out the partial sums made carrying unnecessary. In other examples you might have to repeat the partial-sum process several times to avoid carrying.

$$
\begin{array}{r}
208 \\
95 \\
\hline
13 \\
90 \\
200 \\
\hline
3 \\
100 \\
200 \\
\hline
303
\end{array}
\qquad
\begin{array}{r}
878 \\
79 \\
54 \\
\hline
21 \\
190 \\
800 \\
\hline
1 \\
110 \\
900 \\
\hline
1 \\
10 \\
1000 \\
\hline
1011
\end{array}
$$

The child might best understand the addition algorithm if it were explained in economic terms:

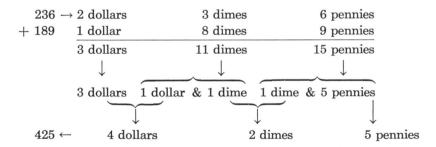

Carrying amounts to turning in ten pennies for a dime, ten dimes for a dollar, etc.

EXERCISES 5–14

1. a) Fill in reasons in this rather detailed proof that $76 + 87 = 163$.

$$
\begin{aligned}
76 + 87 &= (7 \cdot 10 + 6) + (8 \cdot 10 + 7) \quad \text{\textit{exp form}} \\
&= [(7 \cdot 10 + 6) + 8 \cdot 10] + 7 \quad \text{\textit{ass}} \\
&= [7 \cdot 10 + (6 + 8 \cdot 10)] + 7 \quad \text{\textit{ass}} \\
&= [7 \cdot 10 + (8 \cdot 10 + 6)] + 7 \\
&= [(7 \cdot 10 + 8 \cdot 10) + 6] + 7 \\
&= (7 \cdot 10 + 8 \cdot 10) + (6 + 7) \\
&= (7 \cdot 10 + 8 \cdot 10) + 13 \\
&= (7 \cdot 10 + 8 \cdot 10) + (1 \cdot 10 + 3) \\
&= [(7 \cdot 10 + 8 \cdot 10) + 1 \cdot 10] + 3 \\
&= [1 \cdot 10 + (7 \cdot 10 + 8 \cdot 10)] + 3 \\
&= [1 \cdot 10 + (7 + 8) \cdot 10] + 3 \\
&= [1 + (7 + 8)] \cdot 10 + 3 \\
&= [(1 + 7) + 8] \cdot 10 + 3 \\
&= (8 + 8) \cdot 10 + 3 \\
&= 16 \cdot 10 + 3 \\
&= (1 \cdot 10 + 6) \cdot 10 + 3 \\
&= [(1 \cdot 10) \cdot 10 + 6 \cdot 10] + 3 \\
&= [1 \cdot (10 \cdot 10) + 6 \cdot 10] + 3 \\
&= [1 \cdot 10^2 + 6 \cdot 10] + 3 \\
&= 163
\end{aligned}
$$

Therefore $76 + 87 = 163$

b) Is it clear why we must cut a few corners in analyzing algorithms?

2. Fill in the reasons and the chant.

WHAT IS REALLY GOING ON		*THE CHANT*
Statements	*Reasons*	
$26 + 87$		
$= (2 \cdot 10 + 6) + (8 \cdot 10 + 7)$		
$= 2 \cdot 10 + 8 \cdot 10 + 6 + 7$		
$= 2 \cdot 10 + 8 \cdot 10 + 13$		
$= 2 \cdot 10 + 8 \cdot 10 + 1 \cdot 10 + 3$		
$= 1 \cdot 10 + 2 \cdot 10 + 8 \cdot 10 + 3$		
$= (1 + 2 + 8) \cdot 10 + 3$		
$= (3 + 8) \cdot 10 + 3$		
$= 11 \cdot 10 + 3$		
$= (1 \cdot 10 + 1) \cdot 10 + 3$		
$= 1 \cdot 10 \cdot 10 + 1 \cdot 10 + 3$		
$= 1 \cdot 10^2 + 1 \cdot 10 + 3$		
$= 113$		
Therefore $26 + 87 = 113$		

3. Fill in statements, reasons, and chant for the problem $319 + 343$. (This is the sort of explanation you can give at a cocktail party someday.)

4. Fill in statements and reasons for the problem $296 + 95$. Be careful!

5. Fill in a reason or reasons for each step in this analysis of $929 + 84 + 489$ which corresponds to the partial-sum computation.

$929 + 84 + 489$

$$= (9 \cdot 10^2 + 2 \cdot 10 + 9) + (8 \cdot 10 + 4) + (4 \cdot 10^2 + 8 \cdot 10 + 9) \qquad 929$$
$$= (9 \cdot 10^2 + 4 \cdot 10^2) + (2 \cdot 10 + 8 \cdot 10 + 8 \cdot 10) + (9 + 4 + 9)$$
$$\text{``lining up''} \qquad 84$$
$$= (9 + 4) \cdot 10^2 + (2 + 8 + 8) \cdot 10 + (9 + 4 + 9) \qquad 489$$
$$* = 13 \cdot 10^2 + 18 \cdot 10 + 22 \qquad\qquad 22$$
$$= (1 \cdot 10 + 3) \cdot 10^2 + (1 \cdot 10 + 8) \cdot 10 + (2 \cdot 10 + 2) \qquad 180$$
$$= 1 \cdot 10^3 + 3 \cdot 10^2 + 1 \cdot 10^2 + 8 \cdot 10 + 2 \cdot 10 + 2 \qquad 1300$$
$$= 1 \cdot 10^3 + (3 + 1) \cdot 10^2 + (8 + 2) \cdot 10 + 2 \qquad 2$$
$$= 1 \cdot 10^3 + 4 \cdot 10^2 + 10 \cdot 10 + 2 \qquad 100$$
$$= 1 \cdot 10^3 + 4 \cdot 10^2 + 10^2 + 2 \qquad 400$$
$$= 1 \cdot 10^3 + (4 + 1) \cdot 10^2 + 2 \qquad 1000$$
$$= 1 \cdot 10^3 + 5 \cdot 10^2 + 2 \qquad 2$$
$$= 1502 \qquad 00$$
$$\qquad 500$$
$$\qquad 1000$$
$$\rightarrow 1502$$

6. Carry out the indicated base-7 computations. You'll need to recall the elementary addition facts for base 7.

   a) $(245)_7 + (506)_7 \ =$ b) $(162)_7 + (10)_7 \ =$

   c) $(4163)_7 + (2504)_7 \ =$ d) $(245)_7 + (66)_7 + (1301)_7 \ =$

7. Carry out the indicated base-12 computations. You'll need to recall the elementary addition facts for base 12.

   a) $(365)_{12} + (326)_{12} \ =$ b) $(8T7)_{12} + (246)_{12} \ =$

   c) $(EEE)_{12} + (9T7)_{12} \ =$ d) $(35)_{12} + (8T7E)_{12} + (106)_{12} \ =$

5–8   the subtraction algorithm analyzed

There is a good theoretical reason for refusing to discuss subtraction until after the system of integers (negatives as well as whole numbers) has been studied. In the system of integers one can look on every subtraction problem as a special sort of addition problem. There are, however, two good practical reasons for

---

* You may be hard put for a reason here because of the many steps omitted. The reason "addition algorithm, simple case" seems a plausible one to use.

discussing subtraction in the system of whole numbers. One is that the child meets (and learns to solve) subtraction problems years before he is introduced to negative numbers. The other is that to obtain a numerical answer to any specific numerical subtraction problem, even in the context of the integers, one needs to know how to subtract a "smaller" whole number from a "larger" one. Two reasons are, of course, better than one.

When you are asked to subtract 79 from 148 you are really being asked to find a number which, when added to 79, gives 148; that is, you are being asked to solve the equation $79 + x = 148$. We'll speak more of equations and their solutions when we discuss the integers and the rationals. For now let's just work our example.

We are looking for a two-digit number, ab, such that $79 + ab = 148$. That is,

$$(7 \cdot 10 + 9) + (a \cdot 10 + b) = 1 \cdot 10^2 + 4 \cdot 10 + 8.$$

That is,

$$(7 + a) \cdot 10 + (9 + b) = 1 \cdot 10^2 + 4 \cdot 10 + 8.$$

This looks hard, so we tinker with the right-hand side.

$$
\begin{aligned}
1 \cdot 10^2 + 4 \cdot 10 + 8 &= 1 \cdot 10^2 + (3 + 1) \cdot 10 + 8 & &\text{Why?} \\
&= 1 \cdot 10^2 + 3 \cdot 10 + 1 \cdot 10 + 8 & &\text{Why?} \\
&= 1 \cdot 10^2 + 3 \cdot 10 + 18 & &\text{Why?} \\
&= 10 \cdot 10 + 3 \cdot 10 + 18 & &\text{Why?} \\
&= (10 + 3)10 + 18 & &\text{Why?} \\
&= 13 \cdot 10 + 18.
\end{aligned}
$$

Now it is easy to find a and b so that

$$(7 + a) \cdot 10 + (9 + b) = 13 \cdot 10 + 18.$$

Simply choose $b = 9$ and $a = 6$. The answer is 69.

Compare these computations with the familiar chant. "You can't take 9 from 8 so you borrow (take away) 1 from 4, leaving 3, and take away 9 from 18. Write down 9. Now you can't take 7 from 3 so you borrow (take away) 1 from 1, leaving 0, and take away 7 from 13. Write down 6."

The computations are often arranged as follows to better reveal what is going on.

$$
\begin{array}{rcrcrcr}
148 \rightarrow & & 100 + 40 + 8 \rightarrow & & 100 + 30 + 18 \rightarrow & & 130 + 18 \\
-\ 79 & - & 70 + 9 & - & 70 + 9 & - & 70 + 9 \\
\hline
& & & & & & 60 + 9 \rightarrow 69
\end{array}
$$

▶ *Aside.* We pause to explain the symbol −. We were asked to solve the equation

$$79 + x = 148.$$

We know (after the fact) that there is a solution, namely 69. We also know that, as an easy consequence of "Cancel +," there cannot be any other solution (see Problem 5, page 155). We frequently find it convenient to be able to talk about "the solution to the equation $79 + x = 148$" *before* we have actually computed it. The phrase in quotation marks is a clumsy thing to have to repeat so we give it the shorthand abbreviation $148 - 79$. We could as well have used

but it is conventional to use $148 - 79$. The symbol, $148 - 79$, means precisely "the solution to the equation $79 + x = 148$," although we often pronounce it (again for reasons of economy) "one-forty-eight minus seventy-nine."

The command "subtract 79 from 148" is to be interpreted as "find the solution to $79 + x = 148$." ◀

Consider another subtraction problem:

$$\begin{array}{r} 84316 \\ -\ 46523 \end{array} \rightarrow \begin{array}{r} 8 \cdot 10^4 + 4 \cdot 10^3 + 3 \cdot 10^2 + 1 \cdot 10 + 6 \\ -\ 4 \cdot 10^4 + 6 \cdot 10^3 + 5 \cdot 10^2 + 2 \cdot 10 + 3 \end{array} \rightarrow$$

$$\begin{array}{r} 8 \cdot 10^4 + 4 \cdot 10^3 + 2 \cdot 10^2 + 11 \cdot 10 + 6 \\ -\ 4 \cdot 10^4 + 6 \cdot 10^3 + 5 \cdot 10^2 +\ \ 2 \cdot 10 + 3 \end{array}$$ (Prove $2 \cdot 10^2 + 11 \cdot 10$ $= 3 \cdot 10^2 + 1 \cdot 10$)

$$\begin{array}{r} 8 \cdot 10^4 + 3 \cdot 10^3 + 12 \cdot 10^2 + 11 \cdot 10 + 6 \\ -\ 4 \cdot 10^4 +\ 6 \cdot 10^3 +\ \ 5 \cdot 10^2 +\ \ 2 \cdot 10 + 3 \end{array}$$ (Prove $3 \cdot 10^3 + 12 \cdot 10^2$ $= 4 \cdot 10^3 + 2 \cdot 10^2$)

$$\begin{array}{r} 7 \cdot 10^4 + 13 \cdot 10^3 + 12 \cdot 10^2 + 11 \cdot 10 + 6 \\ -\ 4 \cdot 10^4 +\ \ 6 \cdot 10^3 +\ \ 5 \cdot 10^2 +\ \ 2 \cdot 10 + 3 \end{array}$$ (Prove $7 \cdot 10^4 + 13 \cdot 10^3$ $= 8 \cdot 10^4 + 3 \cdot 10^3$)

$$3 \cdot 10^4 +\ \ 7 \cdot 10^3 +\ \ 7 \cdot 10^2 +\ \ 9 \cdot 10 + 3 = 37793$$

Working backward, we've found a, b, c, d, e (namely 3, 7, 7, 9, 3) such that

$$\begin{aligned} a \cdot 10^4 + 4 \cdot 10^4 &=\ \ 7 \cdot 10^4 \\ b \cdot 10^3 + 6 \cdot 10^3 &= 13 \cdot 10^3 \\ c \cdot 10^2 + 5 \cdot 10^2 &= 12 \cdot 10^2 \\ d \cdot 10\ \ + 2 \cdot 10\ \ &= 11 \cdot 10 \\ e\ \ \ \ \ \ \ \ + 3\ \ \ \ \ \ &=\ \ 6 \end{aligned}$$

Thus, using substitution repeatedly, we obtain

$(a \cdot 10^4 + 4 \cdot 10^4) + (b \cdot 10^3 + 6 \cdot 10^3) + (c \cdot 10^2 + 5 \cdot 10^2)$
$+ (d \cdot 10 + 2 \cdot 10) + (e \cdot 3) = (7 \cdot 10^4 + 13 \cdot 10^3) + 12 \cdot 10^2 + 11 \cdot 10 + 6$
$\qquad\qquad\qquad\qquad = 8 \cdot 10^4 + [3 \cdot 10^3 + 12 \cdot 10^2] + 11 \cdot 10 + 6$
$\qquad\qquad\qquad\qquad = 8 \cdot 10^4 + 4 \cdot 10^3 + (2 \cdot 10^2 + 11 \cdot 10) + 6$
$\qquad\qquad\qquad\qquad = 8 \cdot 10^4 + 4 \cdot 10^3 + 3 \cdot 10^2 + 1 \cdot 10 + 6$

That is,

$(4 \cdot 10^4 + 6 \cdot 10^3 + 5 \cdot 10^2 + 2 \cdot 10 + 3)$
$\qquad\qquad\qquad + (a \cdot 10^4 + b \cdot 10^3 + c \cdot 10^2 + d \cdot 10 + e)$
$\qquad\qquad\qquad = 8 \cdot 10^4 + 4 \cdot 10^3 + 3 \cdot 10^2 + 1 \cdot 10 + 6.$

That is, we have found the solution, the five-digit number *abcde*, to the equation

$46523 + x = 84316.$

The child might best understand the subtraction algorithm if it too were explained in economic terms.

1 dollar	4 dimes	8 pennies
−	7 dimes	9 pennies
1 dollar	3 dimes	18 pennies
−	7 dimes	9 pennies
	13 dimes	18 pennies
−	7 dimes	9 pennies
	6 dimes	9 pennies

Borrowing amounts to cashing in a dime for 10 pennies, a dollar for 10 dimes, etc. Borrowing is just the opposite of carrying.

EXERCISES 5–15

1. Compute by arranging computations as on page 174.

a)   347   b)   1952   c)   3737
     − 158   −   36   − 2664

d)   23548   e)   2673   f)   4210
     − 13563   − 1074   − 2943

2. Is subtraction a binary operation on *W*?

3. Find the solution to each of the following equations.
   a) $4005 + x = 5703$
   b) $x + 29 = 318$
   c) $261 = x + 84$

4. (a) through (f) Perform the subtractions in Exercise 1, interpreting all numerals as base-12 numerals.

5. (a) through (f) In each case in Exercise 1 in which the problem makes sense as a base-9 problem, perform the subtraction.

6. Suppose that there is a solution to $a + x = b$.
   Denote it, as usual, by $b - a$. Thus $a + (b - a) = b$.
   Suppose that there is also a solution to $b + x = c$.
   Denote it, as usual, by $c - b$. Thus $b + (c - b) = c$.
   Prove that $(c - b) + a$ is the solution to $(b - a) + x = c$, and thus that $c - (b - a) = (c - b) + a$.

5–9   the multiplication algorithm analyzed

We begin our investigation of the multiplication algorithm with a simple example, $148 \cdot 9$.

WHAT IS REALLY GOING ON   *THE CHANT*

Statements	*Reasons*	
$148 \cdot 9$		
$= (1 \cdot 10^2 + 4 \cdot 10 + 8)9$	Expanded form	
$= 9 \cdot 1 \cdot 10^2 + 9 \cdot 4 \cdot 10 + 9 \cdot 8$	Dist, Comm ·, Assoc ·	9 times 8 is
$= 9 \cdot 1 \cdot 10^2 + 9 \cdot 4 \cdot 10 + 72$	Elem mult fact	72. Write
$= 9 \cdot 1 \cdot 10^2 + 9 \cdot 4 \cdot 10 + 7 \cdot 10 + 2$	Expanded form	down the 2
$= 9 \cdot 1 \cdot 10^2 + (9 \cdot 4 + 7) \cdot 10 + 2$	Dist	and carry the
$= 9 \cdot 1 \cdot 10^2 + (36 + 7) \cdot 10 + 2$	Elem mult fact	7. 9 times 4
$= 9 \cdot 1 \cdot 10^2 + 43 \cdot 10 + 2$	Addn algorithm	is 36 and 7 is
		43.
$= 9 \cdot 1 \cdot 10^2 + (4 \cdot 10 + 3) \cdot 10 + 2$	Expanded form	Write down
$= 9 \cdot 1 \cdot 10^2 + 4 \cdot 10^2 + 3 \cdot 10 + 2$	Dist, Law of exponents	the 3 and
$= (9 \cdot 1 + 4)10^2 + 3 \cdot 10 + 2$	Dist	carry the 4.
$= (9 + 4)10^2 + 3 \cdot 10 + 2$	Elem mult fact	9 times 1 is 9
$= 13 \cdot 10^2 + 3 \cdot 10 + 2$	Elem addn fact	and 4 is 13.
$= (1 \cdot 10 + 3)10^2 + 3 \cdot 10 + 2$	Expanded form	Write down
$= 1 \cdot 10^3 + 3 \cdot 10^2 + 3 \cdot 10 + 2$	Dist, Law of exponents	the 3. Write
$= 1332$	Expanded form	down the 1.
Therefore $148 \cdot 9 = 1332$	Tran $=$	Answer: 1332

A similar analysis can be carried out on the problem $148 \cdot 7 = 1036$. Now consider the more complicated problem, $148 \cdot 79$

$148 \cdot 79$
$= 148 \cdot (7 \cdot 10 + 9)$ Expanded form
$= (148 \cdot 7) \cdot 10 + 148 \cdot 9$ Dist, Assoc ·
$= 1036 \cdot 10 + 1332$ Simple problems already done
$= 10360 + 1332$ Effect of mult by 10 (recall Exercise 3, page 168)
$= 11692$ Addition algorithm

From this analysis it should be clear why, in the multiplication algorithm, we

$$
\begin{array}{r}
148 \\
79 \\
\hline
\end{array}
$$

multiply by 9 $\rightarrow$ 1332
multiply by 7 and indent $\Big\}$ $\rightarrow$ 1036⊙
    (or affix a zero)
add $\rightarrow$ 11692

▶ *Aside.* The more exotic multiplication algorithms, such as the cross-multi-plication method, can be justified by our same principles. For example, the cross-multiplication method of multiplying $148 \cdot 79$ amounts to simply a different arrangement of the terms:

$148 \cdot 79 = (1 \cdot 10^2 + 4 \cdot 10 + 8)(7 \cdot 10 + 9)$
$\qquad\quad = 8 \cdot 9 + (4 \cdot 9 + 8 \cdot 7) \cdot 10 + (1 \cdot 9 + 4 \cdot 7)10^2 + (1 \cdot 7)10^3$
$\qquad\quad = (2 + 7 \cdot 10) + \cdots$

A different chant, a different chart, but the same old reasons. ◀

As with partial sums in addition problems, writing out the partial products in a multiplication problem sheds some light on the inner workings of the algorithm. For example:

$$
\begin{array}{r}
148 \rightarrow \\
\times \ 79 \\
\hline
\end{array}
\qquad
\begin{array}{r}
100 + 40 + 8 \\
\times \qquad 70 + 9 \\
\hline
\end{array}
$$

$\left.\begin{array}{r} 72 \\ 360 \\ 900 \end{array}\right\}$ Multiplying each of top 3 terms by 9. Note that sum of
              these 3 partial products is   1332

$\left.\begin{array}{r} 560 \\ 2800 \\ 7000 \end{array}\right\}$ Multiplying each of top 3 terms by 70. Note that sum of
              these 3 partial products is   10360

       Add   11,692   11,692

For larger numbers the analysis is similar:

$$14087 \rightarrow \quad 10000 + 4000 + 80 + 7$$
$$\times \ 5283 \quad \times \ 5000 + \ 200 + 80 + 3$$

$$\left.\begin{array}{r} 21 \\ 240 \\ 12000 \\ 30000 \end{array}\right\} \quad 42261$$

$$\left.\begin{array}{r} 560 \\ 6400 \\ 320000 \\ 800000 \end{array}\right\} \quad 1126960$$

$$\left.\begin{array}{r} 1400 \\ 16000 \\ 800000 \\ 2000000 \end{array}\right\} \quad 2817400$$

$$\left.\begin{array}{r} 35000 \\ 400000 \\ 20000000 \\ 50000000 \end{array}\right\} \quad 70435000$$

$$\overline{}$$
$$74{,}421{,}621$$

EXERCISES 5–16

1. Fill in the reasons and the chant.

WHAT IS REALLY GOING ON   *THE CHANT*

Statements	Reasons	
$14087 \cdot 3$		
$= (1 \cdot 10^4 + 4 \cdot 10^3 + 0 \cdot 10^2 + 8 \cdot 10 + 7)3$	*expanded form*	
$= 3 \cdot 1 \cdot 10^4 + 3 \cdot 4 \cdot 10^3 + 3 \cdot 0 \cdot 10^2$ $+ 3 \cdot 8 \cdot 10 + 3 \cdot 7$	*disTribuTive*	
$= 3 \cdot 1 \cdot 10^4 + 3 \cdot 4 \cdot 10^3 + 3 \cdot 0 \cdot 10^2$ $+ 3 \cdot 8 \cdot 10 + 21$	*basic fact of mulT,*	
$= 3 \cdot 1 \cdot 10^4 + 3 \cdot 4 \cdot 10^3 + 3 \cdot 0 \cdot 10^2$ $+ 3 \cdot 8 \cdot 10 + 2 \cdot 10 + 1$	*expanded form*	
$= 3 \cdot 1 \cdot 10^4 + 3 \cdot 4 \cdot 10^3 + 3 \cdot 0 \cdot 10^2$ $+ [3 \cdot 8 + 2] \cdot 10 + 1$	*DisTribuTive*	

(Continued)

WHAT IS REALLY GOING ON	*THE CHANT*

$= 3 \cdot 1 \cdot 10^4 + 3 \cdot 4 \cdot 10^3 + 3 \cdot 0 \cdot 10^2$
   $+ [24 + 2] \cdot 10 + 1$ *basic mult. fact*

$= 3 \cdot 1 \cdot 10^4 + 3 \cdot 4 \cdot 10^3 + 3 \cdot 0 \cdot 10^2$
   $+ 26 \cdot 10 + 1$ *algorithym*

$= 3 \cdot 1 \cdot 10^4 + 3 \cdot 4 \cdot 10^3 + 3 \cdot 0 \cdot 10^2$
   $+ (2 \cdot 10 + 6) \cdot 10 + 1$ *expanded form*

$= 3 \cdot 1 \cdot 10^4 + 3 \cdot 4 \cdot 10^3 + 3 \cdot 0 \cdot 10^2$
   $+ 2 \cdot 10^2 + 6 \cdot 10 + 1$ *distributive law of exp.*

$= 3 \cdot 1 \cdot 10^4 + 3 \cdot 4 \cdot 10^3 + (3 \cdot 0 + 2)10^2$
   $+ 6 \cdot 10 + 1$ *distrib.*

$= 3 \cdot 1 \cdot 10^4 + 3 \cdot 4 \cdot 10^3 + (0 + 2)10^2$
   $+ 6 \cdot 10 + 1$ *mult. of zeroes*

$= 3 \cdot 1 \cdot 10^4 + 3 \cdot 4 \cdot 10^3 + 2 \cdot 10^2$
   $+ 6 \cdot 10 + 1$ ~~*base*~~ *add of zeroes*

$= 3 \cdot 1 \cdot 10^4 + 12 \cdot 10^3 + 2 \cdot 10^2$
   $+ 6 \cdot 10 + 1$ *mult. fact*

$= 3 \cdot 1 \cdot 10^4 + (1 \cdot 10 + 2)10^3 + 2 \cdot 10^2$
   $+ 6 \cdot 10 + 1$ *exp. form*

$= 3 \cdot 1 \cdot 10^4 + 1 \cdot 10^4 + 2 \cdot 10^3 + 2 \cdot 10^2$
   $+ 6 \cdot 10 + 1$ *dist. law of exp.*

$= (3 \cdot 1 + 1)10^4 + 2 \cdot 10^3 + 2 \cdot 10^2$
   $+ 6 \cdot 10 + 1$ *Dist.*

$= (3 + 1)10^4 + 2 \cdot 10^3 + 2 \cdot 10^2$
   $+ 6 \cdot 10 + 1$ *basic of mult or mult. of 1*

$= 4 \cdot 10^4 + 2 \cdot 10^3 + 2 \cdot 10^2 + 6 \cdot 10 + 1$ *basic add fact*

$= 42261$ *expanded form*

Therefore $14087 \cdot 3 = 42261$ *Transitive prop of equality*

---

2. Assuming that $14087 \cdot 3 = 42261$
                 $14087 \cdot 8 = 112696$
                 $14087 \cdot 2 = 28174$
                 $14087 \cdot 5 = 70435$

Justify the computational procedure

$$
\begin{array}{r}
14\ 087 \\
5\ 283 \\
\hline
42\ 261 \\
1\ 126\ 960 \\
2\ 817\ 400 \\
70\ 435\ 000 \\
\hline
74{,}421{,}621
\end{array}
$$

3. Explain as in Exercise 1 (statements, reasons, chant) the computation
   $8906 \cdot 5 = 44{,}530$

4. Explain why $800{,}000{,}000{,}000 \cdot 3{,}000{,}000 = 2{,}400{,}000{,}000{,}000{,}000{,}000$

5. Compute, exhibiting partial products as in the example on page 178:

   a) $816 \cdot 37$ b) $205 \cdot 174$ c) $296 \cdot 450$ d) $829 \cdot 301$ e) $7060 \cdot 506$

6. (a) through (e): Do Exercise 5, assuming that all numerals are base-12 numerals.

7. (a) through (e): In each case of Exercise 5 in which the problem makes sense as a base-9 problem, perform the multiplications.

5–10   the division algorithm analyzed

There is a good theoretical reason for deferring a discussion of division until after the system of rational numbers has been studied. In the system of rationals one can look on every division problem as a special sort of multiplication problem. But again there are two good practical reasons for studying division now, in the system of whole numbers. One is that the child meets (and learns to solve) division problems long before he studies rational numbers. The other is that to obtain a numerical answer to any specific numerical division problem, even in the context of the rationals, one needs to know how to divide one whole number by another.

Does this sound like a broken record? If it does, congratulations! You are aware of the analogy between subtraction and division which parallels the analogy between addition and multiplication (recall laws 1 through 8). We shall investigate this analogy further and exploit it rather fully in Chapter 8.

Division is really a subtraction–multiplication problem. When you are asked to divide 2156 by 37 you are really being asked to subtract the largest possible multiple of 37 from 2156. The multiplier of 37 is called the *quotient;* the difference between 2156 and this multiple of 37 is called the *remainder.* For example:

$$
\begin{array}{r}
58 \\
\hline
37 \,\big|\, 2156 \\
185 \\
\hline
306 \\
296 \\
\hline
10
\end{array}
$$

conveys the information
that $2156 - 58 \cdot 37 = 10$

↖   ↖

quotient   remainder

↙   ↙

That is $2156 = 58 \cdot 37 + 10$

The number being divided, 2156, is called the *dividend* (divisee would be a better word); the number 37 is called the divisor. Thus

DIVIDEND = QUOTIENT · DIVISOR + REMAINDER

And note. The remainder must be "less than" the divisor, for otherwise the "largest" multiple of the divisor has not been subtracted (compare this with the discussion of order which follows in Section 11).

▶ *Aside.* A word on terminology. If 37 little boys decide to divide up 2156 marbles, then each boy gets 58 ("quotient" comes from the Latin stem *quot*, meaning "how many") and 10 marbles remain left over. ◀

The calculation

$$
\begin{array}{r}
5\,0 \\
\hline
37\,|\,2156 \\
185\,0 \\
\hline
306
\end{array}
$$

signifies that $2156 - 50 \cdot 37 = 306$ or $2156 = 50 \cdot 37 + 306$. The calculation

$$
\begin{array}{r}
8 \\
\hline
37\,| \\
306 \\
296 \\
\hline
10
\end{array}
$$

signifies that $306 - 8 \cdot 37 = 10$ or $306 = 8 \cdot 37 + 10$. Putting the two equations together (substitution), we get

$$
\begin{aligned}
2156 &= 50 \cdot 37 + 8 \cdot 37 + 10 \\
&= (50 + 8)37 + 10 \\
&= 58 \cdot 37 + 10.
\end{aligned}
$$

Sometimes these calculations are arranged as follows, to better illustrate what is happening:

$$
\begin{array}{r|r|r}
37 & 2156 & 50 \\
& 1850 & \\
\hline
& 306 & 8 \\
& 296 & \\
\hline
& 10 & 58
\end{array}
$$

37 | 2156 | 50 ← First partial quotient
    | 1850 |

First trial remainder; process →   306 | 8 ← Second partial quotient
is not complete since 306 is   296 | Add
greater than 37   → 10 | 58 ← Quotient
      (Genuine) remainder ⸺
      It is less than 37

The equations involved are again:

$2156 = 50 \cdot 37 + 306,$
$\quad 306 = 8 \cdot 37 + 10.$

Thus, when we substitute from the second into the first,

$2156 = 50 \cdot 37 + (8 \cdot 37 + 10)$
$\quad\quad = (50 + 8) \cdot 37 + 10$
$\quad\quad = 58 \cdot 37 + 10.$

Let's look at a more complicated division problem in this systematic fashion: Divide 973,425 by 28.

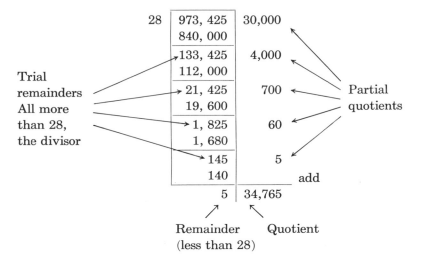

The equations involved are

$973{,}425 = 30{,}000 \cdot 28 + 133{,}425$
$133{,}425 = \qquad\qquad 4000 \cdot 28 + 21{,}425$
$\ \ 21{,}425 = \qquad\qquad\qquad\quad 700 \cdot 28 + 1{,}825$
$\ \ \ \ 1{,}825 = \qquad\qquad\qquad\qquad\qquad 60 \cdot 28 + 145$
$\ \ \ \ \ \ 145 = \qquad\qquad\qquad\qquad\qquad\qquad 5 \cdot 28 + 5$

Substituting four times yields

$973{,}425 = 30{,}000 \cdot 28 + 4{,}000 \cdot 28 + 700 \cdot 28 + 60 \cdot 28 + 5 \cdot 28 + 5$
$\qquad\quad = (30{,}000 + 4{,}000 + 700 + 60 + 5) \cdot 28 + 5$
$\qquad\quad = 34{,}765 \cdot 28 + 5$

Therefore $973{,}425 = 34{,}765 \cdot 28 + 5$

           ↑   ↑   ↑   ↖

     Dividend   Quotient   Divisor   Remainder

From this arrangement of the computations, it is a short step to the more economical (and more mysterious) arrangement:

```
         34765
     _____
 28 | 973425
      84↓
      ___
      133
      112↓
      ___
       214
       196↓
       ___
       182
       168↓
       ___
        145
        140
        ___
          5
```

We now know why the division algorithm works. The only question remaining is, "How did you choose the partial quotients?" The answer is: educated guessing. However, uneducated guessing works almost as well. Consider the following solution to the problem of dividing 5280 by 18.

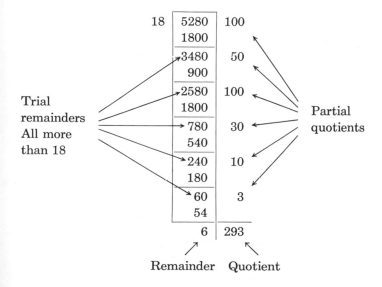

Trial remainders All more than 18

Partial quotients

Remainder   Quotient

The equations are

$$5280 = 100 \cdot 18 + 3480$$
$$3480 = \qquad 50 \cdot 18 + 2580$$
$$2580 = \qquad\qquad 100 \cdot 18 + 780$$
$$780 = \qquad\qquad\qquad 30 \cdot 18 + 240$$
$$240 = \qquad\qquad\qquad\qquad 10 \cdot 18 + 60$$
$$60 = \qquad\qquad\qquad\qquad\qquad 3 \cdot 18 + 6$$

Substituting 5 times yields

$$5280 = 100 \cdot 18 + 50 \cdot 18 + 100 \cdot 18 + 30 \cdot 18 + 10 \cdot 18 + 3 \cdot 18 + 6$$
$$= (100 + 50 + 100 + 30 + 10 + 3) \cdot 18 + 6$$
$$= 293 \cdot 18 + 6$$

The reason for giving so much good space to such bad guessing is that it illustrates a favored method of teaching division. You tell the child that dividing 5280 by 18 means taking away as many 18's as possible. He begins taking them away in a piecemeal fashion. Perhaps he first takes away 100 18's. This leaves him with 3480 and now maybe he takes away 50 18's . . .

After doing a number of division problems in this piecemeal fashion, he *discovers* that he can take away 200 18's at the first step because 18 goes into 52 twice, and that at the next step he can take away 90 18's because 18 goes into 168 9 times, and that at the next step he can take away 3 18's because 18 goes into 60 3 times. The final step to the economical display of computation is then easy, and he knows what he is doing.

$$
\begin{array}{r|r|r}
18 & 5280 & 200 \\
   & 3600 & \\ \hline
   & 1680 & 90 \\
   & 1620 & \\ \hline
   & 60 & 3 \\
   & 54 & \\ \hline
   & 6 & 293
\end{array}
$$

▶ *Aside A.* In careful axiomatic approaches one proves the following theorem. *Division theorem:* Given any whole numbers n and d with $d \neq 0$, there exist unique whole numbers q and r satisfying the two conditions

i) $n = qd + r$,

ii) $0 \leq r < d$.

We won't be able to prove this from our list of fundamental principles even after all the symbols in (ii) have been defined. If it makes you feel more secure, add this to the list of fundamental principles. If you have no fear that every division problem leads to a unique quotient and remainder, then forget this theorem. ◀

▶ *Aside B* (compare with the aside on page 174). When one number divides evenly into another (i.e., remainder is 0), then the quotient is given a special label. For example, 4 divides evenly into 12. The quotient 3 is given the label $\frac{12}{4}$. More generally, when an equation of the form

$$nx = m, \qquad n \neq 0,$$

has "a" solution in W, that solution is denoted by $\dfrac{m}{n}$.

Problem   a) Prove that if $n \neq 0$, then the equation $nx = m$ has at most one solution in W. This justifies the word "a" above.

b) Say what you can about the existence and uniqueness of solutions to the equation $0x = m$. ◀

EXERCISES 5–17

1. Perform the indicated divisions, using the partial-quotient, trial-remainder arrangement of computations. Write out the equations involved and substitute to arrive at a final equation of the form

   dividend = quotient · divisor + remainder.

   (In at least 2 cases make a special effort to be a bad guesser.)

   a) $71\,\overline{\smash{\big)}\,546}$ b) $18\,\overline{\smash{\big)}\,40051}$ c) $263\,\overline{\smash{\big)}\,324}$

   d) $263\,\overline{\smash{\big)}\,9{,}723{,}456}$ e) $27\,\overline{\smash{\big)}\,1728}$ f) $87\,\overline{\smash{\big)}\,63}$

2. Do (e) of 1 as a base-9 problem.

3. What happens to bad guessers who use the short-form arrangement of computations?

4. Figure out what on earth is going on here and why.

$$15 \cdot 39 = 585 \qquad \text{because}$$

15	39	odd
30	19	odd
60	9	odd
~~120~~	~~4~~	~~even~~
~~240~~	~~2~~	~~even~~
480	1	odd

Add $\dfrac{480}{585}$

5. Try Exercise 16, page 88, again.

5–11   order in W, additional fundamental principles

Before we leave the system of whole numbers W, let us speak once again of order. Order was first encountered when we learned to count. It came up again in our discussion of division when we spoke of "largest" multiples and the remainders being "less than" the divisor.

We would like to reintroduce the notion of order without having to rely on counting notions. We do so by making the following reasonable definition. (Bear in mind that throughout this section "number" means "whole number.")

Definition   "a is less than b" if there is a nonzero number c such that $a + c = b$. We shall also sometimes say that b is greater than a, meaning that a is less than b. (The nonzero whole numbers are called the *natural numbers*, and are denoted by N.)

Notation $a < b$ denotes "a is less than b"
$b > a$ denotes "b is greater than a"

Examples $3 < \ \ 7$ because $3 + 4 = 7$
$1 > \ \ 0$ because $0 + 1 = 1$
$8 < 10$ because $8 + 2 = 10$

The relation $<$ has a number of properties which play such important roles in mathematics that they have acquired rather exotic names: the Trichotomy, Transitivity, and Monotony theorems. (Monotony refers to stability, not to dullness.) To deserve the name theorem each should be derivable from our list of assumptions (fundamental principles). They are not. We need to add to the list to prove these theorems.

This defect is again a result of our having to forego a completely rigorous approach, in which approach the things we are now about to assume are proved as theorems.

ADDITIONAL ARITHMETIC FACTS

15. If a and b denote whole numbers, then either $a = b$ or $a < b$ or $a > b$.
16. If $a \neq 0$ and $b \neq 0$, then $a + b \neq 0$.

Another fact we'll need, but this one we proved (Ex. 5 p. 164) is:

If $a \neq 0$ and $b \neq 0$, then $ab \neq 0$.

Trichotomy theorem   If a and b denote whole numbers, then exactly one of the following holds: $a = b$, $a > b$, $a < b$.

Proof   We note that Fact 15 says that *at least* one of the alternatives holds. It only remains for us to show that no two can hold simultaneously.

Suppose that $a = b$ and $a < b$. Then:

1. $a + 0 = a = b$ Add 0, Given
2. $\exists c \neq 0$ such that $a + c = b$ Defn $<$, Given
3. Therefore $a + 0 = a + c$ Tran $=$

4. Therefore $c = 0$ Cancel $+$

5. Therefore $c \neq 0$ and $c = 0$ Steps 2, 4

which is absurd, and hence our assumption that $a = b$ and $a < b$ is untenable.

     Suppose that $a < b$ and $a > b$. Then:

1. $\exists c \neq 0$ such that $a + c = b$ Defn $<$, Given

2. $\exists d \neq 0$ such that $b + d = a$ Defn $<$, Given

3. Therefore $(a + c) + d = a$ Subst

4. Therefore $a + (c + d) = a + 0$ Assoc $+$, Add 0

5. Therefore $c + d = 0$ Cancel $+$

6. But $c + d \neq 0$ Steps 1, 2 and fact 16

So again we have an absurdity.

Transitivity theorem $a < b$ and $b < c \Rightarrow a < c$.

Proof $\exists d \neq 0$ such that $a + d = b$.   Why?

        $\exists e \neq 0$ such that $b + e = c$.   Why?

        Therefore $a + d + e = c$.   Why?

        But $d + e \neq 0$.   Why?

        Therefore $a < c$.   Why?

Monotony theorem for $+$ $a < b \Rightarrow a + c < b + c$.

Proof $\exists d \neq 0$ such that $a + d = b$.   Why?

        Therefore $(a + d) + c = b + c$.   Why?

        Therefore $(a + c) + d = b + c$.   Why?

        Therefore $a + c < b + c$.   Why?

Monotony theorem for $\cdot$ $a < b$ and $c \neq 0 \Rightarrow ac < bc$

Proof $\exists d \neq 0$ such that $a + d = b$ Why?

        Therefore $(a + d)c = bc$ Why?

        Therefore $ac + dc = bc$ Why?

        But $d \neq 0$ and $c \neq 0 \Rightarrow dc \neq 0$ Why?

        Therefore $ac < bc$ Why?

EXERCISES 5–18

1. Complete the proof of the trichotomy theorem by assuming that $a = b$ and $a > b$ and finding an absurdity. Compare this type of proof with the argument of the lawyer who "proves" that his client is innocent of a bank robbery in Chicago by establishing his presence in Boston at the time of the robbery.

2. Show that (a) $10 < 11$, (b) $87 < 5341$, (c) $348 < 916$.

3. Prove that

   a) $a \neq 0 \Leftrightarrow a > 0$. [*Hint:* Use definition of $<$ and Trichotomy.]

   b) $a, b > 0 \Rightarrow a + b > 0$.

   c) $a, b > 0 \Rightarrow ab > 0$.

4. Prove that

   a) $a < b$ and $b < c$ and $c < d \Rightarrow a < d$.

   b) $a < b$ and $c < d \Rightarrow a + c < b + d$.

   [*Hint:* $a + c < b + c$. (Why?) $b + c < b + d$. (Why?)]

   c) $a < b$ and $c < d \Rightarrow ac < bd$.

   [*Hint:* Compare with (b).]

5. Prove these "cancellation laws for $<$."

   a) $a + c < d + c \Rightarrow a < b$. [*Hint:* Suppose that $a \not< b$.]

   b) $ac < bc \Rightarrow a < b$.   [*Hint:* Compare with (a).]

6. We denote "a is less than b or a is equal to b" by $a \leq b$. We define "a divides b" (written $a \mid b$) by $a \mid b$ if there is a c such that $ac = b$. Explore the properties of $\mid$ and $\leq$. Look for analogies. (Test for reflexivity, symmetry, transitivity, trichotomy, monotony.)

7. Is our definition of $<$ reasonable at the set-counting stage of abstraction? Does it translate, into careful mathematics, your intuitive notion of what it means for one set to be smaller than another?

8. Let a, b, c in the proofs of the transitivity and monotony theorems be 2, 7, 9, respectively.

   a) What are the numerical values of d and e in the proof of transitivity?

   b) What is the numerical value of d in the proof of monotony $+$?

   c) What is the numerical value of d in the proof of monotony $\cdot$?

SUMMARY

From the child's point of view, the nine basic principles of whole-number arithmetic isolated in this chapter

Assoc $+$	Assoc $\cdot$
Comm $+$	Comm $\cdot$
Add 0	Mult 1
Cancel $+$	Cancel $\cdot$
Dist	

are consequences of the relationships between operations on sets and operations on numbers. One characteristic of modern mathematics programs is that statements of these principles are found in elementary texts and teachers are expected to utilize them in their teaching. But the principles should be mentioned only as they are actually used. In early counting experiences, children find commutativity and associativity useful. When a child thinks of 12 eights as 10 eights and 2 eights he is using the distributive principle.

From the long-range point of view, the basic principles have far greater significance than their applicability to whole-number computation. They provide the key for an understanding of the structure of arithmetic. It makes sense to codify the rules of the game so that one need not go all the way back to the physical world in order to validate properties of numbers. As students progress to the study of other sets of numbers, integers, rationals, and real numbers, these principles persist and furnish a basic core of concepts that gives unity to all number systems.

You should be able to break down any calculation with whole numbers into a series of tiny moves, each justified by a single basic principle. Note that the multiplicative property of zero is not assumed. It follows from the other principles that

$$\forall a, b \in W, a \cdot b = 0 \quad \text{if and only if} \quad a = 0 \text{ or } b = 0.$$

Order concepts for whole numbers are more subtle than they appear to be on the surface. Actually two new principles need to be added to our list in order to prove the basic Trichotomy, Transitivity, and Monotony theorems. You should understand the definition:

$$a < b \text{ means } \exists c \neq 0 \text{ such that } a + c = b,$$

and you should know the statements of the three theorems:

Trichotomy $\forall a, b \in W$, exactly one of $a = b$, $a < b$, $a > b$ is true.

Transitivity $\forall a, b, c \in W$, $a < b$ and $b < c \Rightarrow a < c$.

Monotony $\forall a, b, c \in W$:

    i) $a < b \Rightarrow a + c < b + c$.

    ii) If $c \neq 0$, $a < b \Rightarrow a \cdot c < b \cdot c$.

These theorems, in slightly altered form, will recur in each successive number system: the integers, the rationals, the reals.

6 the abstraction of positive rational arithmetic from the real world

6-1 stage 1: the invention of symbols

In earlier chapters we have examined the abstraction process by which whole-number arithmetic is drawn from the real world. We invented symbols to record the number of elements in any set, devised useful ways of "calculating" with those symbols in order to gain further information about the sets they describe, abstracted the resulting symbolic game from its environment, and then, in Chapter 5, made a careful study of the game itself. As an end result of our efforts we can now view the system of whole numbers as an interesting object in its own right, independent of the world of reality which mothered it.

We now repeat this process for the rational number system. Our first task, the Stage-1 abstraction, is to recognize the possible usefulness of inventing new symbols to describe some particular physical situations. Consider the following statement:

In a set of children there are 2 boys for every 3 girls.

This language immediately evokes the mental image of two sets which stand in a particular relationship.

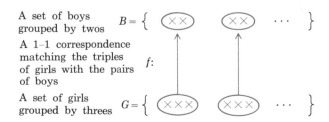

A set of boys grouped by twos

A 1–1 correspondence matching the triples of girls with the pairs of boys

A set of girls grouped by threes

The expression "2 boys for every 3 girls" suggests a 1–1, onto function whose *domain* is a set of triples and whose *range* is a set of pairs.

A little reflection shows that functions of this type occur frequently in the real world, and so we decide to establish a convention for *naming* these functions. Again and again we are led to consider the following sort of physical situation.

i) A set A is partitioned into a-element subsets.

ii) A set B is partitioned into b-element subsets.

iii) There is a 1–1 function from the partition of B *onto* the partition of A.

We agree to name the function of (iii) *by the symbol* $\frac{a}{b}$. In our example the set of boys is partitioned into 2-element subsets and the set of girls is partitioned into 3-element subsets. By our naming convention, the 1–1, onto function f matching triples of girls with pairs of boys is named $\frac{2}{3}$. Thus

$$f = \tfrac{2}{3}.$$

Obviously we could just as well have drawn our arrows in the other direction and pictured the inverse of the function f.

$$B = \{(\times\times)\ (\times\times)\ldots\}$$
$$f^{-1}:$$
$$G = \{(\times\times\times)(\times\times\times)\ldots\}$$

By our naming agreement,

If $f = \tfrac{2}{3}$, then $f^{-1} = \tfrac{3}{2}$.

Note the connection between our naming convention and the diagrams we draw. In naming a function $\frac{a}{b}$, the a denotes the number of elements in subsets pictured in the diagrams at the *heads* of the arrows. The b describes sets at the *bases* of the arrows. (A helpful mnemonic device is that *d*enominator goes with *d*omain.)

If there are 2 boys for every 3 girls, then there are

4 boys for every 6 girls,
6 boys for every 9 girls,
$\vdots$

Explain when some functions in the set below can be used interchangeably and when they cannot when we are comparing two sets.

$$\left\{\frac{2}{3}, \frac{4}{6}, \frac{6}{9}, \ldots, \frac{n \cdot 2}{n \cdot 3}, \ldots\right\}.$$

EXERCISES 6–1

1. Set A contains 80 elements and set B 60 elements. The symbol $\frac{80}{60}$ names a function from a set of one 60-tuple onto a set of one 80-tuple.

   a) Write several other such symbols naming functions which compare the two sets.

   b) Which function, mapping b-tuples of elements in B upon a-tuples of elements in A, involves the smallest possible whole numbers b and a?

   c) Sketch arrow diagrams picturing one of the functions f you noted in (a) and also the function f^{-1}.

2. In a group C of children there are 5 boys for every 8 children. Denoting the set of boys by B, the set of girls by G, write a symbol for a 1–1, onto function whose domain and range are, respectively:

   a) A partition of the children into 8-tuples and a partition of the boys into 5-tuples.

   b) A set of 3-tuples of girls and a set of 8-tuples of children.

   c) A set of 3-tuples of girls and a set of 5-tuples of boys.

   Check our notational agreement and assure yourself that you have not written any of these names "upside down."

3. In 2(a) above, the domain of the function is a set of 8-tuples. Each 8-tuple is itself a set. What is the union of the 8-tuples? What is the union of the 5-tuples?

4. A segment $\overline{AB}$ is subdivided into 40 congruent segments. Segment $\overline{CD}$ is subdivided into 48 segments congruent to those of $\overline{AB}$.

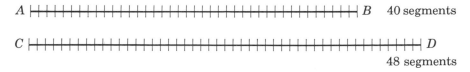

   A ┣┼┼┼┼┼┼┼┼┼┼┼┼┼┼┼┼┼┼┼┼┼┼┼┼┼┼┼┼┼┼┼┼┼┼┼┼┤ B 40 segments

   C ┣┼┼┤ D
                                                    48 segments

   a) Write symbols for several functions which compare these segments. Specify domain and range of each function.

   b) Which symbols indicate the *length* of $\overline{CD}$ when $\overline{AB}$ is taken as the *unit segment*? Which indicate the length of $\overline{AB}$ with $\overline{CD}$ as unit?

5. If an amount of hamburger is described as weighing $\frac{3}{2}$ pounds, then the symbol $\frac{3}{2}$ compares the meat purchased with a unit quantity called a *pound*. Visualize the hamburger purchased as formed into 24 small patties of equal weight. Visualize a pound of hamburger partitioned into patties of the same weight. Name several functions which compare the hamburger purchased with the pound unit. Sketch an arrow diagram for one of these functions.

▶ *Aside.* At this point we have agreed to write specific symbols for certain functions which compare in a very special way a first set of physical objects with a second. Exercises 4 and 5 above suggest that our symbolism may have wide applicability. Note that the introduction of our new symbolism is essentially the invention of a new "language" for talking about familiar relationships between sets. You may call these new *symbols*

$$\tfrac{2}{3}, \tfrac{7}{4}, \tfrac{8}{5}, \ldots$$

numbers or *numerals* as you please so long as you remember that no matter what you *call* them they are, at the moment, no more and no less than names for functions that exist in the physical world.

In our use of these new symbols it will be convenient to have a special language that is descriptive both of the symbols themselves and of the ways in which we utilize them in computation. Hence, we begin to develop a language for our symbols which is a "mirror" reflection of the language we use in referring to the functions named by them. This is one of the developments of Stage 2 of the abstraction process as we begin to recognize the desirability of defining "operations" on our new symbols. ◀

6–2   stage 2: operations on fractions

We agree to call each of the new symbols $\tfrac{a}{b}$ a *fraction*. We call the whole numbers a and b, respectively, the *numerator* and *denominator* of the fraction $\tfrac{a}{b}$. For the moment we require that neither a nor b be zero. We read the symbol $\tfrac{a}{b}$ as "a over b" or "a $b$ths." (You know special names for the cases $b = 2, 3, 5$.)

We shall replace diagrams of the sort used in Section 6–1 with simpler ones, as illustrated below.

$$f = \tfrac{4}{7}$$

$$A \xrightarrow{\;\tfrac{3}{5}\;} B \qquad\qquad C \overset{}{\underset{f^{-1} = \tfrac{7}{4}}{\dashrightarrow}} D$$

The diagram on the left indicates that set B is partitioned into 3-tuples, A into 5-tuples, and that the function $\tfrac{3}{5}$ is a 1–1 correspondence *from* the set of 5-tuples *onto* the set of 3-tuples. The diagram on the right pictures a function named $\tfrac{4}{7}$ and its inverse: the inverse of $\tfrac{4}{7} = \left(\tfrac{4}{7}\right)^{-1} = \tfrac{7}{4}$.

In general, the diagram

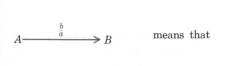

means that

1) A is partitioned into a-element subsets,

2) B is partitioned into b-element subsets,

3) $\tfrac{b}{a}$ is a 1–1, onto function from the partition of A to the partition of B.

Note that if $\frac{a}{b}$ is any fraction, then the two fractions, $\frac{a}{b}$ and $\frac{b}{a}$, name functions which are inverses of each other. We shall say that these *fractions* are *reciprocals* of each other. Sometimes instead of saying, "Write the reciprocal of the fraction $\frac{a}{b}$," we shall say

"*Invert* the fraction $\frac{a}{b}$."

We have seen that all the functions in the set

$$\frac{2}{3}, \frac{4}{6}, \frac{6}{9}, \ldots, \frac{n \cdot 2}{n \cdot 3}, \ldots$$

are "almost" alike. We shall say that any two fractions naming two such functions are *equivalent* fractions.

As the diagram indicates, the fractions $\frac{1}{3}$, $\frac{2}{6}$, and $\frac{5}{15}$ are *equivalent* to one another because they can all be used to compare the same two sets. The set of all fractions equivalent to a single fraction will be called an *equivalence class* of fractions. Abbreviating, we have

Eq. $(\frac{5}{15})$ = $\{\frac{1}{3}, \frac{2}{6}, \frac{3}{9}, \frac{4}{12}, \frac{5}{15}, \ldots\}$

Read "Eq. $(\frac{5}{15})$" as "the equivalence class of $\frac{5}{15}$."

EXERCISES 6–2

1. Prove that $\frac{9}{15}$ and $\frac{15}{25}$ are equivalent fractions by choosing A to be a set of 150 elements, B a set of 90 elements, and showing how to group the elements in two different ways.

2.

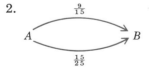

Given that the set A has 75 elements, show that the *domain* of the function $\frac{15}{25}$ consists of three elements, each of which is a 25-tuple. Describe the *range* of the function $\frac{15}{25}$. Describe domain and range of the function $\frac{9}{15}$.

3. What is the least number of elements that set A and set B can have so
that the diagram

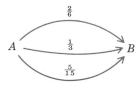

makes sense? Find another pair of such numbers.

4. Describe the relationship between *domain* and *range* of a *function* $\frac{a}{b}$ and
denominator and *numerator* of the corresponding *fraction* $\frac{a}{b}$.*

As you may anticipate, we shall soon be adding, multiplying, subtracting,
and dividing fractions in the approved manner. But now we are concerned with
the way in which these operations are drawn from the real world. The exercise
list below indicates the origin of operations on fractions.

EXERCISES 6–3

1.
$$A \xrightarrow{\ \ \frac{3}{5}\ \ } B$$

a) If B has 12 elements, how many has A?

b) Explain how, in answering (a), you visualized the *domain* of the *function* $\frac{3}{5}$.

c) Explain how the number 12 and the numerator and denominator of the
fraction $\frac{3}{5}$ are used in answering the question of part (a).

d) Why would it be nonsensical to ask for the number of elements in A,
assuming that B has 20 elements?

e) Answer the question of (a), assuming that B has 21 elements; 3; 300.

f) Because problems of this type occur so often, we facilitate their solution
by *defining* an *operation* on certain ordered pairs of whole numbers and
fractions. As you have computed:

$(12, \frac{3}{5}) \rightarrow 20; \qquad (21, \frac{3}{5}) \rightarrow 35; \qquad (3, \frac{3}{5}) \rightarrow 5.$

* Note that when we look at the symbol $\frac{a}{b}$ we may think of the symbol itself (a fraction)
or the thing named by it (a function). You will have to decide from context how the
authors are thinking. For example, when we talk about "the inverse of $\frac{a}{b}$" we mean
function; when we talk about "the reciprocal of $\frac{a}{b}$" we mean fraction. It may be helpful
to remember that we only think about functions while we may both think about and
write fractions.

In order for you to perform this operation on a pair $(n, \frac{b}{a})$, what relationship must hold between the whole numbers b and n? Choose a mellifluous name for this operation.

2.

$$A \xrightarrow{\quad \frac{3}{5} \quad} B$$

a) If A has 25 elements, how many has B?

b) Explain how in answering (a) you visualize the *range* of the function $\frac{3}{5}$.

c) Explain how the number 25 and the *numerator* and *denominator* of the *fraction* $\frac{3}{5}$ are used in answering the question of part (a).

d) Because problems of this type occur so often, we facilitate their solution by defining an operation on certain ordered pairs of fractions and whole numbers:

$$(\tfrac{3}{5}, 25) \rightarrow 15; \qquad (\tfrac{3}{5}, 40) \rightarrow 24.$$

In order for you to perform this operation on a pair $(\frac{b}{a}, n)$, what relationship must hold between the whole numbers a and n? Choose a name for this operation.

3. A B $A \cup B$

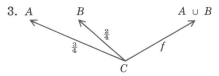

a) Assuming that $A \cap B = \emptyset$, compute a fraction name for the function f.

b) Explain how you visualized the *domains* and *ranges* of the *functions* $\frac{3}{4}$ and $\frac{2}{4}$ as you computed the fraction name for f.

c) Explain how one can get the fraction name for f by working mechanically with the numerators and denominators of the *fractions* $\frac{3}{4}$ and $\frac{2}{4}$.

4. Replace the function $\frac{2}{4}$ in Exercise 3 by $\frac{5}{8}$ and repeat parts (a), (b), and (c).

5. Replace the functions $\frac{3}{4}$ and $\frac{2}{4}$ in Exercise 3 by $\frac{2}{3}$ and $\frac{7}{5}$ and repeat parts (a), (b), and (c).

6. The "general" problem is suggested below. $A \cap B = \emptyset$.

A B $A \cup B$

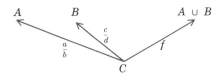

a) Explain how to visualize the domains and ranges of the functions $\frac{a}{b}$ and $\frac{c}{d}$ as you compute a name for f.

b) Explain how one can get a fraction for f by working mechanically with the numerators and denominators of the fractions $\frac{a}{b}$ and $\frac{c}{d}$.

Because problems of the type described in Exercise 6 occur so often, we facilitate their solution by defining an operation on all ordered pairs of fractions. As you have computed:

$$(\tfrac{3}{4}, \tfrac{2}{4}) \to \tfrac{5}{4}; \qquad (\tfrac{3}{4}, \tfrac{5}{8}) \to \tfrac{11}{8}; \qquad (\tfrac{2}{3}, \tfrac{7}{5}) \to \tfrac{31}{15}.$$

Choose a pleasant name for this operation.

Before we continue, let us consider the direction in which we are heading. The image is beginning to shape up of a large set of "numbers" including our old whole numbers and our new fractions. (Temporarily we exclude zero.)

$$\{1, 2, 3, \ldots; \tfrac{1}{1}, \tfrac{1}{2}, \tfrac{2}{1}, \tfrac{1}{3}, \tfrac{2}{2}, \tfrac{3}{1}, \tfrac{1}{4}, \tfrac{2}{3}, \ldots\}.$$

(Continue the systematic list of fractions above, writing the next 10 symbols.) In this set we have our old familiar operations, $+$, $-$, $\cdot$, $\div$, for whole numbers. We have also invented three new operations. The chances are excellent that you used the familiar signs $\div$, $\cdot$, $+$, for these operations also.

$$12 \div \tfrac{3}{5} = 20; \qquad \tfrac{3}{5} \cdot 25 = 15; \qquad \tfrac{3}{4} + \tfrac{5}{8} = \tfrac{11}{8}.$$

It would have been more imaginative to choose new symbols for these new operations, but these choices will work out well. Note that we have *not* associated meanings with symbols like $8 \div \tfrac{3}{4}$; $12 \cdot \tfrac{3}{4}$; $\tfrac{3}{4} \div 12$; $\tfrac{1}{2} + 2$; $\tfrac{2}{3} \cdot \tfrac{1}{5}$. One of our objectives will be to remedy this "defect." It would be more pleasing if we could "add," "multiply," and "divide" any two numbers in our large set. (In the next exercise list you will be led to a natural way of assigning meaning to symbols like $\tfrac{3}{5} \div n$ and $n \cdot \tfrac{3}{5}$.)

The diagram below suggests the invention of a subtraction operation. Suppose that $A \subset B$ and we have the relationships pictured below; $B - A$ denotes the set of all elements which are in B, but not in A.

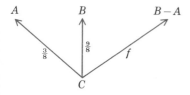

Explain why the fraction $\tfrac{6}{8}$ is a suitable name for the function f, and show how to compute f if $\tfrac{3}{8}$ is replaced by $\tfrac{2}{3}$. Use this example to motivate the definition of a subtraction operation that associates some (why not all?) ordered pairs of fractions with fractions.

$$(\tfrac{9}{8}, \tfrac{3}{8}) \rightarrow \tfrac{9}{8} - \tfrac{3}{8} = \tfrac{6}{8}; \qquad (\tfrac{9}{8}, \tfrac{2}{3}) \rightarrow \tfrac{9}{8} - \tfrac{2}{3} = \tfrac{11}{24}.$$

Explain how to work mechanically with numerators and denominators of two fractions $\tfrac{a}{b}$ and $\tfrac{c}{d}$ to compute the fraction $\tfrac{a}{b} - \tfrac{c}{d}$.

In our work with addition and subtraction, the usefulness of some new terminology becomes apparent. If we wish to *tell* someone how to add two fractions we can say: "Look at the denominators. If they are the same, write the *sum* of the numerators above this *common denominator*."

$$\tfrac{3}{5} + \tfrac{7}{5} = \tfrac{10}{5}.$$

"If the denominators are not the same, examine the *equivalence classes* for the two fractions. Pick two fractions, one from each class, with equal denominators. Add these fractions as in the previous case."

Eq. $(\tfrac{3}{10}) = \{\tfrac{3}{10}, \tfrac{6}{20}, \tfrac{9}{30}, \ldots\}$; Eq. $(\tfrac{7}{4}) = \{\tfrac{7}{4}, \tfrac{14}{8}, \tfrac{21}{12}, \ldots\}$;
$$\tfrac{3}{10} + \tfrac{7}{4} = \tfrac{150}{500} + \tfrac{875}{500} = \tfrac{1025}{500}.$$

As our example (facetiously chosen) emphasizes, our directions are not specific enough to insure that two different persons will produce the same answers. We have several choices. (1) We can require that everyone choose fractions from the equivalence classes with the smallest possible common denominators:

$$\tfrac{3}{10} + \tfrac{7}{4} = \tfrac{6}{20} + \tfrac{35}{20} = \tfrac{41}{20}.$$

(2) We can instruct everyone to multiply the old denominators to get a common denominator:

$$\tfrac{3}{10} + \tfrac{7}{4} = \tfrac{12}{40} + \tfrac{70}{40} = \tfrac{82}{40}.$$

(3) We can observe that all the fraction answers that we get,

$$\tfrac{41}{20}, \tfrac{82}{40}, \ldots, \tfrac{1025}{500}, \ldots$$

no matter how we choose a common denominator, fall in the same equivalence class and decide that all answers are equally acceptable. (4) We can require that all answers, no matter how obtained, be *reduced to lowest terms:*

$$\tfrac{3}{10} + \tfrac{7}{4} = \tfrac{30}{100} + \tfrac{175}{100} = \tfrac{205}{100} = \tfrac{41}{20}.$$

This multiplicity of choices illustrates the complexity of rational arithmetic. It is small wonder that fractions confuse children! How were these matters handled by your own teachers?

   The need to describe the operation of adding fractions motivates invention of the terminology "common denominator," "least common denominator," "lower terms," "higher terms," "lowest terms," "reduce to lowest terms," . . . Note again that this is a language invented in order to describe the ways we *work* with our fraction symbols as we *think* about the functions that they represent. Our language continues to proliferate.

   The exercise list below outlines the development of the multiplication and division operations.

EXERCISES 6–4

1. Recall the concept of composition of functions. Let A be the set of all people who have ever lived. Let

   $f(x)$ = the father of x; $m(x)$ = the mother of x.
   $f: A \rightarrow A$ $m: A \rightarrow A$

   Of course neither f nor m is either 1–1 or onto. (Why?) Two compositions are shown below.

   f of $f(x)$ = the father of the father of x
   m of $f(x)$ = the mother of the father of x

   $$x \xrightarrow{\quad f \quad} f(x) \xrightarrow{\quad m \quad} m(f(x))$$
   $$\underbrace{\qquad\qquad\qquad}_{m \text{ of } f}$$

   We may call m of f the paternal-grandmother function.
   a) Give common names for the functions f of f; f of m; m of m.
   b) Are f of m and m of f the same?
2. Consider the diagram below.

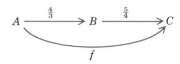

$$A \xrightarrow{\quad \frac{4}{3} \quad} B \xrightarrow{\quad \frac{5}{4} \quad} C$$
$$\underbrace{\qquad\qquad\qquad}_{f}$$

   To each 3-tuple of A is associated a 4-tuple of B; to each 4-tuple of B is associated a 5-tuple of C.

   a) With our agreement on composition of functions, is it possible to form the composition of the functions $\frac{4}{3}$ and $\frac{5}{4}$?

b) With our notational agreements, should we write f as $\frac{4}{3}$ of $\frac{5}{4}$ or as $\frac{5}{4}$ of $\frac{4}{3}$?

c) Compute a fraction for f.

d) Point out a mechanical method for manipulating numerators and denominators of $\frac{4}{3}$ and $\frac{5}{4}$ to get a fraction name for f.

3. In the diagram below we reverse the order of the functions in Exercise 2.

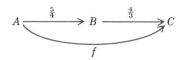

a) Explain why it is impossible to form the composition of the functions $\frac{5}{4}$ and $\frac{4}{3}$.

b) Explain how to regroup the elements of A, B, and C and choose new functions, named by fractions equivalent to $\frac{5}{4}$ and $\frac{4}{3}$, so that the composition of these functions can be formed.

c) Write f as the composite of these new functions and compute a fraction for f.

d) Compare answers in parts (c) of Exercises 2 and 3.

4. Let E, S, B be, respectively, the amount of money a man earns, saves, and invests in bonds. Let the relationships between these amounts of money be described below.

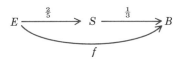

a) Think in terms of the *domains* and *ranges* of the *functions* $\frac{2}{5}$ and $\frac{1}{3}$ and explain how to compute a fraction for f. Interpret your result.

b) Explain how to manipulate the *numerators* and *denominators* of the *fractions* $\frac{2}{5}$ and $\frac{1}{3}$ and compute a fraction name for f.

c) Interchange the functions $\frac{2}{5}$ and $\frac{1}{3}$ and repeat parts (a) and (b).

5. In a group of people there are $\frac{3}{4}$ as many boys as girls and $\frac{2}{5}$ as many girls as adults. We denote the sets involved by B, G, and A.

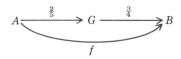

a) Compute a fraction for f and interpret your result. Make your computation by *thinking* about domains and ranges of functions.

b) Explain how to compute f mechanically from the fractions.

c) Interchange the functions $\frac{2}{5}$ and $\frac{3}{4}$ and repeat parts (a) and (b).

6. Invent a word problem to fit the diagram shown below and solve the problem both by thinking about functions and by mechanical manipulation of fractions.

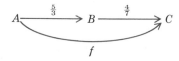

7. Solve the suggested problems below in any way you choose.

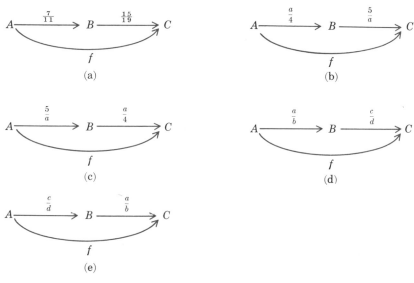

(a)

(b)

(c)

(d)

(e)

8. Solve the suggested problems below in any way that you choose.

a) On assembly line B, 3 items are produced for every 5 produced on A and 2 items are produced for every 3 produced on C. Explain the diagram below, compute f, and interpret the result.

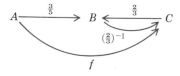

b) Pose and solve the assembly-line problem suggested by the diagram below.

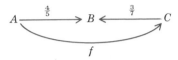

9. Relate the computation performed in Exercise 8 to the mysterious rule for dividing fractions.

10. We indicate below how reasonable meanings may be assigned to $\frac{a}{b} \div n$ and $n \cdot \frac{a}{b}$ for every natural number n. We agree that

$$\overbrace{\phantom{\frac{a}{b} + \frac{a}{b} + \cdots + \frac{a}{b}}}^{n \text{ addends}}$$

i) $1 \cdot \frac{a}{b} = \frac{a}{b}$, and if $n \neq 1$, $n \cdot \frac{a}{b} = \frac{a}{b} + \frac{a}{b} + \cdots + \frac{a}{b}$. (If it takes $\frac{1}{2}$ hour to walk 1 mile how long does it take to walk n miles?)

ii) $n \cdot (\frac{a}{b} \div n) = \frac{a}{b}$; that is, $\frac{a}{b} \div n$ is the number which when multiplied by n (added to itself $n - 1$ times) yields $\frac{a}{b}$. (If you walked $7\frac{1}{2}$ miles in 3 hours, at a constant rate, how far did you walk in 1 hour?)

Use these definitions to compute

a) $1 \cdot \frac{7}{4}$ b) $5 \cdot \frac{7}{4}$ c) $4 \cdot \frac{3}{8}$ d) $\frac{7}{4} \div 1$ e) $\frac{35}{4} \div 7$

f) $\frac{3}{2} \div 4$ g) $6 \cdot \frac{1}{3}$ h) $6 \cdot \frac{3}{1}$ i) $\frac{5}{11} \div 13$

From the problems of the above list we extract the following definition. To each ordered pair of fractions $(\frac{a}{b}, \frac{c}{d})$ we assign the fraction $\frac{a \cdot c}{b \cdot d}$. We call the fraction $\frac{a \cdot c}{b \cdot d}$ the *product* of the fractions $\frac{a}{b}$ and $\frac{c}{d}$. We call the binary operation thus defined in the set of all fractions *multiplication of fractions*. We denote this operation by the same symbols used to denote multiplication of whole numbers, namely $\times$ and . Thus

$$\frac{a}{b} \times \frac{c}{d} = \frac{a \cdot c}{b \cdot d} = \frac{a}{b} \cdot \frac{c}{d}.$$

Problem   Write out definitions of division and addition of fractions paralleling the above definition of multiplication.

The work of this section is drawing to a close. Let us look at the structure that we now possess. We have a system whose elements are the natural numbers and fractions. If we denote the set of natural numbers by N and the set of fractions by F, then we are concerned with the set $N \cup F$. In this set we can add and multiply *any* two elements of N. We can subtract and divide *some* pairs of elements of N. In F we also have operations that we have *called* addition, subtraction, multiplication, and division, although they are vastly different from the corresponding operations for whole numbers. We can add, multiply, and divide *any* two fractions. We can subtract only *some* pairs of fractions. We do not add whole numbers to fractions. (Why?) We do have four "mixed" operations, involving whole numbers and fractions denoted by the overworked signs of operation $\cdot$ (or $\times$) and $\div$. We summarize these ideas below. Note that all operations in this set are defined in terms of operations on whole numbers.

$$N \cup F = \{1, 2, 3, \ldots ; \tfrac{1}{1}, \tfrac{1}{2}, \tfrac{2}{1}, \tfrac{1}{3}, \tfrac{2}{2}, \tfrac{3}{1}, \tfrac{1}{4}, \ldots\}.$$

1. $\forall a, b \in N,\ +\ (a, b)\ =\ a + b \in N$

2. $\forall a, b \in N,\ \cdot\ (a, b)\ =\ a \cdot b \in N$

3. For some $a, b \in N,\ -\ (a, b)\ =\ a - b \in N$

4. For some $a, b \in N,\ \div\ (a, b)\ =\ a \div b \in N$

5. $\forall \dfrac{a}{b}, \dfrac{c}{d} \in F,\ +\left(\dfrac{a}{b}, \dfrac{c}{d}\right) = \dfrac{ad + bc}{bd} \in F$ (cf. Exercise 6, page 196)

6. $\forall \dfrac{a}{b}, \dfrac{c}{d} \in F,\ \cdot\left(\dfrac{a}{b}, \dfrac{c}{d}\right) = \dfrac{a \cdot c}{b \cdot d} \in F$ (cf. Exercise 7, page 201)

7. $\forall \dfrac{a}{b}, \dfrac{c}{d} \in F,\ \div\left(\dfrac{a}{b}, \dfrac{c}{d}\right) = \dfrac{a \cdot d}{b \cdot c} \in F$ (cf. Exercise 8, page 202)

8. For some $\dfrac{a}{b}, \dfrac{c}{d} \in F,\ -\left(\dfrac{a}{b}, \dfrac{c}{d}\right) = \dfrac{ad - bc}{bd} \in F$ (cf. page 197)

9. For some $n \in N$ and $\dfrac{a}{b} \in F,\ \cdot\left(\dfrac{a}{b}, n\right) = a \cdot (n \div b) \in N$

(cf. Exercise 2(d), page 196)

10. For some $n \in N$ and $\dfrac{a}{b} \in F,\ \div\left(n, \dfrac{a}{b}\right) = b \cdot (n \div a) \in N$

(cf. Exercise 1, page 195)

11. $\forall n \in N, \forall \dfrac{a}{b} \in F,\ \cdot\left(n, \dfrac{a}{b}\right) = \dfrac{n \cdot a}{b} \in F$ (cf. Exercise 10, page 202)

12. $\forall n \in N, \forall \dfrac{a}{b} \in F,\ \div\left(\dfrac{a}{b}, n\right) = \dfrac{a}{n \cdot b} \in F$ (cf. Exercise 10, page 202)

Problem For each of the 12 operations listed above, formulate a word problem and apply the appropriate formula in solving the problem.

The four different formulas for each of the operations $\cdot$ and $\div$ forcibly call attention to our confusing habit of using one name for many different things. At this stage we have an extremely complex mathematical structure. It will be the goal of the next section to effect many simplifications.

▶ *Aside.* We submit that our construction of the above mathematical system with its complex of 12 distinct operations is an accurate description of the manner in which a child's mind first grasps rational number concepts. The child meets fraction symbols first as tools to describe his world. As he is introduced to operations on fractions, he should visualize clearly the functional relationships that are associated with these operations. As he solves a problem like

Joe has $\frac{3}{5}$ as much money as Kate.
Kate has 80 cents.
How much has Joe?

he should visualize two sets of coins and picture the functional relationships. The type of thinking we have emphasized suggests the visual image below

$J = \{ \boxed{\times \times \times} \quad \boxed{\times \times \times} \ldots \}$

$K = \{ \boxed{\times \times \times \times \times} \quad \boxed{\times \times \times \times \times} \ldots \}$

Our approach here is not the only way to wrest rational arithmetic from the real world. One could also picture Kate's money split into 5 sets of 16¢ each and visualize Joe's money accordingly. However, in any systematic approach, all the 12 operations above loom up, and the function concept is the dominating concept. The ability to visualize *functions* is an important skill that must be developed in the early stages of learning.

The careful reader should have many questions about our approach. For example, we use operations on fractions in a wide variety of practical situations. Is it conceivable that this function approach is a *universal* interpretation applicable to all practical problems involving fractions? For example, if I buy $\frac{7}{2}$ pounds of beef at $\frac{148}{100}$ dollars per pound, the product $\frac{7}{2} \times \frac{148}{100}$ gives me my cost. Is composition of functions present in this example? To find the area of a rectangle, $\frac{2}{3}$ by $\frac{3}{4}$, I compute the product,

$\frac{2}{3} \cdot \frac{3}{4}.$

How is composition of functions involved here? Is the "invert and multiply" rule for division always associated with composing one function with the inverse of another?

There are two possible answers to such questions:

i) It is not necessary that in all applications of fractions these fractions name functions of the sort we have described here. An abstract mathematical system is often found to have far wider application than its inventor anticipated. When we develop such an abstract system, however, it is important to have clearly in mind *some* model (in this case our functions which exist in the real world) so that we shall be sure we are developing a consistent system which will have some usefulness.

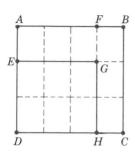

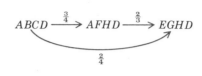

ii) Although it is not *necessary* that we interpret all practical applications of fractions to the real world in the light of function concepts, a little thought convinces us that it is indeed *possible* to do so. From a theoretical point of view this is very satisfying. We need no longer speak vaguely of the many different interpretations of fractions. We have one unifying concept: the concept of function. Any examination of the use of a fraction to describe the real world will reveal two sets *and* a function which "compares" them. Any "practical" problem in which we multiply two fractions can be seen to involve the composition of two functions. We illustrate this for the area problem mentioned above. Visualize a $\frac{2}{3}$ by $\frac{3}{4}$ rectangle embedded in a unit square and examine the figure. The function $\frac{2}{4}$ compares the area of the rectangle to that of the unit square. It is an interesting exercise of one's geometric intuition to see this function as the composition of two functions.

We hasten to emphasize that, although function concepts unify the study of rational arithmetic from the standpoint of the theoretical ideas involved, yet, in teaching rational numbers, it is not appropriate to always keep function ideas in the foreground. For problems traditionally treated as ratio problems, certainly the function ideas should be stressed. One of the useful characteristics of the terminology of ratio is that it evokes images of the functions that underlie rational number concepts. But in problems involving measurement, cutting up pies, etc., in general in many problems of a geometrical flavor, function concepts should be pushed into the background. For example, when we are measuring with a ruler, our *unit* may be established once and for all in the beginning of the discussion as an inch. Now we know very well that when we say that a segment is three eighths of an inch long, the $\frac{3}{8}$ refers to the relationship between our segment and the unit. Our attention is not centered on the functional relationship, however, but rather on the *range* of the function, that is, on the $\frac{3}{8}$-inch segment. Our mathematical reader will think of many mathematical situations in which functions are deliberately downgraded and the ranges of the functions are given nearly all the attention.   (Sequences constitute a classic example of this.) ◄

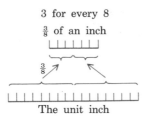

3 for every 8

$\frac{3}{8}$ of an inch

The unit inch

DISCUSSION EXERCISE

The diagrams below illustrate standard devices for motivating the definitions of addition and multiplication of fractions.   Here $\frac{m}{n}$ names the function (rule), "carve into n equal parts and unite m such parts."   Discuss the downgrading of the functions and the emphasizing of their domains.   Observe that addition of fractions continues to "reflect" disjoint union, and that multiplication of fractions continues to "reflect" composition.

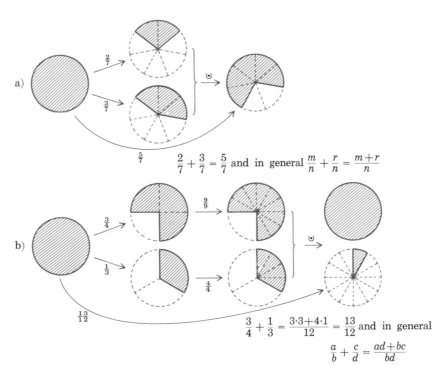

$$\frac{2}{7} + \frac{3}{7} = \frac{5}{7} \text{ and in general } \frac{m}{n} + \frac{r}{n} = \frac{m+r}{n}$$

$$\frac{3}{4} + \frac{1}{3} = \frac{3\cdot3+4\cdot1}{12} = \frac{13}{12} \text{ and in general}$$

$$\frac{a}{b} + \frac{c}{d} = \frac{ad+bc}{bd}$$

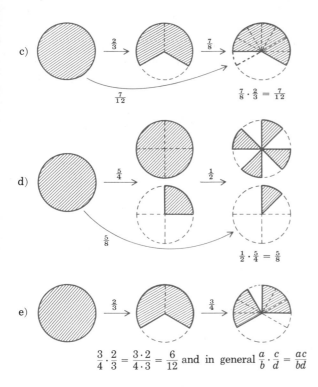

$$\frac{3}{4}\cdot\frac{2}{3}=\frac{3\cdot2}{4\cdot3}=\frac{6}{12}\ \text{and in general}\ \frac{a}{b}\cdot\frac{c}{d}=\frac{ac}{bd}$$

6–3   stage 3: the game of rational arithmetic

The system that we have dragged from the real world in the preceding sections is not a very pleasing mathematical object, although there is much to be said for its practical value.   Most nonmathematicians probably think of the rational number system pretty much as we have described it: a set of fractions and whole numbers with lots of different operations that they don't understand too well. The mathematician always tries to simplify things, if he can do so without destroying their essential characteristics. We can greatly simplify the game of rational arithmetic by allowing a player to

1)   Replace any fraction by any equivalent fraction,

2)   Replace any whole number a by the fraction $\frac{a}{1}$.

The significance of (1) is that our fractions are now packaged up in bundles, the equivalence classes. We think in terms of adding and multiplying these classes instead of individual fractions. Each class is called a *rational number*. When we apply (2), not only do all our whole numbers go away, but also 8 of our 12 operations vanish.* We use only the 4 operations (5–8 on page 203) that we have developed for fractions. This last advantage is not so great as it sounds. Since all operations on fractions are defined in terms of operations on whole numbers, we continue using these whole-number operations (1–4 on page 203) in rational arithmetic.

We need to say a bit more about our rational numbers (the equivalence classes). Our original definition of equivalence for fractions was dictated to us by the way we used fractions to describe the real world.

$\frac{a}{b}$ and $\frac{c}{d}$ are equivalent if there are sets A and B which can be "compared" by both fractions.

For example, $\frac{24}{42}$ and $\frac{40}{70}$ are equivalent because both name functions comparing sets of 210 and 120 elements, respectively. Verify this assertion.

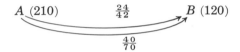

Note that the significance of this definition is that in order to prove that two fractions like $\frac{24}{42}$ and $\frac{40}{70}$ are equivalent we must find two numbers, in this case 210 and 120, which are equimultiples of 42 and 24,

$$210 = \underline{5} \cdot 42 \quad \text{and} \quad 120 = \underline{5} \cdot 24,$$

and also equimultiples of 70 and 40,

$$210 = \underline{3} \cdot 70 \quad \text{and} \quad 120 = \underline{3} \cdot 40.$$

For mathematical purposes this definition of equivalence is too clumsy. From now on we shall do without it. We list below some basic facts about equivalence classes that can be derived from our definition. Embarrassingly, these assertions are too difficult for us to prove at the moment, although they may seem obvious to you. For convenience we write $\frac{a}{b} \sim \frac{c}{d}$ as an abbreviation for "$\frac{a}{b}$ is equivalent to $\frac{c}{d}$."

1) $\frac{a}{b} \sim \frac{c}{d}$ if and only if $a \cdot d = b \cdot c$.

For example,

$\frac{24}{42} \sim \frac{40}{70}$ since $24 \cdot 70 = 42 \cdot 40$; $\quad \frac{3}{5} \nsim \frac{4}{7}$ since $3 \cdot 7 \neq 5 \cdot 4$.

2) Each equivalence class contains exactly one lowest-terms fraction.

For example,

In Eq. $(\frac{40}{70})$ this lowest-terms fraction is $\frac{4}{7}$.

---

* See the problem on page 213.

3) If the lowest-terms fraction in Eq. ($\frac{a}{b}$) is the fraction $\frac{r}{s}$, then *every* fraction in this class can be written as $\frac{n \cdot r}{n \cdot s}$ for some natural number n. For example,

$\frac{24}{42} \in$ Eq. $(\frac{40}{70})$ and $\frac{24}{42} = \frac{6 \cdot 4}{6 \cdot 7}$.

4) Each fraction belongs to one and only one equivalence class. That is, the set of equivalence classes is a *partition* of the set of all fractions.

The last property (5) explains why, in our calculations, we can replace fractions by equivalent fractions.

5) The formulas for computing with fractions,

  i) $\dfrac{a}{b} + \dfrac{c}{d} = \dfrac{ad + bc}{bd}$

  ii) $\dfrac{a}{b} - \dfrac{c}{d} = \dfrac{ad - bc}{bd}$

  iii) $\dfrac{a}{b} \cdot \dfrac{c}{d} = \dfrac{ac}{bd}$

  iv) $\dfrac{a}{b} \div \dfrac{c}{d} = \dfrac{ad}{bc}$

respect equivalence classes in the sense that if $\frac{r}{s} \sim \frac{a}{b}$ and $\frac{u}{v} \sim \frac{c}{d}$, then

  i) $\dfrac{r}{s} + \dfrac{u}{v} = \dfrac{rv + su}{sv} \sim \dfrac{ad + bc}{bd} = \dfrac{a}{b} + \dfrac{c}{d}$.

    For example, $\dfrac{2}{3} \sim \dfrac{10}{15}, \dfrac{3}{12} \sim \dfrac{1}{4}$,

    and

$$\frac{2}{3} + \frac{3}{12} = \frac{2 \cdot 12 + 3 \cdot 3}{3 \cdot 12} = \frac{33}{36} \sim \frac{55}{60} = \frac{10 \cdot 4 + 15 \cdot 1}{15 \cdot 4} = \frac{10}{15} + \frac{1}{4}.$$

  ii) $\dfrac{r}{s} - \dfrac{u}{v} = \dfrac{rv - su}{sv} \sim \dfrac{ad - bc}{bd} = \dfrac{a}{b} - \dfrac{c}{d}$.

    For example,

$$\frac{2}{3} - \frac{3}{12} = \frac{2 \cdot 12 - 3 \cdot 3}{3 \cdot 12} = \frac{15}{36} \sim \frac{25}{60} = \frac{10 \cdot 4 - 15 \cdot 1}{15 \cdot 4} = \frac{10}{15} - \frac{1}{4}.$$

  iii) $\dfrac{r}{s} \cdot \dfrac{u}{v} - \dfrac{ru}{sv} \sim \dfrac{ac}{bd} = \dfrac{a}{b} \cdot \dfrac{c}{d}$.

    For example, $\dfrac{2}{3} \cdot \dfrac{3}{12} = \dfrac{2 \cdot 3}{3 \cdot 12} = \dfrac{6}{36} \sim \dfrac{10}{60} = \dfrac{10 \cdot 1}{15 \cdot 4} = \dfrac{10}{15} \cdot \dfrac{1}{4}$.

  iv) $\dfrac{r}{s} \div \dfrac{u}{v} = \dfrac{rv}{su} \sim \dfrac{ad}{bc} = \dfrac{a}{b} \div \dfrac{c}{d}$.

    For example, $\dfrac{2}{3} \div \dfrac{3}{12} = \dfrac{2 \cdot 12}{3 \cdot 3} = \dfrac{24}{9} \sim \dfrac{40}{15} = \dfrac{10 \cdot 4}{15 \cdot 1} = \dfrac{10}{15} \div \dfrac{1}{4}$.

EXERCISES 6-5

1. List several fractions in Eq. $(\frac{4}{3})$. Pick three pairs $\frac{a}{b}$, $\frac{c}{d}$ and verify that $a \cdot d = b \cdot c$.

2. In each set of fractions below exactly one is not equivalent to any of the others. Locate the miscreant.

   a) $\{\frac{24}{36}, \frac{14}{21}, \frac{22}{33}, \frac{12}{16}\}$ b) $\{\frac{91}{119}, \frac{169}{221}, \frac{221}{287}\}$

3. Find the lowest-terms fraction in

   a) Eq. $(\frac{42}{36})$ b) Eq. $(\frac{156}{234})$ (c) Eq. $(\frac{70597}{25813})$

4. Note that $\frac{12}{18} \sim \frac{4}{6}$ and $\frac{1}{5} \sim \frac{5}{25}$. Using the computational rules for fractions, show that

   a) $\frac{12}{18} + \frac{1}{5} \sim \frac{4}{6} + \frac{5}{25}$ b) $\frac{12}{18} \cdot \frac{1}{5} \sim \frac{4}{6} \cdot \frac{5}{25}$

   c) $\frac{12}{18} - \frac{1}{5} \sim \frac{4}{6} - \frac{5}{25}$ d) $\frac{12}{18} \div \frac{1}{5} \sim \frac{4}{6} \div \frac{5}{25}$

5. Use the computational rules to compute

   a) $\frac{2}{3} \cdot (\frac{5}{4} + \frac{1}{2})$ b) $\frac{2}{3} \cdot \frac{5}{4} + \frac{2}{3} \cdot \frac{1}{2}$

   Verify that the answers are different but equivalent fractions. Explain how this problem illustrates the fact that multiplication of *rational numbers* is distributive with respect to addition.

6. Use the properties listed above for equivalence classes and prove that

   a) Eq. $(\frac{27}{72})$ = Eq. $(\frac{45}{120})$ b) Eq. $(\frac{15}{42}) \neq$ Eq. $(\frac{18}{45})$

7. Consider the binary operation * in the set of all fractions defined by

   $$* \left(\frac{a}{b}, \frac{c}{d}\right) = \frac{a}{b} * \frac{c}{d} = \frac{a+c}{b+d}$$

   a) Prove that $\frac{a}{b} * \frac{c}{d} = \frac{c}{d} * \frac{a}{b}$ b) Prove that $\left(\frac{a}{b} * \frac{c}{d}\right) * \frac{e}{f} = \frac{a}{b} * \left(\frac{c}{d} * \frac{e}{f}\right)$

   c) Prove that $\frac{e}{f} \cdot \left(\frac{a}{b} * \frac{c}{d}\right) = \frac{e}{f} \frac{a}{b} * \frac{e}{f} \frac{c}{d}$

   d) Show that although $\frac{2}{4} \sim \frac{1}{2}$ and $\frac{3}{9} \sim \frac{1}{3}$, $\frac{2}{4} * \frac{3}{9} \not\sim \frac{1}{2} * \frac{1}{3}$, and on the basis of this fact explain why the * operation cannot be a very *useful* operation on fractions. Can you find some use for it?

8. a) Explain the significance of the following addition diagram.

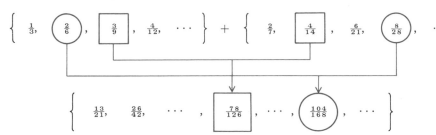

   b) Draw a corresponding subtraction diagram.

   c) Draw a corresponding multiplication diagram.

   d) Draw a corresponding division diagram.

9. Prove "fact 1" about equivalence classes.

From now on we shall use our fraction symbols to denote rational numbers, that is, our equivalence classes. Hence

$\frac{6}{12} = \frac{4}{8}$ is an abbreviation for Eq. $(\frac{6}{12})$ = Eq. $(\frac{4}{8})$.

Keep in mind that we are working with a set whose only elements are equivalence classes of fractions. We denote this set by Q^+, the set of *positive rational numbers**,

$$Q^+ = \{\frac{1}{1}, \frac{1}{2}, \frac{2}{1}, \frac{1}{3}, \frac{3}{1}, \ldots\},$$

where, remember, $\frac{1}{2}$ is an abbreviation for Eq. $(\frac{1}{2})$. In this set we can add, multiply or divide any pair of rational numbers and subtract some pairs according to the rules:

To add (subtract, multiply, divide) two positive rational numbers (equivalence classes of fractions), choose any fraction from the first and any fraction from the second and add (subtract, multiply, divide) them according to the rules for computing with fractions. The equivalence class of the resulting fraction is the sum (difference, product, quotient) of the given rational numbers.

Note (cf. Exercise 8 above) that sums, products, quotients, and differences (when they exist) of positive rational numbers are *unique*; i.e., they do *not* depend on what fractions one happened to choose from each rational.

   We have not examined the disappearance of the natural numbers as yet. You will remember computing in school arithmetic in the following fashion.

$$4 \times \tfrac{3}{5} = \tfrac{4}{1} \times \tfrac{3}{5} = \tfrac{12}{5}, \qquad 4 \div \tfrac{3}{5} = \tfrac{4}{1} \div \tfrac{3}{5} = \tfrac{20}{3},$$

$$4 + \tfrac{3}{5} = \tfrac{4}{1} + \tfrac{3}{5} = \tfrac{23}{5}, \qquad 4 - \tfrac{3}{5} = \tfrac{4}{1} - \tfrac{3}{5} = \tfrac{17}{5}.$$

In other words, in calculations involving whole numbers and fractions you exchange whole numbers for fractions having denominator 1. It is worth looking at this exchange with some care. The mathematical ideas are exactly the same as those we developed in Chapter 2 when we pointed out that the *counting function* enabled us to replace the operation of *counting the disjoint union of two sets* by the operation of *adding the numbers of the two sets*. So here also we observe that

---

* After negative integers have been introduced, these equivalence classes are enlarged. For example, Eq. $(\frac{1}{2})$ also contains $\frac{-1}{-2}, \frac{-2}{-4}, \frac{-3}{-6}, \ldots$ Properties 1–5 on pages 208, 209 remain true providing "lowest terms" is suitably redefined (cf. page 282).

the function which matches each natural number n with the rational number $\frac{n}{1}$ enables us to replace all operations on natural numbers by corresponding operations on fractions. At first glance it doesn't seem that this is much of an advantage. No one in his right mind is going to compute $3 + 4$ and $3 \cdot 4$, calculating as below

$$3 + 4 \rightarrow \tfrac{3}{1} + \tfrac{4}{1} = \tfrac{7}{1} \rightarrow 7, \qquad 3 \cdot 4 \rightarrow \tfrac{3}{1} \cdot \tfrac{4}{1} = \tfrac{12}{1} \rightarrow 12.$$

But note that this does suggest an interpretation of *division* of any two natural numbers:

$$3 \div 4 \rightarrow \tfrac{3}{1} \div \tfrac{4}{1} = \tfrac{3}{4}.$$

Until now we have not considered such an extension of the division operation. We have divided only certain pairs of whole numbers.

The main advantage that results from observing the relationships between whole-number and rational number computations is that we can think of the familiar whole-number system as a subsystem of the rational number system. We diagram the key relationships below.

$$
\begin{array}{ccc}
N & \xrightarrow{\;f\;} & Q^+ \\
n & \longrightarrow & \dfrac{n}{1} \\
m & \longrightarrow & \dfrac{m}{1} \\
n+m & \rightarrow \dfrac{n+m}{1} & = \dfrac{n}{1} + \dfrac{m}{1}
\end{array}
\qquad
\begin{array}{ccc}
N & \xrightarrow{\;f\;} & Q^+ \\
n & \longrightarrow & \dfrac{n}{1} \\
m & \longrightarrow & \dfrac{m}{1} \\
n\cdot m & \rightarrow \dfrac{n\cdot m}{1} & = \dfrac{n}{1} \cdot \dfrac{m}{1}
\end{array}
$$

As the diagrams show, the function $f\colon N \rightarrow Q^+$ defined by

$$f(n) = \frac{n}{1}, \; \forall n \in N$$

has the properties that, $\forall m, n \in N$,

$$f\,(m + n) = f(m) + f(n), \qquad f(m \cdot n) = f(m) \cdot f(n).$$

We say that f is a *homomorphism of the natural numbers into* (not onto) *the system Q^+ relative to addition and multiplication.*

▶ *Aside.* The embedding of the natural numbers in Q^+ is chiefly of theoretical interest. From an abstract point of view it is immaterial whether we throw away all the rational numbers $\frac{n}{1}$ and replace them by whole numbers n, or discard the whole numbers and replace them by rationals. In practical work we do neither. We keep both types of symbols around and through much use *identify* them with each other. That is, we unblushingly write 4 to denote not the cardinal number of a set, but rather a functional relationship between two sets, matching each element of the first set with 4 of the second, and we may even write $\frac{4}{1}$ to report the cardinal number of a set. Some people think that this is a sloppy way to do things, but no one pays much attention to their complaints. We have better things to do with our time than to worry about whether $\frac{12}{3}$ is 4 or $\frac{4}{1}$. When you use mathematics, what is really important is that you visualize clearly the real-world relationships described by the symbols you employ. One of our greatest failures in teaching arithmetic is that children do not learn to form clear mental images of the functional relationships with which their rational arithmetic deals. ◀

Problem   In the list of operations on page 203:

a) Is operation 1 consistent with operation 5 when m, n are identified with $\frac{m}{1}$, $\frac{n}{1}$?

b) Same question for operations 3 and 8.

c) Similar questions for operations 2, 6, 9, 11.

d) Similar questions for operations 4, 7, 10, 12.

If you work this problem carefully you will understand how the twelve operations shrink to four.

  In the final pages of this chapter we turn our attention to computation with little concern for applications. It is convenient to invent a zero! The easiest way to do this is just to write a tall thin "0" and agree that for every rational number a,

$$a + 0 = 0 + a = a; \qquad a \cdot 0 = 0 \cdot a = 0.$$

It seems more mannerly to observe that if we use the symbol $\frac{0}{1}$ according to our rules for computing with fractions, then

$$\forall n \in N, \frac{0}{1} \sim \frac{0}{n}, \text{ since } n \cdot 0 = 1 \cdot 0,$$

$$\forall \frac{a}{b} \in Q^+, \frac{a}{b} + \frac{0}{1} = \frac{a}{b} + \frac{0}{b} = \frac{a}{b}, \text{ and } \frac{a}{b} \cdot \frac{0}{1} = \frac{a \cdot 0}{b \cdot 1} = \frac{0}{b} = \frac{0}{1}.$$

  These observations justify the absorption of the entire set of whole numbers into rational arithmetic. However, one rarely gets something for nothing. Now we should no longer refer to our system as the positive rationals, and we can no longer view division as an operation applicable to every pair of rational numbers. (Why?)

  One of the most interesting problems of rational arithmetic is that of reducing a fraction to lowest terms. Students expend a great deal of energy on this activity in school arithmetic without ever really coming to grips with the basic ideas involved. Over 2000 years ago the Greek mathematicians discovered a solution to this problem that has had far-reaching theoretical significance. Earlier we listed properties of equivalence classes and remarked, rather lamely, that we were in no position to prove their validity. The Greek technique for reducing fractions to lowest terms is useful in making some of these proofs. We illustrate this technique by applying it to problem 3(c) of Exercise List 6–5. The calculation below is referred to as an application of the *Euclidean algorithm*.

$$
\begin{array}{r|r}
2 \\
\hline
25813 & 70597 \\
& 51626 \\
\hline
& 18971
\end{array}
\qquad
\begin{array}{r|r}
1 \\
\hline
18971 & 25813 \\
& 18971 \\
\hline
& 6842
\end{array}
\qquad
\begin{array}{r|r}
2 \\
\hline
6842 & 18971 \\
& 13684 \\
\hline
& 5287
\end{array}
$$

$$
\begin{array}{r|r}
1 \\
\hline
5287 & 6842 \\
& 5287 \\
\hline
& 1555
\end{array}
\qquad
\begin{array}{r|r}
3 \\
\hline
1555 & 5287 \\
& 4665 \\
\hline
& 622
\end{array}
\qquad
\begin{array}{r|r}
2 \\
\hline
622 & 1555 \\
& 1244 \\
\hline
& 311
\end{array}
$$

$$
\begin{array}{r|r}
2 \\
\hline
311 & 622
\end{array}
$$

The calculation assures us that 311 is the *greatest common divisor* of 70597 and 25813. Dividing each number by 311, we get the *lowest-terms fraction*:

$$\frac{70597}{25813} = \frac{70597 \div 311}{25813 \div 311} = \frac{227}{83}.$$

At this stage you are not expected to understand why the Euclidean algorithm works. An explanation of why it works will be given in paragraph 12.3.

    If numerator and denominator are factored into prime factors, their gcd (greatest common divisor) can be recognized and the fraction reduced to the lowest terms.

Examples

$$\frac{30}{42} = \frac{2 \cdot 3 \cdot 5}{2 \cdot 3 \cdot 7} = \frac{5}{7}; \qquad \text{the gcd is } 2 \cdot 3.$$

$$\frac{252}{600} = \frac{2^2 \cdot 3^2 \cdot 7}{2^3 \cdot 3 \cdot 5^2} = \frac{3 \cdot 7}{2 \cdot 5^2}; \qquad \text{the gcd is } 2^2 \cdot 3.$$

    Prime factorizations of denominators enable one to choose least common denominators easily in addition problems.

Examples

$$\frac{5}{4} + \frac{1}{10} = \frac{5}{2 \cdot 2} + \frac{1}{2 \cdot 5} = \frac{5 \cdot 5}{2 \cdot 2 \cdot 5} + \frac{2 \cdot 1}{2 \cdot 2 \cdot 5} = \cdots$$

$$\frac{3}{133} + \frac{4}{95} = \frac{3}{7 \cdot 19} + \frac{4}{5 \cdot 19} = \frac{5 \cdot 3}{5 \cdot 7 \cdot 19} + \frac{7 \cdot 4}{5 \cdot 7 \cdot 19} = \cdots$$

EXERCISES 6–6

1. Use the Euclidean algorithm to compute the gcd of numerator and denominator and reduce to lowest terms.

   a) $\frac{255}{204}$ b) $\frac{3288}{4384}$ c) $\frac{49183}{293303}$

2. Using the given prime factorizations, reduce to lowest terms:

   a) $\frac{20}{25} = \frac{2^2 \cdot 5}{5 \cdot 5}$ b) $\frac{24}{56} = \frac{2^3 \cdot 3}{2^3 \cdot 7}$ c) $\frac{68}{119} = \frac{2^2 \cdot 17}{7 \cdot 17}$

   d) $\frac{144}{391} = \frac{2 \cdot 3^2 \cdot 23}{17 \cdot 23}$ e) $\frac{1106}{1738} = \frac{2 \cdot 7 \cdot 79}{2 \cdot 11 \cdot 79}$

3. Determine a and b and reduce to lowest terms.

   a) $\frac{14}{21} = \frac{a \cdot 7}{b \cdot 7}$ b) $\frac{100}{175} = \frac{a \cdot 25}{b \cdot 25}$ c) $\frac{672}{672} = \frac{a \cdot 672}{b \cdot 672}$

   d) $\frac{904}{2260} = \frac{a \cdot 113}{b \cdot 113}$ e) $\frac{0}{527} = \frac{a \cdot 527}{b \cdot 527}$ f) $\frac{1482}{2223} = \frac{a \cdot 57}{b \cdot 57}$

4. The gcd of two numbers is also called their *greatest common factor*. Give the greatest common factor of each pair of numbers below.

   a) $7 \cdot 11 \cdot 13$; $11 \cdot 13 \cdot 17$ b) $2^3 \cdot 5 \cdot 7$; $2 \cdot 5^2 \cdot 11$

   c) $2 \cdot 3 \cdot 5$; $7 \cdot 11^2$ d) $17^2 \cdot 23$; $17 \cdot 23 \cdot 37$

5. The least common denominator for two fractions is also called the *least common multiple* (lcm) of the two denominators. Give in factored form the lcm of each pair of numbers below.

   a) $7 \cdot 11$; $11 \cdot 13$ b) $3 \cdot 5 \cdot 7$; $5 \cdot 7 \cdot 17$

   c) $2^2 \cdot 3$; $3^2 \cdot 2$ d) $2 \cdot 5^2 \cdot 7$; $2^3 \cdot 5 \cdot 11$

   e) $3^5 \cdot 5^4$; $3^4 \cdot 5^3$ f) $11^2 \cdot 19 \cdot 31$; $11 \cdot 19^3 \cdot 43$

6. Give the values for a, and b, and c

   a) $\frac{1}{5} + \frac{2}{7} = \frac{a \cdot 1}{5 \cdot 7} + \frac{b \cdot 2}{5 \cdot 7} = \frac{c}{5 \cdot 7}$

   b) $\frac{5}{2^2 \cdot 3} + \frac{7}{2 \cdot 3^2} = \frac{a \cdot 5}{2^2 \cdot 3^2} + \frac{b \cdot 7}{2^2 \cdot 3^2} = \frac{c}{2^2 \cdot 3^2}$

c) $\dfrac{3}{5 \cdot 7 \cdot 11} + \dfrac{4}{7 \cdot 11 \cdot 13} = \dfrac{a \cdot 3}{5 \cdot 7 \cdot 11 \cdot 13} + \dfrac{b \cdot 4}{5 \cdot 7 \cdot 11 \cdot 13} = \dfrac{c}{5 \cdot 7 \cdot 11 \cdot 13}$

d) $\dfrac{5}{19 \cdot 31} + \dfrac{1}{2 \cdot 3 \cdot 19 \cdot 31} = \dfrac{a \cdot 5}{2 \cdot 3 \cdot 19 \cdot 31} + \dfrac{b \cdot 1}{2 \cdot 3 \cdot 19 \cdot 31} = \dfrac{c}{2 \cdot 3 \cdot 19 \cdot 31}$

e) $\dfrac{3}{7^2 \cdot 13 \cdot 19} + \dfrac{5}{7 \cdot 13^2 \cdot 23} = \dfrac{a \cdot 3}{7^2 \cdot 13^2 \cdot 19 \cdot 23} + \dfrac{b \cdot 5}{7^2 \cdot 13^2 \cdot 19 \cdot 23}$

$$= \dfrac{c}{7^2 \cdot 13^2 \cdot 19 \cdot 23}$$

7. Prove that $\frac{a}{b} \cdot \frac{c}{d} = \frac{a}{d} \cdot \frac{c}{b}$ and explain how this fact is used to get answers in lowest terms in the examples below.

a) $\frac{9}{5} \cdot \frac{10}{21} = \frac{9}{21} \cdot \frac{10}{5} = \frac{3}{7} \cdot \frac{2}{1} = \frac{6}{7}$

b) $\frac{12}{50} \cdot \frac{175}{15} = \frac{6}{25} \cdot \frac{35}{3} = \frac{6}{3} \cdot \frac{35}{25} = \frac{2}{1} \cdot \frac{7}{5} = \frac{14}{5}$

c) $\frac{84}{225} \cdot \frac{30}{14} = \frac{28}{75} \cdot \frac{15}{7} = \frac{28}{7} \cdot \frac{15}{75} = \frac{4}{1} \cdot \frac{1}{5} = \frac{4}{5}$

d) $\dfrac{\cancel{5} \cdot \cancel{7} \cdot 13}{7 \cdot \cancel{11}^2 \cdot \cancel{19}} \cdot \dfrac{\overset{19}{\cancel{11}} \cdot \cancel{19}^2 \cdot \cancel{23}}{\cancel{5} \cdot \cancel{23}^2} = \dfrac{13 \cdot 19}{11 \cdot 23}$

8. Prove that $\left(\frac{c}{d} \cdot \frac{a}{b}\right) \div \frac{c}{d} = \frac{a}{b}$ for all rational numbers $\frac{a}{b}$ and $\frac{c}{d}$ with $\frac{c}{d} \neq 0$.

9. Use the result of Exercise 8 to explain the statements below.

a) Because $\frac{3}{4} \cdot \frac{5}{7} = \frac{15}{28}$, $\frac{15}{28} \div \frac{3}{4} = \frac{5}{7}$.

b) Because $\frac{7}{11} \cdot \frac{13}{8} = \frac{91}{88}$, $\frac{91}{88} \div \frac{13}{8} = \frac{7}{11}$.

c) Because $\dfrac{r}{s} \cdot \dfrac{t}{u} = \dfrac{r \cdot t}{s \cdot u}$, $\dfrac{r \cdot t}{s \cdot u} \div \dfrac{r}{s} = \dfrac{t}{u}$.

10. Use a technique suggested by Exercise 9 as a shortcut to solve the following division problems.

a) $\frac{12}{15} \div \frac{6}{5}$ b) $\frac{20}{14} \div \frac{10}{2}$ c) $\frac{27}{18} \div \frac{9}{9}$

d) $\frac{35}{24} \div \frac{7}{8}$ c) $\frac{220}{165} \div \frac{20}{11}$ f) $\frac{84}{75} \div \frac{12}{15}$

g) $\dfrac{7 \cdot 11 \cdot 13}{3 \cdot 5 \cdot 19} \div \dfrac{7 \cdot 11}{3 \cdot 19}$ h) $\dfrac{3^2 \cdot 5 \cdot 11^3}{7 \cdot 13^2 \cdot 19} \div \dfrac{3 \cdot 11^2}{7 \cdot 13 \cdot 19}$

11. Use the idea illustrated in the example to replace each division problem below by one like the problems of Exercise 10.

Example

$\frac{12}{5} \div \frac{3}{2} = \frac{24}{10} \div \frac{3}{2} = \frac{8}{5}$

a) $\frac{6}{5} \div \frac{3}{2}$ b) $\frac{7}{9} \div \frac{2}{3}$ c) $\frac{30}{25} \div \frac{12}{5}$

d) $\dfrac{7 \cdot 2}{11} \div \dfrac{2}{3}$ e) $\dfrac{2 \cdot 3 \cdot 5}{7 \cdot 11} \div \dfrac{2 \cdot 3}{5 \cdot 7}$

12. Explain the following development of the "invert and multiply" rule for division.

$$\frac{a}{b} \div \frac{c}{d} = \frac{a \cdot c}{b \cdot c} \div \frac{c}{d} = \frac{a \cdot c \cdot d}{b \cdot c \cdot d} \div \frac{c}{d} = \frac{a \cdot d}{b \cdot c}$$

13. Division can be defined in terms of multiplication, as indicated below, and then the "invert and multiply" rule can be derived.

   Definition Given that $\frac{c}{d} \cdot \frac{x}{y} = \frac{a}{b}$ and $\frac{c}{d} \neq 0$, then $\frac{x}{y}$ is called the quotient of $\frac{a}{b}$ and $\frac{c}{d}$ and is written

$$\frac{x}{y} = \frac{a}{b} \div \frac{c}{d}$$

   Observe that $\frac{c}{d} \cdot (\frac{d}{c} \cdot \frac{a}{b}) = \frac{a}{b}$. (Why?)   Hence $\frac{a}{b} \div \frac{c}{d} = \frac{a}{b} \cdot \frac{d}{c}$. (Why?)

14. For each pair of numbers below, give the number you must multiply the first number by to get the second, and then state the division problem you have solved.

   Examples   i) 4, 12;   3, $12 \div 4 = 3$

   ii) 12, 4; $\frac{1}{3}$, $4 \div 12 = \frac{1}{3}$

   iii) $\frac{3}{5}, \frac{12}{25}$; $\frac{4}{5}$, $\frac{12}{25} \div \frac{3}{5} = \frac{4}{5}$

   a) $\frac{3}{4}, \frac{9}{20}$ b) $\frac{7}{3}, \frac{28}{15}$ c) $\frac{8}{7}, 1$ d) $\frac{23}{59}, 0$

   e) $\frac{35}{35}, \frac{23}{23}$ f) 18, 7   g) $1, \frac{3}{11}$ h) $\frac{3}{7}, 1$

   i) $\frac{3}{7}, \frac{5}{9}$

15. Determine the rational number $\frac{a}{b}$ such that:

   a) $\frac{3}{4} \cdot (\frac{4}{3} \cdot \frac{a}{b}) = \frac{9}{7}$ b) $\frac{3}{4} \cdot (\frac{a}{b} \cdot \frac{7}{11}) = \frac{7}{11}$

   c) $\frac{a}{b} \cdot (\frac{13}{17} \cdot \frac{4}{9}) = \frac{4}{9}$ d) $\frac{11}{15} \cdot (\frac{15}{11} \cdot \frac{a}{b}) = \frac{23}{19}$

16. Explain how parts (a) and (d) of Exercise 15 show, respectively, that

$$\frac{9}{7} \div \frac{3}{4} = \frac{9}{7} \cdot \frac{4}{3} \qquad \text{and} \qquad \frac{23}{19} \div \frac{11}{15} = \frac{23}{19} \cdot \frac{15}{11}.$$

   We have not compared the *sizes* of rational numbers. When we list the whole numbers, we nearly always list them in order of size:

0, 1, 2, 3, . . .

The three dots indicate that this listing is suitably described by the few symbols we have written. Everyone "knows" how to order the whole numbers by size. But the few times we have listed rational numbers, we have used the style

$$\frac{0}{1}, \frac{1}{1}, \frac{1}{2}, \frac{2}{1}, \frac{1}{3}, \frac{3}{1}, \frac{1}{4}, \frac{2}{3}, \ldots$$

You probably understand the ellipsis marks and can continue this listing indefinitely, but this is certainly not an ordering of the rational numbers that makes use of their size. We are quite certain that $\frac{0}{1}$ is the smallest number in our set, but $\frac{2}{1}$ is surely not smaller than the number $\frac{1}{3}$ which follows it.

Problem   Why did we omit $\frac{2}{2}$ in the list above? What will be the next three fractions omitted?

The crucial question is: "Why do we not list the rationals in order of increasing size, just as we list the whole numbers?" Before answering, we must decide precisely what we mean by saying that one rational is smaller than another. The natural thing to do is to return to the real world and search for a reasonable definition.
Consider the diagram below.

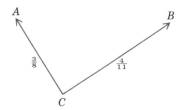

Which set contains the fewer elements, A or B? The easy way to decide is to replace the functions $\frac{3}{8}$ and $\frac{4}{11}$, as indicated below.

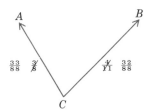

We see that for every 88 elements in C there are 33 in A and 32 in B. Since set B has fewer elements than A, it is natural to say that $\frac{4}{11}$ is less than $\frac{3}{8}$, and we write $\frac{4}{11} < \frac{3}{8}$.
The "rule" that comes out of this example is:

Choose two fractions from the equivalence classes (rational numbers) with common denominators. Now if the numerators are the same, of course the rational numbers are equal. Otherwise the smaller numerator indicates the smaller rational number.

Sometimes a geometrical interpretation of this test is made. The set C is taken to be a unit segment. Then A and B are segments and the rational numbers indicate their lengths. Intuitively we know what it means to say that one segment is shorter than another. The geometric interpretation only suggests, just as our first example does, that we are being reasonable in our definition of order for rational numbers. If two rational numbers are nearly the same size, the geometric interpretation is little help in deciding which of them is smaller.

If $\frac{a}{b}$ and $\frac{c}{d}$ are any fractions, we can compare

$$\frac{a \cdot d}{b \cdot d} \quad \text{and} \quad \frac{b \cdot c}{b \cdot d}.$$

Recall that:

If $a \cdot d = b \cdot c$, then $\dfrac{a}{b} = \dfrac{c}{d}$.

Now, if $a \cdot d < b \cdot c$, then $\frac{a}{b} < \frac{c}{d}$, and if $a \cdot d > b \cdot c$, then $\frac{a}{b} > \frac{c}{d}$.

Our definition of order for rational numbers enables us to understand why we do not list rational numbers in order of size. Between 0 and 1 we have many infinite strings of decreasing rational numbers. One of these is

$$1, \tfrac{1}{2}, \tfrac{1}{3}, \tfrac{1}{4}, \tfrac{1}{5}, \tfrac{1}{6}, \ldots,$$

Our smallest rational number is 0, but *we have no next-larger number.*

Another way to look at the situation is to recognize that if $\frac{a}{b}$ and $\frac{c}{d}$ are any unequal rational numbers, then there are many rational numbers between them. No rational number has a "next-larger" rational number. For whole numbers, each whole number has a "next-larger" one.

EXERCISES 6–7

1. Arrange in order of size from smallest to largest.
   a) $\frac{8}{17}, \frac{5}{17}, \frac{12}{17}, \frac{0}{17}, \frac{31}{17}$
   b) $\frac{17}{8}, \frac{17}{5}, \frac{17}{12}, \frac{17}{31}$
   c) $\frac{3}{4}, \frac{7}{8}, \frac{11}{16}, \frac{1}{2}, \frac{19}{32}$

2. The *average* of two rational numbers $\frac{a}{b}$ and $\frac{c}{d}$ is the rational number $\frac{1}{2} \cdot (\frac{a}{b} + \frac{c}{d})$. This "average" should be *between* the two numbers. Show that this is the case for
   a) $\frac{1}{3}$ and $\frac{1}{2}$
   b) $\frac{4}{12}$ and $\frac{5}{12}$
   c) 0 and $\frac{1}{2}$

   Why is the average of $\frac{3}{5}$ and $\frac{6}{10}$ not *between* these numbers?

3. A technique for inserting many rational numbers between any two distinct numbers is illustrated below.

$\frac{1}{5}, \frac{1}{3} \rightarrow \frac{3}{15}, \frac{5}{15}$ Now we see that we can insert $\frac{4}{15}$ between $\frac{1}{5}$ and $\frac{1}{3}$.

$\frac{1}{4}, \frac{1}{3} \rightarrow \frac{3}{12}, \frac{4}{12} \rightarrow \frac{30}{120}, \frac{40}{120}$ This suggests several rational numbers which lie between $\frac{1}{4}$ and $\frac{1}{3}$. What are they?

Indicate how to use this technique to insert more than 100 numbers between $\frac{1}{6}$ and $\frac{1}{5}$.

4. Find a whole number n such that

a) $\dfrac{n}{10} < \dfrac{1}{3} < \dfrac{n+1}{10}$ b) $\dfrac{n}{100} < \dfrac{5}{8} < \dfrac{n+1}{100}$

c) $\dfrac{n}{100} < \dfrac{17}{13} < \dfrac{n+1}{100}$ d) $\dfrac{n}{1000} < \dfrac{63}{179} < \dfrac{n+1}{1000}$

5. A 13-ounce box of soap flakes costs 23¢. An 18-ounce box of the same brand costs 33¢.

a) Which is the larger number, $\frac{23}{13}$ or $\frac{33}{18}$?

b) Which box is the better buy?

6. A 16-ounce loaf of bread costs 21¢. A 20-ounce loaf costs 26¢.

a) Which is the larger fraction, $\frac{16}{21}$ or $\frac{20}{26}$?

b) If the loaves are of equal quality, which is the better buy?

7. On the number line below, decide whether point A is to the right or left of point B.

a) $A = \frac{31}{23}$, $B = \frac{74}{55}$ b) $A = \frac{93}{29}$, $B = \frac{117}{36}$

8. Use your intuitive understanding of the order relation for rational numbers and insert the proper symbol in the box.

a) Since $\frac{5}{4} > \frac{4}{5}$, $\frac{7}{3} + \frac{5}{4} \square \frac{7}{3} + \frac{4}{5}$.

b) Since $\frac{5}{4} > \frac{4}{5}$, $\frac{7}{3} - \frac{5}{4} \square \frac{7}{3} - \frac{4}{5}$.

c) If $\dfrac{a}{b} > \dfrac{c}{d}$ and $\dfrac{c}{d} > \dfrac{e}{f}$, then $\dfrac{a}{b} \square \dfrac{e}{f}$.

d) If $\dfrac{a}{b} > \dfrac{c}{d} > \dfrac{e}{f}$, then $\dfrac{a}{b} - \dfrac{c}{d} \square \dfrac{a}{b} - \dfrac{e}{f}$.

e) If $\dfrac{a}{b} \cdot \dfrac{c}{d} > \dfrac{e}{f} \cdot \dfrac{c}{d}$, then $\dfrac{a}{b} \square \dfrac{e}{f}$,

f) If $\dfrac{a}{b} - \dfrac{c}{d} > \dfrac{r}{s} - \dfrac{t}{u}$ and $\dfrac{a}{b} < \dfrac{r}{s}$, then $\dfrac{c}{d} \square \dfrac{t}{u}$.

REVIEW EXERCISES

1. In a group of children there are 2 boys for every 3 girls.

   a) How many boys are there if there are 15 girls?

   b) How many boys are there if there are 7 more girls than boys?

   c) Write a fraction comparing the number of boys with the total number of children in the group.

   d) After 12 more boys joined the group, there were 4 boys for every 3 girls. How many girls are there?

   e) After 8 more girls joined the group, there were 4 boys for every 7 girls. How many boys are there?

2. Joe's age is two-thirds of Jim's. If Jim is 12 years old, how old is Joe?

3. Bob's age is two-thirds of Alan's. If Bob is 12 years old, how old is Alan?

4. After spending three-fifths of my money I had $30 left. How much did I spend?

5. In a group of people there are three-fourths as many men as women and six-fifths as many children as women.

   a) Express the number of men as a fraction of the number of children.

   b) If there are 10 more women than men, how many more children are there than men?

   c) If there are 354 men, women, and children altogether, how many of each are there?

6. In city A, 3 persons out of 5 are over 20 years old. In city B, 2 out of 3 are over 20. What fraction of the people in the combined cities is over 20 if:

   a) The cities have the same population?

   b) City A has twice the population of city B?

   c) The ratio of the population of A to the population of B is 8 to 5?

7. One boy can mow a lawn in 4 hours, another in 3. If they work simultaneously, how long will it take them to mow the lawn?

8. Eight men can complete a job in 12 days. Six men work for 4 days. How long will it take 4 men to complete the job?

9. Consider the sequence of rational numbers below.

   $$\frac{1}{1}, \frac{3}{2}, \frac{7}{5}, \frac{17}{12}, \frac{41}{29}, \frac{99}{70}, \cdots$$

   a) Identify a pattern and write the next 3 fractions.

   b) Square each of these numbers and compare the result with 2.

SUMMARY

This chapter has covered the first three stages of abstraction for the rational number system. Many different situations suggest the invention of fraction symbols: pie cutting, measurement, comparison of sets of discrete objects, etc. The analysis of various physical situations in this chapter should make it clear that in all these cases we can interpret fraction symbols as names for functions. This brings a unity to all physical applications of fractions. This unity is esthetically pleasing and has considerable practical significance for teaching rational numbers.

The summary on page 203 presents the heart of the chapter. The eight operations, 5 through 12, listed there are the result of carrying out Stage 2 of the abstraction process. These eight operations—three called multiplication, three division, one addition, and one subtraction—have been drawn from the real world because we have observed eight broad categories of problems. Each of these operations enables us to solve all the problems of one category. It is not essential that you remember the classification of problems that leads to these operations. When we agree to replace each whole number n by the fraction $\frac{n}{1}$, we find that we can get along with just one multiplication, one division, etc. But it is important that you realize that physical situations which seem on the surface to differ widely are handled by the same abstract mathematical operation. The significance of these ideas for teaching is that there should be no hurried rush in the elementary school to master the abstract rational number system. The approach should be a leisurely one in which students work many problems by thinking carefully about relationships between the various sets involved in each problem.

You should understand the set-theoretic basis for equivalence of fractions; relate reciprocals of fractions to inverses of functions; see clearly that multiplication of fractions is based on composition of functions; observe that the addition operation on fractions, like the addition operation on whole numbers, is closely related to the union operation on disjoint sets; and recognize that the "invert and multiply" technique taught in school mathematics for division has a simple set-theoretic interpretation. You should think of a single rational number as an equivalence class of fractions, and understand the rule for equivalence: $\frac{a}{b} \sim \frac{c}{d}$ if and only if $a \cdot d = b \cdot c$. In Chapter 8 we shall look at the structure of the rational number system as it is determined by basic principles.

7 the abstraction of the integers from the real world

7–1 introduction

The most straightforward way to obtain the system I of integers is to abstract it from the set W of whole numbers without reference to the real world. One simply decides that it would be a good idea to have an *opposite* or *negative* of each number in W so that each equation of the form

$$a + x = 0$$

has a solution in this new system. Hence, for each $a \in W$ we invent a number $-a$, which we call *the opposite of* a or *the negative of* a. These new numbers, together with the old numbers of W, form our new set I:

$$I = \{\ldots -3,\, -2,\, -1, 0, 1, 2, 3, \ldots\}.$$

In I we can add any two elements of W, and we know many other facts such as

$$\ldots;\ -3 + 3 = 0;\ -2 + 2 = 0;\ -1 + 1 = 0;\ \ldots$$

The next problem is to decide how to add, subtract, and multiply *any* two numbers in I so that the resulting system will have a simple, pleasing structure. This approach to the integers is presented in Chapter 8.

Here we are interested in ways in which we can pull the system of integers out of the real world. Many physical situations suggest the integers.

Elevators go up and down.

We can walk east or west on a road.

Income is canceled off by expenses.

We have the advantage of knowing exactly what we want. We intend to end our investigation with the abstract set

$$I = \{\ldots -3, -2, -1, 0, 1, 2, 3, \ldots\}$$

in which addition, subtraction, multiplication, and division are operations on which we place *no physical interpretation*. But we wish to analyze carefully the process by which we obtain this system from the real world. We want to show that the system of integers *can* be used to study real situations, that the operations on the integers are natural, not artificial.

EXERCISES 7–1

1. An elevator moves successively 7 floors, 3 floors, 5 floors, 4 floors, 1 floor, and has returned to its starting point. Explain.

2. A man walks on a north-south road successively 2 miles, 5 miles, 4 miles, 3 miles, 6 miles, and is 2 miles south of his starting point. Explain.

3. A gambler places even-money bets of $50, $25, $100, $30, and $200. At the end of this series of bets he has won $5. What happened?

7–2   stage 1: new symbols

Consider a hypothetical gambler who can risk any whole number of dollars on an even-money bet. For each whole number n in the set

$$W = \{0, 1, 2, \ldots\},$$

two events can happen. The gambler can win n dollars or lose n dollars.

We have observed the existence of two functions from the set W into a set of events E. These functions are diagrammed below.

$\forall n \in W,$ $w(n) =$ the event of winning n dollars; and

$l(n) =$ the event of losing n dollars.

$$W = \{0, 1, 2, \ldots\}$$
$$w:$$
$$E = \{w(0) = l(0), w(1), w(2), \ldots; l(1), l(2), \ldots\}$$
$$l:$$
$$W = \{0, 1, 2, \ldots\}$$

Note that we consider the events of winning and losing 0 dollars to be identical. In the symbol "$w(3)$," the 3 *names* a whole number, the w *names* a function, and the entire symbol $w(3)$ *names* the event of winning 3 dollars.

7–3 stage 2: operations on the new symbols

In the set of events E, there is a natural binary operation. With this operation we can keep track of the gambler's financial standing during a series of bets. We denote this operation by the sign $*$ (read as "star"). Thus, for example,

$$w(3) * w(4) = w(7); w(3) * l(6) = l(3).$$

EXERCISES 7–2

1. Complete the table below, which explains how to compute with $*$ in E.

   $\forall a, b \in W,$ $w(a) * w(b) = w(a + b)$

                       $l(a) * l(b) = $ _____

                       If $a \geq b, w(a) * l(b) = w(a - b)$

                       If $a \leq b, w(a) * l(b) = $ _____

   Explain why you are sure that $*$ is commutative and associative.

2. What operations and relations in W are used in the definition of the operation $*$ in E?

3. Explain the statement: $*$ is a function: $E \times E \to E$ but $*$ is not 1–1.

4. Practice computation in E.

   a) $w(7) * w(3)$ b) $l(4) * l(8)$ c) $w(6) * l(9)$ d) $l(9) * w(6)$

   e) $w(4) * l(11)$ f) $l(11) * w(4)$ g) $w(7) * w(0)$ h) $w(9) * l(9)$

5. Show how to use the commutative and associative laws and compute very rapidly.

   a) $w(473) * l(219) * l(473)$ b) $w(864) * l(769) * l(864) * w(769)$

6. Illustrate the associativity of $*$ by computing both

   (i) $[w(9) * l(b)] * w(20)$ and   (ii) $w(9) * [l(b) * w(20)]$:

   a) under the assumption that $b < 9$;

   b) under the assumption that $b > 29$;

   c) under the assumption that $9 < b < 29$.

7. The operation $*$ possesses a *neutral* (or identity) event e such that

   $$\forall x \in E, \quad x * e = e * x = x.$$

   What is the event e?

8. To each event $x \in E$, there is associated an event that we call "the *opposite* of x" or "the *negative* of x" and denote by $-x$, such that

   $$x * (-x) = e.$$

 a) If $x = w(7)$, what is $-x$?

 b) If $y = l(3)$, what is $-y$?

 c) If $z = w(0)$, what is $-z$?

Note that the symbol $-$ used in Exercise 8 denotes a 1–1 function from E to E:

$$-: E \xrightarrow{1\text{-}1} E$$

We sometimes call a function a *unary* operation. The usual functional notation would be $-(x)$; $-[w(3)]$; $-[l(7)]$, etc. To simplify the notation we drop the parentheses. We introduce another notational change. We shall replace the symbol $*$ by the familiar symbol $+$ and call the operation in E *addition*.

EXERCISES 7–3

1. Complete each statement.

 a) $\forall n \in W,\ -w(n) =$ b) $\forall n \in W,\ -l(n) =$

 c) $\forall n \in W,\ -[-w(n)] =$ d) $\forall n \in W,\ -[-l(n)] =$

 e) $\forall n \in W,\ -\{-[-w(n)]\} =$

2. Compute:

 a) $w(7) + -w(4)$ b) $l(7) + -l(4)$

 c) $w(3) + -l(5)$ d) $l(3) + -w(5)$

 e) $l(9) + -w(0)$ f) $-l(5) + -l(4)$

 g) $-w(6) + -w(5)$ h) $-w(4) + -[-w(7)]$

3. Explain why the symbols

  $w[w(3)]$ and $l[w(3)]$

 are meaningless.

4. Note that

 $-(w(3) + w(4)) = -w(7) = l(7),$

 $-w(3) + -w(4) = l(3) + l(4) = l(7).$

 This suggests that possibly

 $\forall x, y \in E,\ -(x + y) = -x + (-y).$

 Use the table you developed in Exercise 1 of Exercises 7–2, and by considering all possible cases prove that this formula is correct.

5. a) Explain what it means to say that *a function is its own inverse,* and show that the function $-$ is its own inverse.

$$E = \{\ldots l(2),\ l(1),\ l(0),\ w(0),\ w(1),\ w(2),\ \ldots\}$$

b) Show that the function, *the reciprocal of,* in the set of (nonzero) fractions, is its own inverse.

As our calculations become more complicated, it should be comforting to keep in mind that we are dealing with a simple physical situation. You know perfectly well how to watch a series of bets and keep track of what is happening. Note that you are observing the same stages of abstraction that you have seen twice before, once for whole numbers and again for fractions. We have invented a system of new symbols and operations which is useful for describing a familiar situation. Soon we shall be more interested in our symbolic game than in the real-world situation which suggested it.

It is convenient to view E as the union of two sets,

$$E^w = \{w(0), w(1), \ldots\}; \qquad E^l = \{l(0), l(1), \ldots\}.$$

Note that

$$E = E^w \cup E^l; \qquad E^w \cap E^l = \{w(0)\}$$

$$w: W \xrightarrow[\text{onto}]{1\text{-}1} E^w; \qquad l: W \xrightarrow[\text{onto}]{1\text{-}1} E^l$$

If we inspect E^w and E^l closely, we see that each is a "copy" of W so far as the addition operation is concerned. Note that

$$4 + 5 \xrightarrow{w} w(4) + w(5) = w(9) \xrightarrow{w^{-1}} 9,$$

$$w(3) + w(7) \xrightarrow{w^{-1}} 3 + 7 = 10 \xrightarrow{w} w(10).$$

Just as the *counting function* enabled us to substitute *addition of whole numbers* for the operation *disjoint union* of sets, and just as the function associating each whole number n with the rational number $\frac{n}{1}$ enabled us to pass back and forth between calculations with whole numbers and calculations with fractions, so do the functions w and l enable us to replace calculations in E^w or E^l by calculations in W. We can describe this relationship by saying that

w is a *homomorphism* of W onto E^w relative to the addition operations.

A similar statement holds for l.

The importance of the relationship we have noted above is that, so far as addition is concerned, we can *embed* W in E just as we embedded W in the set of rational numbers. We can replace the elements of E^w or of E^l by those of W. It is traditional to replace the elements of E^w by W, and we bow to tradition. Hence we consider the set

$$(E - E^w) \cup W = \{0, 1, 2, \ldots ; l(1), l(2), \ldots\}.^*$$

Of course when we compute in this new set we face problems like

$$l(2) + 4; \qquad l(3) + (-4).$$

To solve such problems, simply replace (mentally) each whole number a by the event $w(a)$ and carry out the computation. For example, we compute the sum

$$l(2) + (-4)$$

by thinking:

      i) Replace 4 by $w(4)$.

      ii) $-w(4) = l(4)$.

      iii) The sum is $l(6)$.

Explain how one thinks in computing $l(2) + 4$.

EXERCISES 7–4

1. In the examples below, explain how the symbolism describes our way of thinking as we compute in $(E - E^w) \cup W$.

    a) $5 + l(8) \rightarrow w(5) + l(8) = l(3)$

    b) $8 + l(5) \rightarrow w(8) + l(5) = w(3) \rightarrow 3$

2. Let us call our set I instead of $(E - E^w) \cup W$. Thus

$$I = \{\ldots l(2), l(1), 0, 1, 2, \ldots\}.$$

In I we have a binary operation $+$ and a unary operation: (the opposite of or the negative of). This system was drawn from a particular physical situation, but other interpretations are possible. Interpret $l(n)$ as "walking n steps to the left on a road" ("left" as viewed from a particular side of the road). Make the natural interpretations of n, $+$, and $-$.

      Left   Road   Right

$\longleftarrow$————————————————————————$\longrightarrow$

                · Observer

---

* The symbol $E - E^w$ designates the set of all elements of E which are not in E^w.

Interpret the equations below.

a) $l(5) + l(3) = l(8)$ b) $l(8) + 6 = l(2)$

c) $l(4) + 9 = 5$ d) $3 + 4 = 7$

e) $l(3) + (-5) = l(8)$ f) $-l(4) + (-6) = l(2)$

3. With the interpretations of Exercise 2, perform the calculations below. Give all answers in terms of our basic symbols. That is, in your answers replace $-n$ by $l(n)$ and $-l(n)$ by n.

a) $4 + 3$ b) $l(4) + l(3)$ c) $l(4) + 3$

d) $4 + l(3)$ e) $-4 + 3$ f) $-l(4) + 3$

g) $l(4) + (-3)$ h) $-4 + [-l(3)]$ i) $-[-l(4)] + [-(-3)]$

4. Either use the interpretations of Exercise 2 or compute mechanically.

a) $7 + 6$ b) $l(10) + 8$ c) $12 + l(4)$

d) $l(5) + l(4)$ e) $-3 + l(5)$ f) $-l(5) + l(2)$

g) $-l(4) + -l(3)$ h) $-6 + -l(8)$ i) $-l(5) + -l(8)$

5. Solve each equation below. Either use the interpretation of Exercise 2 or compute mechanically.

a) $x + l(4) = 3$ b) $4 + x = l(3)$

c) $4 + l(x) = l(3)$ d) $x + x = l(8)$

e) $-x = l(5)$ f) $-x = 7$

g) $-(x + 2) = l(5)$ h) $-[x + l(2)] = l(6)$

i) $-[l(3) + -x] = 7$ j) $-[l(3) + -x] = -6$

6. Explain why each equation below has no solution.

a) $4 + l(x) = 8$. (Why is $l(-4)$ meaningless?)   b) $-l(x) = l(7)$

In I we can define a subtraction operation by agreeing that the equation

$$l(8) - l(5) = x$$

poses the problem:

"I have bet and lost \$5. What event must occur to make my total loss \$8?"

Thus, symbolically, we define $l(8) - l(5)$ so that the reasonable equation, $l(5) + [l(8) - l(5)] = l(8)$, holds.

EXERCISES 7–5

1. The definition of subtraction assures us that in I,

$$x - y = z \qquad \text{if and only if} \qquad x = y + z.$$

Prove that each "answer" below is *incorrect*.

a) $l(8) - l(3) = l(4)$ b) $6 - l(2) = 4$ c) $l(9) - 2 = l(7)$

d) $l(4) - l(7) = l(3)$ e) $l(4) - (-2) = l(6)$ f) $-3 - [-l(5)] = 2$

2. Give correct answers for the subtraction problems of Exercise 1.

3. Solve the subtraction problems below.

a) $l(7) - l(5)$ b) $8 - 3$ c) $l(5) - l(7)$

d) $3 - 8$ e) $5 - l(2)$ f) $2 - l(5)$

g) $3 - l(7)$ h) $l(7) - 3$ i) $-8 - l(3)$

j) $l(5) - (-7)$

4. Explain the way of thinking described below and use the method to rework the subtraction problems of Exercise 3.

Example $5 - l(2) = x.$

i) I must determine x so that $l(2) + x = 5.$

ii) $l(2) + 2 = 0.$

iii) Hence $l(2) + 2 + 5 = 5$ and $x = 2 + 5 = 7.$

Instead of continuing our investigation of I, we turn to a second illustration of how the integers may be drawn from the real world.

Consider the set V of all *vectors* on a line having a common initial point and whole-number length.

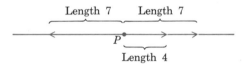

Length 7   Length 7

P

Length 4

Think of each vector as an arrow fastened to the line at point P. We imagine one vector of zero length at P. It is natural to split V into two sets, the set of vectors directed in one direction on the line, and the set of vectors oppositely directed. For convenience we put the zero vector in both of these sets.

If we look at either one of these sets of vectors, say the vectors directed to the right, then it is natural to construct the 1–1 correspondence from W to this set of vectors which associates each vector with its length.

$+3$

$W = \{ 0, \quad 1, \quad 2, \quad 3, \quad 4, \quad 5, \cdots \}$

We denote this function by the symbol $+$. For computational convenience we write ^+n instead of $+(n)$. Note that in the symbol

$+(n)$ or ^+n

the symbol $+$ names our function; n names a whole number; and the entire symbol ^+n names the vector that the function $+$ matches with n. This is just another illustration of our standard convention in using the functional notation, $f(x)$.

For the corresponding 1–1 function matching W with vectors directed to the left, we use the symbol $-$ and write

^-n rather than $-(n)$

The names V^+ and V^- are convenient choices for the sets of vectors above. Explain the statements below.

$$+: W \xrightarrow[\text{onto}]{1\text{-}1} V^+; \qquad -: W \xrightarrow[\text{onto}]{1\text{-}1} V^-$$
$$V^+ \cup V^- = V; \qquad V^+ \cap V^- = \{^+0\} = \{^-0\}$$

The reader can anticipate the notation that lies ahead. Soon we shall be using the $+$ sign in *two* ways: to "add" vectors in V and as a function from W to V^+. The versatile sign $-$ will be used in *three* ways: to indicate subtraction in V, and to indicate *the opposite of* a vector in V, as well as our initial use as a function from W to V^-. This threefold use of the sign $-$ has a tendency to confuse students when they are introduced to the integers.

There is a natural way to define an "addition" in V. To find the sum of two vectors,

$r + s,$

"unhook" vector s from point P. Slide s to right or left and "hook" its initial point to the terminal point of vector r. Now the terminal point of s coincides with that of some vector, say the vector t. Then

$r + s = t.$

For example,

$^+3 + {}^-1 = {}^+2$

Slide -1 three units right.   The terminal point of $^-1$ now falls on that of $^+2$.

EXERCISES 7–6

1. Compute the sums.

   a) $^+7 + {}^+3$ b) $^-4 + {}^-8$
   c) $^+6 + {}^-9$ d) $^-9 + {}^+6$
   e) $^+4 + {}^-11$ f) $^-11 + {}^+4$
   g) $^+7 + {}^+0$ h) $^+9 + {}^-9$

2. Compute quickly. (Why are you sure that vector addition is associative and commutative?)

  a) $^+473 + {}^-219 + {}^-473$ b) $^+864 + {}^-769 + {}^-864 + {}^+769$

3. Complete the statements below.

$$\forall a, b \in W, \qquad {}^+a + {}^+b =$$
$${}^-a + {}^-b =$$
$$\text{If } a \geq b, \ {}^+a + {}^-b =$$
$$\text{If } a \leq b, \ {}^+a + {}^-b =$$

4. What operations and relations in W are used to define addition in V?

5. Explain:

$$+: V \times V \xrightarrow{\text{onto}} V.$$

6. Illustrate the associative property for the binary operation $+$ in V by computing (i) $({}^+8 + {}^-b) + {}^+6$ and (ii) ${}^+8 + ({}^-b + {}^+6)$:

  (a) assuming that $b < 8$; (b) assuming that $b > 14$; (c) assuming that $8 < b < 14$.

7. The operation $+$ in V has an identity (neutral) element. What is it?

8. We define a function from V to V, denoted by $-$ and called *the opposite of* (or *the negative of*) by the conditions

$$\forall a \in W, \qquad \text{i) } -({}^+a) = {}^-a,$$
$$\text{ii) } -({}^-a) = {}^+a.$$

  (We suggest that you say "plus a" for ${}^+a$ and "minus a" for ${}^-a$. With the suggested language one reads $--a = {}^+a$ as, "the negative (or opposite) of minus a is plus a." One reads $-(-x)$ as "the negative of the negative of x.") Show that $-$ is a 1–1 correspondence: $V \to V$.

9. Explain why each of the following symbols is sheer nonsense.

  a) $^{+}{}^{+}a$ b) $+{}^+a$ c) $^-{}^+a$ d) $^-{}^-a$ e) $^-(-x)$ f) $^+(-x)$

10. Find the sums. Give all answers in terms of our basic symbols for vectors, that is, as ${}^+a$ or ${}^-a$.

  a) $^+4 + {}^+3$ b) $^-4 + {}^+3$ c) $- {}^+4 + {}^-3$

  d) $- {}^-4 + {}^-3$ e) $- {}^+5 + (- {}^-7)$ f) $-(- {}^-3) + [-(- {}^+2)]$

11. Solve each equation below.

  a) $x + {}^-4 = {}^+3$ b) $^+4 + x = {}^-3$

  c) $x + x = {}^-8$ d) $-x = {}^-5$

  e) $-x + {}^+7$ f) $-(x + {}^+2) = {}^-9$

  g) $-[{}^-3 + (-x)] = {}^+7$ h) $^+4 + (-x) = {}^-3$

12. Explain why each equation below has no solution.

  a) $^+4 + {}^-x = {}^+8$ b) $- {}^-x = {}^-7$

13. The subtraction operation in V (the third use of the sign $-$) is defined by $x - y = x + (-y)$. Compute the following.

   a) $^+7 - {}^+3$ b) $^+7 - {}^-3$ c) $^+7 - (- {}^+3)$

   d) $^+7 - (- {}^-3)$ e) $^-4 - {}^-8$ f) $^-8 - {}^-4$

   g) Reconcile this definition with the implicit definition (page 229), $y + (x - y) = x$.

14. Explain the triple use of the sign $-$ in part 13(d).

15. Explain the statements below.

   i) $-: W \xrightarrow[\text{onto}]{\text{1-1}} V^-$, and $-$ is a homomorphism of W on V^- relative to addition in these sets.

   ii) $-: V \xrightarrow[\text{onto}]{\text{1-1}} V$. Also $-: V^+ \xrightarrow[\text{onto}]{\text{1-1}} V^-$, and $-: V^- \xrightarrow[\text{onto}]{\text{1-1}} V^+$. The function $-: V \xrightarrow[\text{onto}]{\text{1-1}} V$ is its own inverse.

   iii) $-: V \times V \xrightarrow{\text{onto}} V$. The binary operation $-$ is neither commutative nor associative.

16. Make statements using the symbol $+$ which correspond to (i) and (iii) in Exercise 15. Why do we make no statement for $+$ corresponding to (ii)?

17. Define a multiplication operation between whole numbers and vectors by agreeing that, for all vectors v, $0 \cdot v = {}^+0$, $1 \cdot v = v$, and $n \cdot v = v + v + \cdots + v$ (n addends). For example, $0 \cdot {}^-2 = {}^+0$, $1 \cdot {}^+4 = {}^+4$, $3 \cdot {}^+2 = {}^+6$, and $3 \cdot {}^-4 = {}^-12$. Explain how your definition of multiplication suggests a division operation such that

   $$^+6 \div 3 = {}^+2; \quad {}^+6 \div {}^+2 = 3.$$

18. Compute products and quotients below.

   a) $4 \cdot {}^-5$ b) $^-3 \cdot 6$ c) $(- {}^-3) \cdot 3$

   d) $(- {}^+3) \cdot 4$ e) $^+12 \div 4$ f) $^-12 \div 4$

   g) $^+12 \div 4$ h) $^-12 \div {}^-4$ i) $(- {}^-12) \div (- {}^-4)$

Using the facts that both $+$ and $-$ are homomorphisms of W onto V^+ and V^-, respectively, of course we can embed W in V. We shall consider this embedding in the next section.

7–4   stage 3: the system of integers

In this section we disregard physical interpretations and study our abstract system. At the close of Section 7–3 we were actually considering the set

$$V \cup W = \{0, 1, 2, \ldots; \; {}^+0, {}^+1, {}^+2, \ldots; \; {}^-1, {}^-2, \ldots\},$$

in which we could compute in the familiar ways with whole numbers, add or subtract any two vectors, multiply any vector by any whole number, and divide every vector by at least one whole number and at least one vector.

$^+6 \div 1 = {}^+6;\ {}^-5 \div {}^-1 = 5.$

We have also the function $-$ which maps each vector on its negative. (Naturally we shall not expect to perform calculations like

$^+3 \div 8.$

Fractions are back in Chapter 6. We chose, for reasons of simplification, not to bring them along for this work of Chapter 7, although we could easily have done so.)

We can drop out of the set $V \cup W$ either the elements of V^+ or of V^-, letting the whole numbers take over their tasks. Since we have not established an order in V, we have no reason to prefer one choice over another. Only the weight of tradition suggests the elimination of V^+. Hence we consider the set

$I = (V - V^+) \cup W = \{0, 1, 2, \ldots; {}^-1, {}^-2, {}^-3, \ldots\}.$

To add and subtract in I, we pass back and forth freely between I and V. Explain the calculations below.

$8 + {}^-5 \to {}^+8 + {}^-5 = {}^+3 \to 3$
$3 + {}^-5 \to {}^+3 + {}^-5 = {}^-2$
$4 - {}^-3 \to {}^+4 - {}^-3 = {}^+4 + -{}^-3 = {}^+4 + {}^+3 = {}^+7 \to 7$
$3 - 7 \to {}^+3 - {}^+7 = {}^+3 + -{}^+7 = {}^+3 + {}^-7 = {}^-4$

We round out our multiplication rule by deciding that for all $a, b \in W$,

${}^-a \cdot {}^-b = a \cdot b.$

It is easy to see that no other rule would be satisfactory. For example,

${}^-2 \cdot (3 + {}^-3)$ should be 0. (Why?)

But

${}^-2 \cdot (3 + {}^-3)$ should be ${}^-2 \cdot 3 + {}^-2 \cdot {}^-3.$ (Why?)

Hence

${}^-6 + {}^-2 \cdot {}^-3$ should be 0. (Why?)

And hence we had better agree that

${}^-2 \cdot {}^-3 = 6.$ (Why?)

With this agreement we automatically get the division rules

$$(a \cdot b) \div {}^-a = {}^-b; \; (a \cdot b) \div {}^-b = {}^-a$$

We can simplify the notation for I by eliminating the raised minus signs. Note that for all $a \in W$,

$$-a = {}^-a.$$

Hence wherever a symbol ${}^-a$ occurs we replace it by $-a$. Thus

$$I = \{\ldots -2, -1, 0, 1, 2, \ldots\}.$$

The sign $-$ is used now in only two ways:

$$a \xrightarrow{-} -a; \qquad (a, b) \xrightarrow{-} a - b = a + (-b).$$

But even the use of $-$ to indicate subtraction, as in $a - b$, is unnecessary, since we can always rewrite $a - b$ as $a + (-b)$. In this sense there is only one necessary interpretation of the sign $-$, the "opposite" interpretation.

Below we summarize computational rules in I, the set of *integers*.

The unary operation $-$ *in I:* $\forall a \in W$,

    i) $a + (-a) = 0$ ii) $-(-a) = a$

Addition (a binary operation) in I: $\forall a, b \in W$,

    i) $a + b$ is the familiar sum in W
    ii) $(-a) + (-b) = -(a + b)$
    iii) $a + (-b) = a - b$ if $a \geq b$; $-(b - a)$ if $a \leq b$.

Addition is associative and commutative, 0 is a neutral (identity) element, and every element of I has a negative (or additive inverse).

Subtraction (a binary operation) in I: $\forall x, y \in I$,

$$x - y = x + (-y).$$

(Remember: Subtraction in I is an "unnecessary" operation.)

Multiplication (a binary operation) in I: $\forall a, b \in W$,

    i) $a \cdot b$ is the familiar product in W.
    ii) $(-a) \cdot b = a \cdot (-b) = -(a \cdot b)$.
    iii) $(-a) \cdot (-b) = a \cdot b$.

Multiplication is commutative and associative and is distributive with respect to addition. The number 1 is the neutral element for multiplication. Not every element of I has a multiplicative inverse. (Which do?)

Division in I: $\forall a, b \in W$ with $b \neq 0$,

    i) $(a \cdot b) \div b = a$ (the familiar quotient in W);
       for example, $(3 \cdot 4) \div 4 = 3$.
    ii) $[-(a \cdot b)] \div (-b) = a$; for example, $[-(3 \cdot 4)] \div -4 = 3$.
    iii) $(a \cdot b) \div (-b) = -(a \cdot b) \div b = -a$;
       for example $(3 \cdot 4) \div -4 = -(3 \cdot 4) \div 4 = -3$.

There is another very useful function in I, the *absolute-value function*, denoted by the sign $|\ |$.

$$\forall a \in W, \qquad |a| = a \qquad \text{and} \qquad |-a| = a.$$

Note that the absolute-value function maps I on W:

$$|\ |: I \xrightarrow{\text{onto}} W.$$

Examples $|3| = 3$; $|-3| = 3$; $|0| = 0$.

We have not discussed order in I systematically. When considered as elements of I, the natural numbers

$$1, 2, 3, \ldots$$

are called the *positive* integers. Their opposites,

$$-1, -2, -3, \ldots$$

are called the *negative* integers. The integer 0 is neither positive nor negative. The order we have in mind is displayed below:

$$\ldots < -2 < -1 < 0 < 1 < 2 < \ldots$$

A precise definition of this order relation is given below in terms of subtraction and the concept of a positive integer.

$$\forall a, b \in I, \qquad a < b \qquad \text{if and only if} \qquad b - a \text{ is a positive integer.}$$

Note that, according to this definition,

$$-4 < 0 \text{ for } 0 - (-4) = 4 \text{ (a } \textit{positive} \text{ integer)}.$$

EXERCISES 7–7

  1. Verify that $a + (-a) = 0$ for
      a) $a = 3$ b) $a = -4$ c) $a = 0$

2. Verify that $(-a) + (-b) = -(a + b)$ for:
   a) $a = 3, b = 2$ b) $a = 3, b = -2$
   c) $a = -3, b = 2$ d) $a = -3, b = -2$

3. Verify that $(-a) \cdot (-b) = ab$ for:
   a) $a = 3, b = 2$ b) $a = 3, b = -2$
   c) $a = -3, b = 2$ d) $a = -3, b = -2$

4. Verify that $(-a) \cdot b = -(a \cdot b)$ for:
   a) $a = 3, b = -4$ b) $a = -3, b = 4$

5. Show that $|a| \cdot |b| = |a \cdot b|$ for:
   a) $a = 3, b = -2$ b) $a = -3, b = -2$

6. Verify the following statements.
   a) If $a = 3$ and $b = 5$, $|a + b| = |a| + |b|$
   b) If $a = -3$ and $b = -5$, $|a + b| = |a| + |b|$
   c) If $a = 3$ and $b = -5$, $|a + b| < |a| + |b|$
   d) If $a = -3$ and $b = -5$, $|a + b| < |a| + |b|$
   e) Offer a conjecture.

7. Test the validity of $|a - b| \geq |a| - |b|$ for several choices of integers a and b.

8. Verify that both numbers 1 and -9 satisfy the equation

   $|x + 4| = 5.$

9. Determine all solutions of each equation below.
   a) $|x + 3| = 6$ b) $|x - 2| = 6$
   c) $|3 - x| = 5$ d) $|2x + 3| = 11$

10. Give all integers satisfying the inequality
    a) $|x| < 5$ b) $|x + 3| < 2$
    c) $|x - 4| < 3$ d) $|8 - x| < |x - 6|$

11. Find as many pairs of integers x, y as possible such that

    $|x + y| = 10$ and $|x - y| = 2.$

12. Reconcile the following definition of the absolute-value function with the one given earlier.

    $\forall x \in I,$ i) If $x \geq 0,$ $|x| = x$
                            ii) If $x < 0,$ $|x| = -x$

13. Using the concept of absolute value, formulate "simple" rules for addition and multiplication in I.

14. Let V denote the set of all vectors on a line having a common initial point and (nonnegative) *rational* length. Retrace the development of pages 230–233 in this situation. Compare the computational rules for Q with those for I. (Here and from now on, Q denotes the set of all rationals.)

7–5   number lines

It is often helpful to visualize numbers as points on a line. We speak of the *whole number* line, the *integer* line, the *rational number* line, and the *real number* line. Each of these phrases refers to a function which associates a certain set of numbers with a set of points on a line. The order of the points on the line reflects the ordering of the numbers matched with them. Each number is said to be the *coordinate* of the point with which it is matched.

$$W = \{\; 0, \quad 1, \quad 2, \quad 3, \; \cdots \}$$

The whole number line

$$I = \{ \cdots -2, \quad -1, \quad 0, \quad 1, \quad 2, \; \cdots \}$$

The integer line

The points matched with the whole numbers (or integers) determine congruent segments. Hence each number line is completely determined as soon as one specifies the points matched with the numbers 0 and 1. These points are called the *origin* and *unit point*, respectively. Because each of the lines pictured above has points which are not matched with any numbers, one says that these number lines have *holes* in them.

The rational number line is best envisioned by thinking first of the integer number line, then mentally adjoining all points of bisection for the segments determined by consecutive integers, all points of trisection, all points dividing each segment into fourths, etc.

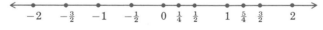

$$-2 \qquad -\tfrac{3}{2} \qquad -1 \qquad -\tfrac{1}{2} \qquad 0 \;\; \tfrac{1}{4} \;\; \tfrac{1}{2} \qquad 1 \;\; \tfrac{5}{4} \;\; \tfrac{3}{2} \qquad 2$$

The rational number line

(Here we have considered the set of *all* rational numbers, both positive and negative.)

The operations addition, subtraction, multiplication, and division can be visualized on the number line, and the relative positions of points present information about the relative sizes of the numbers matched with them. Pictures of number lines are usually drawn so that, if one observes them in the "natural" way, the points matched with positive numbers fall to the right of the zero point. Of course this is not an essential feature.

EXERCISES 7–8

1. For each drawing below, tell what fact of whole-number arithmetic is pictured. Then imagine each arrow reversed and give the corresponding fact.

(a)   (b)

2. For the whole-number line below give the coordinate(s) of:

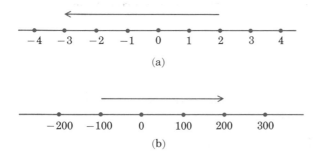

a) The point bisecting AB

b) The two points trisecting AB

c) The three points which divide AB into four congruent segments

d) The four points which divide AB into five congruent segments

3. For each drawing below, give an associated addition fact in the arithmetic of the integers. Then imagine each arrow reversed and give the corresponding addition fact.

(a)

(b)

4. On the integer number line, the coordinates of A and B are -21 and 3, respectively.

a) What is the coordinate of the midpoint of AB?

b) Find the coordinate of a point C such that B is the midpoint of AC.

c) Find the coordinate of a point X between A and B such that the distance from X to B is three times the distance from A to X.

d) Find the coordinate of a point Y *not* between A and B such that the distance from Y to B is three times the distance from Y to A.

5. The diagrams below present multiplication and division facts. Explain.

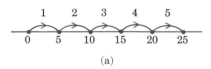

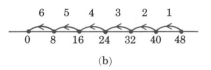

(a)   (b)

6. For the rational number line below, give the coordinates of C and D if they trisect AB, and the coordinates of A and B are, respectively,

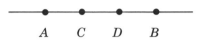

A   C   D   B

a) 0 and 1   b) 2 and $\frac{5}{2}$ c) $\frac{1}{3}$ and $\frac{1}{2}$

7. Work the problems suggested by figures (a) through (d).

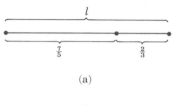

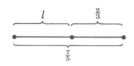

(a)   (b)

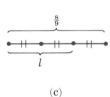

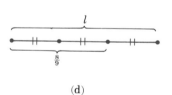

(c)   (d)

8. The diagram below illustrates the fact that algebraic equations can be given geometric interpretations. Consider the problem of determining two numbers x and y such that

$x + y = 13$ and $x - y = 3$.

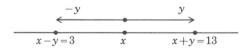

We see that x is the *midpoint* of the segment with endpoints 3 and 13. Determine x and y "geometrically" and use the suggested technique to solve the systems of equations below. Sketch a diagram for each problem.

a) $x + y = 20$ b) $x + y = -18$ c) $x + y = 7$
   $x - y = 4$ $x - y = 12$ $x - y = 30$

d) $2x + y = 15$ e) $x + 3y = 14$ f) $2x + 3y = 40$
   $2x - y = 5$ $x - 3y = -10$ $2x - 3y = 4$

9. The graph of the relation $|x - 3| \leq 2$ on the rational number line consists of all rational points not farther than 2 units from the point 3.

a) What are the endpoints of this "segment"?

b) What is the midpoint of this "segment"?

10. The two numbers that satisfy the equation $|x - 3| = 4$ can be visualized as endpoints of a segment with midpoint 3. One endpoint is 4 units to the right of 3; the other is 4 units to the left. Use this method of reasoning and determine the two numbers which satisfy each equation below.

a) $|x - 2| = 5$ b) $|x - 8| = 2$ c) $|x - 11| = 9$

d) $|x - (-3)| = 5$ e) $|x - (-6)| = 10$ f) $|x + 3| = 6$

Implications for teaching. The teacher has many choices of "style" in introducing the integers. We have indicated the possibility of leaning heavily on the real world. With this approach the student learns techniques of computation by thinking about the physical interpretation of the symbols. There is much to be said for the $w(n)$, $l(n)$ notation, for this emphasizes strongly that one is dealing with something real. With elementary students one should not introduce the symbol *, but rather, from the beginning, write

$w(3) + l(7)$,

and read $+$ as "and." The student should reason as indicated below.

$w(11) + l(3) + l(11) = l(3)$.

(Winning 11 and losing 11 cancel each other . . .)

$w(3) - l(7) = w(10)$.

(I have lost 7 and need to win it all back and 3 more . . .)

$3 \cdot l(5) = l(15)$.

(If I lose 5 three times in a row, then . . .)

Certainly students should be introduced to number lines. When this is done, there is no need to write the raised plus signs. Students will just think of the symbols $-1, -2, \ldots$ as names for "new" points on the "other" side of zero.

The "old" points keep their old names.

The diagram above suggests that

$-3 + 4$ *should be* 1.

The fact, which we have stressed for you, that in all these applications there are two functions from the set W into some large set should not be stressed for children. They unconsciously work with such functions when they think of the number symbols as names for the points.

SUMMARY

When one introduces the integers in elementary school, it is customary to base the introduction on some physical model. All models have much in common. Each nonzero whole number n is identified with two concepts, one denoted by ^+n, the other by ^-n. The concepts $^+0$ and $^-0$ are indistinguishable, and are often denoted by 0. An associative and commutative binary operation $+$ is defined such that, for all $n \in W$,

$^+n + {}^-n = 0.$

A related subtraction operation is defined in terms of addition by agreeing to denote the solution of $a + x = b$ by $b - a$. This yields in each model a simple physical interpretation of subtraction. Multiplication appears naturally as repeated addition, and is defined as a binary operation involving whole numbers and elements of the new system.

$3 \cdot {}^+4 = {}^+4 + {}^+4 + {}^+4 = {}^+12; \qquad 2 \cdot {}^-5 = {}^-5 + {}^-5 = {}^-10.$

For a time we work with the large set containing all the whole numbers and the new symbols ^+n and ^-n. At this stage things are conceptually simple. Each operation has an obvious physical interpretation. In order to simplify the structure of the system we disregard physical interpretations and observe that so far as addition is concerned we can either identify each whole number n with ^+n or with ^-n. In technical terminology, the functions $^+$ and $^-$ which map each whole number n upon ^+n and ^-n, respectively, are isomorphisms (1–1 homomorphisms) relative to addition. It is customary to drop the symbols ^+n, replacing them by n. When we make this change we also replace ^-n by $-n$.

Note that two uses are made of the sign + and three of the sign −. Some confusion is created by overworking these symbols. In the vector example:

In ⁻4, the raised symbol ⁻ indicates that the vector is directed to the left.

In − ⁻4, the centered symbol − indicates that one is to consider a vector directed oppositely to ⁻4 and of the same length.

In ⁺3 − (− ⁻4), the symbol − preceding the parentheses denotes the binary operation subtraction.

The final agreement that in our abstract system $(-a) \cdot (-b)$ shall be the whole number $a \cdot b$ is dictated by structural reasons, and by our desire to have a workable distributive law. Of course it is possible to motivate this definition by constructing a separate physical model, and some teachers prefer to do so.

Absolute value is best treated geometrically by viewing $|a - b|$ as the distance separating two points on a number line.

8 basic principles for integers and rationals

8-1 introduction

We saw in Chapters 6 and 7 how the systems of (positive) rationals and of integers are abstracted from the real world. This was the view from the first three stages of the abstraction process. We now move up one level and analyze the structure of those systems on the basis of the fundamental principles they exhibit (or are assumed to exhibit). In this analysis we return to the spirit of Chapter 5 and The New Math. We shall again be using such terms as associativity, distributivity, commutativity, and cancellation.

Here are a few (carelessly done) examples to illustrate how we shall justify the computational procedures for integers and rationals. Explain each example.

Example 1 $\frac{1}{2} \cdot \frac{1}{3} = \frac{1}{6}$ because

$$6 \cdot \frac{1}{2} \cdot \frac{1}{3} = 3 \cdot 2 \cdot \frac{1}{2} \cdot \frac{1}{3} = 3 \cdot 1 \cdot \frac{1}{3} = 3 \cdot \frac{1}{3} = 1 = 6 \cdot \frac{1}{6}$$

Therefore $\cancel{6} \cdot \frac{1}{2} \cdot \frac{1}{3} = \cancel{6} \cdot \frac{1}{6}$.

Example 2 $2 \cdot (-3) = -6$ because

$$2 \cdot [3 + (-3)] = 2 \cdot 0 = 0 = 6 + (-6).$$
$$\|$$
$$2 \cdot 3 + 2 \cdot (-3) = 6 + 2 \cdot (-3).$$

Therefore $\cancel{6} + (-6) = \cancel{6} + 2 \cdot (-3)$.

Example 3 $(-2) \cdot (-3) = 6$ because

$$[2 + (-2)] \cdot (-3) = 0 \cdot (-3) = 0 = 6 + (-6)$$
$$\|$$
$$2 \cdot (-3) + (-2) \cdot (-3) = (-6) + (-2) \cdot (-3)$$

Therefore $6 + (-\cancel{6}) = (-2) \cdot (-3) + (-\cancel{6})$.

Example 4 $\dfrac{\frac{1}{2}}{\frac{1}{3}} = \dfrac{1}{2} \cdot \dfrac{3}{1}$ because

$$\frac{1}{3} \cdot \frac{\frac{1}{2}}{\frac{1}{3}} = \frac{1}{2} = 1 \cdot \frac{1}{2} = \frac{1}{3} \cdot \frac{3}{1} \cdot \frac{1}{2}$$

Therefore $\cancel{\dfrac{1}{3}} \cdot \dfrac{\frac{1}{2}}{\frac{1}{3}} = \cancel{\dfrac{1}{3}} \cdot \dfrac{1}{2} \cdot \dfrac{3}{1}$.

Our intention in this chapter is to establish a sound mathematical footing for manipulations such as these. We shall systematically exhibit and justify all the "rules for minus signs and fractions" once we have erected a satisfactory mathematical framework. But the framework *must* come first.

Consequently you may find the point of view in this chapter somewhat more abstract than what you are used to. It has been our intention to keep the exposition at a rather sparse and rigorous level so as to reveal clearly the simple structure of the systems of integers and rationals which underlies the rules for computation. In working through this chapter you will have to make a special effort to learn the *precise* statements of the definitions and theorems. They are few in number and clearly displayed, but they do need to be learned *carefully*.

If you survive this regimen you will be doubly rewarded. First, you will gain a new appreciation of the power of a few simple and natural assumptions. Second, if you work very hard at understanding Sections 8–3 through 8–6 (on the integers) you will find Sections 8–7 through 8–12 (on the rationals) much less difficult. You will be helped greatly by your knowledge of the integers and the remarkably close analogy between the development of the rationals from the integers and the development of the integers from the whole numbers.

Three more remarks need to be made before we describe the system of integers.

1. *Structural reasons* dictate that the system of integers be discussed before any mention is made of rationals. In school, of course (recall Chapters 6 and 7), the child meets positive fractions long before he meets negative integers.

2. Since we'll be talking about three different number systems—W (the whole numbers, I (the integers), and Q (the rationals)—we'll follow these notational conventions to help you keep them straight

System	Letters denoting elements in that system
W	k, m, n, p (middle of alphabet)
I	a, b, c, d, e (beginning of alphabet)
Q	r, s, t, u, v, w (end of alphabet)

The third remark, about equations, deserves amplification.

8–2 equations and their solutions

An example: Let S denote the set of all the states in the United States. Consider the following "open sentences."

1. The capital of _____ is Albany.

2. _____ borders on the Pacific Ocean.

3. The legal voting age in _____ is thirteen.

When confronted by problems such as these on an examination, one chooses from S those elements which, when inserted into the blank, make the statement true. The subset of S consisting of all elements which make the statement true is called the *solution set* of the open sentence. For example:

1. The solution set is {New York}. This is an example of a *unique solution*: Precisely *one* element of S makes the statement true.

2. The solution set is {California, Oregon, Washington, Alaska, Hawaii}. This is an example of *distinct* (nonunique) *solutions*: Several different elements of S make the statement true.

3. The solution set is $\varnothing$. This is an example of nonexistence of a solution: No element of S makes the statement true.

Another example: Let W denote, as usual, the set of whole numbers. Consider the following open sentences.

1. $2 + $ _____ $= 7.$ 2. _____ is even.

3. _____ $< 4.$ 4. _____ $- 5 = 3.$

5. $5 + $ _____ $= 2.$ 6. _____$^2 = 6.$

The solution sets are:

1. {5} (unique)   2. {0, 2, 4, 6, . . .} (distinct)

3. {0, 1, 2, 3} (distinct)   4. {8} (unique)

5. $\varnothing$ (nonexistent)   6. $\varnothing$ (nonexistent)

When we look at the open sentences 4 and 6, we see that the use of _____ to indicate a blank leads to some rather strange typographical configurations. A box, $\square$, would make things neater:

4. $\square - 5 = 3.$ 6. $\square^2 = 6.$

So would an x:

4. $x - 5 = 3.$ 6. $x^2 = 6.$

The use of an x to indicate the blank in an open sentence has become traditional in mathematics. The letter x simply means "blank." It has no intrinsic superiority over any other symbol: $\square, \not{5} , \odot$.

The open sentences 1, 4, 5, 6 are examples of *equations*. An equation is an open sentence the verb of which is "equals." Open sentence number 3 is called an *inequality.* (Generally, any open sentence involving $<$, $>$, $\leq$, or $\geq$, is called an inequality.) Open sentence number 2 has no special name.

One further convention: It has become traditional to say "$x = 5$ is the solution to the equation $2 + x = 7$" rather than to say "$\{5\}$ is the solution set to the equation $2 + x = 7$." Strictly speaking, this is a perverse use of the symbol, $=$, because x and 5 are not labels for the same element of W; x means "blank."

EXERCISES 8–1

1. Let S denote the set of all states in the United States. For each of the following open sentences exhibit the solution set (a subset of S) and accompany it with the appropriate word: "unique," "distinct," or "nonexistent."

   a) _____ has a boundary on Lake Superior.

   b) _____ has a boundary on Lake Huron.

   c) _____ has a boundary on Hudson Bay.

   d) x has a common border with Maine.

   e) x has a common border with Florida.

   f) x has borders in common with Washington and Montana.

2. Determine the solution sets (subsets of W) of the following open sentences. Label with the word "unique," "distinct," "nonexistent." In cases in which the solution is unique, denote it using the symbol, $=$, as well as in set notation.

   a) $3x - 4 = 11$ b) $x^2 - 2x = 0$ c) $5 + x = 2$ d) $2x = 3$

   e) $2x < 3$ f) $x + 1 = x + 2$ g) $x^2 - 7x + 10 < 0$

3. A statement is a declarative sentence which is either true or false, not neither and not both. An open sentence can be thought of as a sort of machine. Into one end of the machine go elements of a set S; out of the other end come statements (about S).

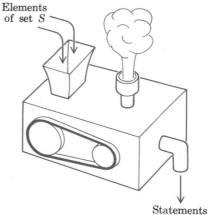

Elements of set S

The statements, in turn, fall into either a basket marked "true" or a basket marked "false." Those elements of S which turn into statements that end up in the basket marked "true" constitute the solution set of the open sentence. Look for *functions* in this situation. Discuss domains, ranges, composition.

Statements

8–3   the system of integers

For many purposes the system of whole numbers, W, is inadequate. Its most obvious failing is that a very simple equation involving only whole numbers, such as

$$5 + x = 2,$$

has no solution in W. In fact, the equation

$$n + x = m$$

has a solution in W if and only if $n \leq m$ (by the very definition of $\leq$). We propose to remedy this defect.

In rough outline, we shall assume the existence of a set I just enough larger than W so that every equation of the form

$$n + x = m, \qquad n, m \in W,$$

has a solution in I. We shall receive as a (perhaps surprising) bonus the theorem that every equation of the form

$$b + x = a, \qquad b, a \in I,$$

also has a (unique) solution in I. This result will permit us to define negatives and differences and to establish all the usual rules for manipulating minus signs.

The assumptions about the system of integers. We assume the existence of a set $I \supset W$ and binary operations $+$ and $\cdot$ on I which satisfy the following conditions:

1) Assoc $+$	2) Assoc $\cdot$
3) Comm $+$	4) Comm $\cdot$
5) Add 0	6) Mult 1
7) Cancel $+$	8) Cancel $\cdot$

9)   Dist

[*Note:* Assumptions 1 through 9 are assumed to hold in I, not just in W.]

10) Every equation of form $n + x = m$ $(n, m \in W)$ has a solution in I.

11) Every element of I is the solution to an equation of form $n + x = m$ $(n, m \in W)$.

The elements of I are called *integers*.

▶ *Aside*

1.   Conditions 1 through 9 are modest demands. We are asking only that the operations $+$ and $\cdot$ behave as well in I as they do in W. Condition 10 says

that I is big enough to remedy the defect of W. Condition 11 says that I is *just* big enough. All the elements of I pay their way; there are no free loaders.

2. Strictly speaking, we should have called the binary operations on $I \oplus$ and $\odot$ and made two further assumptions,

12) $m \oplus n = m + n, \ \forall m, n \in W$

13) $m \odot n = m \cdot n, \ \forall m, n \in W,$

because, strictly speaking, $+$ and $\cdot$ already stand for binary operations on W, and so we should use different symbols to denote the binary operations on the larger set I. Assumptions 12 and 13 tell us that these new binary operations, $\oplus$ and $\odot$, agree with the old ones, $+$ and $\cdot$, whenever the old ones make sense; i.e., whenever the pair being operated on is a pair of whole numbers.

We get the same effect, and keep the notation neater and the list of assumptions shorter, by simply omitting the circles around $+$ and $\cdot$. We *know* that, by the strict definition of binary operation, a binary operation on a set, such as I, cannot be identical to a binary operation on a proper subset, such as W. But we use the same symbol for both to suggest that the two binary operations are to have the same effect on all pairs of elements of W. Assumptions 12 and 13 are implicit, then, in our use of notation.

3. The principles based on our use of the symbol, $=$, continue to hold in I; viz., substitution, reflexivity, symmetry, transitivity. ◀

Two immediate and extremely important consequences of these assumptions are

i) $0 \cdot a = 0, \qquad \forall a \in I,$

ii) $a \neq 0, b \neq 0 \Rightarrow ab \neq 0 \qquad\qquad \forall a, b \in I.$
(or $ab = 0 \Rightarrow a = 0$ or $b = 0$)

We shall not prove these, but refer you instead to pages 160–161 of Chapter 5. There we took great pains to show that these results (for W) were derivable from only the nine basic laws (for W). But now we've assumed that those same nine laws hold in I, so that these results *must* also be true in I!

We would next like to derive the usual "rules for minus signs." To do so we first need to observe some immediate consequences of our assumptions and explain some notation.

Theorem   There exists a unique solution (in I) to the equation

$b + x = 0,$

for every $b \in I$ (not just for every $b \in W$, which is a corollary to Assumption 10).

Proof

Existence: $b \in I \overset{(11)}{\Longrightarrow} b$ is a solution to an equation of form $n + x = m$ $(n, m \in W)$; that is, $n + b = m$. Moreover, we know that there is a solution in I to the equation $m + x = 0$, since $m, 0 \in W$. Call it c; that is, $m + c = 0$. Thus

$$n + b = m \Longrightarrow n + b + c = m + c = 0$$
$$\Longrightarrow b + (n + c) = 0 \text{ and thus } n + c \text{ is a solution to } b + x = 0.$$

Uniqueness: Suppose that d, e both denote solutions to $b + x = 0$. Then $b + d = 0 = b + e$ so, by Cancel $+$, $d = e$. Thus d, e both had to denote a single solution.

It is now legitimate to make the following definition.

Definition   The unique solution (in I) to

$$a + x = 0, \qquad a \in I,$$

will be denoted by $-a$ and will be called *the negative of a*, or *the additive inverse of a*, or *minus a*. Thus, symbolically, $\forall a \in I$,

i) $a + (-a) = 0$,

ii) if $a + b = 0$, then $b = -a$.

If you prefer to memorize words rather than symbols, memorize this:

"Minus a is that integer which when added to a gives zero."

Examples   (a) -2 is that integer which when added to 2 gives 0; (b) $-(3 + 6)$ is that integer which when added to $3 + 6$ gives 0; (c) $-(-2)$ is that integer which when added to -2 gives 0.

Theorem   There exists a unique solution (in I) to the equation

$$b + x = a$$

for every $a, b \in I$; namely, $a + (-b)$.

Proof

Existence: $b + [a + (-b)] = b + [(-b) + a] = [b + (-b)] + a = 0 + a = a$.

Uniqueness: Suppose that d, e both denote solutions to $b + x = a$. Then $b + d = a = b + e$; so, by Cancel $+$, $d = e$.

▶ *Aside.* This is the theorem that you were promised on page 248.

Observe that our first theorem is but a special case of this one. The proof of this one, however, and even the notation used in its statement, required the knowledge of the first theorem. Thus the first theorem cannot simply be forgotten now that a more general theorem has been proved. ◀

We now make another definition (notational convention).

Definition

$a - b = a + (-b)$.

We read $a - b$ as "a minus b." The binary operation on I sending (a, b) to $a - b$ is called the *subtraction* operation.

"a minus b means a plus the negative of b."

Examples $5 - 3 = 5 + (-3)$
$0 - 2 = 0 + (-2)$
$(9 + 6) - (2 + 4) = (9 + 6) + [-(2 + 4)]$

Our previous theorem could thus be restated:

i) $b + (a - b) = a$;

ii) if $b + c = a$, then $c = a - b$.

EXERCISES 8–2

1. Assumption 11 about I would be hopelessly optimistic were it not true that every element of W is the solution to an equation of the form $n + x = m$ $(n, m \in W)$.

   a) Find whole numbers n and m such that 5 is the solution to $n + x = m$.

   b) If $k \in W$, find whole numbers n, m such that k is the solution to $n + x = m$.

   c) Repeat part (b), finding a different pair of values for m, n.

2. Given that S is a proper subset of T, explain why, in the strict sense of the word, no binary operation on S can be a binary operation on T.

3. Write the additive inverse for each of the following:

   a) 6   b) $2 + 7$ c) -3 d) $a + 5$ e) $-4a$ f) $-(8 + a)$

4. The integers which are not whole numbers are called the negative integers. If a is an integer, is $-a$ necessarily a negative integer? What about $-(-a)$?

5. Compute (a) through (f) as in the example.

   Example $14 + (-8) = (6 + 8) + (-8)$ Elem + Fact
   $= 6 + [8 + (-8)]$ Assoc +
   $= 6 + 0$ Defn of -8
   $= 6$ Add 0

a) $17 + (-3)$ b) $26 + [(-4) + (-8)]$
c) $[(-6) + 35] + (-10)$ d) $8 + (-18)$
e) $18 + [(-12) + (-6)]$ f) $-8 + 20$

6. Using the definition of "minus a," prove the following.
   a) $(-a) + a = 0$ for any $a \in I$
   b) $(-2) + [-(-2)] = 0$
   c) $(-2) + 2 = 0$
   d) $-(-2) = 2$ [*Hint:* Use (b) and (c).]
   e) $-[-(-2)] = -2$ [*Hint:* Don't work too hard.]
   f) $-(-a) = a$ for any *integer* a.
   g) $-(3 + 6) = (-3) + (-6)$ [*Hint:*   Compute $(3 + 6) + [-(3 + 6)]$ and $(3 + 6) + [(-3) + (-6)]$ and compare.]
   h) $-(a + b) = (-a) + (-b)$ for any *integers* a, b.
   i) $-0 = 0$

7. Compute (a) through (n), using the definition of subtraction and the results of Exercise 6, as in the example.

   Example $20 - (a - 6)$
                  $= 20 + [-(a - 6)]$ Defn subtr
                  $= 20 + \{-[a + (-6)]\}$ Defn subtr
                  $= 20 + \{(-a) + [-(-6)]\}$ Ex. 6(h)
                  $= 20 + [(-a) + 6]$ Ex. 6(f)
                  $= 20 + [6 + (-a)]$ Comm +
                  $= (20 + 6) + (-a)$ Assoc +
                  $= 26 + (-a)$ Addn algorithm in W
                  $= 26 - a$ Defn subtr

   a) $7 - (-4)$ b) $10 - 15$
   c) $(12 - 6) - 3$ d) $(9 + 18) - (a + 3)$
   e) $-7 - 13$ f) $-8 + 12$
   g) $16 - 45$ h) $(a - 6) + (b - 4)$
   i) $20 - (4 - a)$ j) $(a + 12) - (-2)$
   k) $6 - [14 - (3 - 7)]$ l) $6 - (a - 2)$
   m) $(a + 2) - [(2 - a) + (6 - b)]$ n) $-5 + (-21)$

8. Prove, using the definition of subtraction and Exercise 6(i).
   a) $0 - a = -a$
   b) $0 - 0 = 0$
   c) $a - 0 = a$

9. Suppose that, in place of our Assumption 7, "Cancel +," we had assumed "Negatives exist"; i.e., every element a of I has an additive inverse, denoted by $-a$.

a) Prove that every element a of I has *just one* additive inverse. [*Hint:* You can't use "Cancel +." Suppose that d and e are both additive inverses of a. Consider $d + a + e$. Use Assoc + and Add 0.]

b) Prove "Cancel +" as a theorem.

c) Prove that there is a solution to any equation of the form

$$a + x = b, \qquad a, b \in I.$$

[*Hint:* Take a good guess and verify.]
[*Note.* Our first proof of this result (page 250) relied, ultimately, on Assumption 11. We now know that if "negatives exist," then we don't need Assumption 11 to get it. This will be seen to be important later on when we discuss Q and don't have Assumption 11.]

10. Prove the following, using the definition of "a minus b."

a) $5 - 3$ is the unique solution to

$$x + 3 = 5.$$

[*Hint:* Write $5 - 3$ as $5 + (-3)$, "plug it in," and reassociate terms.]

b) $5 - 3$ is the unique solution to

$$3 + x = 5.$$

c) $2 - 7$ is the unique solution to both

$$x + 7 = 2 \qquad \text{and} \qquad 7 + x = 2.$$

d) $a - b$ is the unique solution to both

$$x + b = a \qquad \text{and} \qquad b + x = a.$$

(The equations $x + b = a$ and $b + x = a$ are said to be *equivalent equations* because they have the same solution set.)

11. (Discussion problem) We defined $a - b$ to equal $a + (-b)$ for any integers a and b, in particular for any whole numbers. But when a and b are whole numbers and $b < a$, the symbol $a - b$ already has a meaning (cf. Chapter 5, page 174); it denotes the solution in W to the equation $b + x = a$. Does our new definition leave us in the embarrassing position of having a single symbol, $a - b$, denote two different elements of I?

These two different views of $a - b$ are exemplified in two different approaches to subtraction. Consider the problem of finding 86 minus 59.

Viewpoint 1: Finding the (unique) solution in W to the equation $59 + x = 86$. "What must I add to 59 to get 86?" One needn't know of the existence of the "negative integers" to ask and answer this question: What is more, this interpretation is a natural one in real-life situations. "I have 59 pennies. How many more must I save in order to buy this 86¢ toy?"

Viewpoint 2: Finding the unique solution in I to the equation $59 + x = 86$. "I know that the solution is expressible as $86 + (-59)$; the problem is to simplify this expression." To say this requires a knowledge of the negative integers. Also the connection to real-life situations is not very clear. This viewpoint does, however, have the virtue of being conceptually neater. You add -59 to both sides of the equation $59 + x = 86$ to isolate x. You *know* that there is a solution.

Must the two viewpoints lead to the same answer (in this specific problem)? Does the person with Viewpoint 2 get by with any less work in obtaining a simplified answer when he computes

$$86 + (-59) = (27 + 59) + (-59)$$
$$= 27 + [59 + (-59)] = 27 + 0 = 27?$$

How would the person with Viewpoint 1 react to the problem: find 32 minus 75? How would the person with Viewpoint 2 react to this same problem?

12. Check the binary operation (on I), subtraction, for associativity, commutativity, existence of neutral element, cancellation laws, and distributivity with respect to multiplication.

8–3a   the system of integers: another point of view

We present here an alternate description of the system of integers which has the advantage of concreteness. One knows what the integers "look like" from the very beginning. (Furthermore this description is the one widely used in teaching the integers to school children.) It has the disadvantage of having no neat analogue for the rational numbers.

The assumptions about the system of integers. We assume the existence of a set $I \supset W$, denoted by

$$I = \{\ldots\ ^-3,\ ^-2,\ ^-1, 0, 1, 2, 3, \ldots\},$$

and binary operations $+$ and $\cdot$ on I which satisfy

1) Assoc $+$	2) Assoc $\cdot$
3) Comm $+$	4) Comm $\cdot$
5) Add 0	6) Mult 1
7) $n + {}^-n = 0, \forall n \in N$	8) Cancel $\cdot$

9) Dist

[*Note:* (1) through (9) are assumed to hold in I, not just in W; for example, we are assuming

$$^-3 + (6 + \,^-2) = (^-3 + 6) + \,^-2, \qquad 1 \cdot (^-7) = \,^-7,$$
$$^-4 \cdot (5 + \,^-1) = \,^-4 \cdot 5 + \,^-4 \cdot \,^-1.]$$

An important consequence of these assumptions is the following.

Theorem   Every element of I has a unique additive inverse. Specifically,

1. $n + \,^-n = 0 \ (n \in N)$ (the unique additive inverse of n is ^-n)
2. $^-n + n = 0 \ (n \in N)$ (the unique additive inverse of ^-n is n)
3. $0 + 0 = 0$ (the unique additive inverse of 0 is 0)

Proof   The three equations are immediate consequences of our assumptions. Thus every element of I has at least one additive inverse. Only the uniqueness requires further explanation.

1. Suppose that $n \in N$. Could there be an element $a \in I$, $a \neq \,^-n$, such that $n + a = 0$? Certainly such an a could not belong to $\{1, 2, 3, \ldots\}$ for $n + m = 0$ $(n, m \in N)$ would contradict our Assumption 16 about W: $n \neq 0$, $m \neq 0 \Rightarrow$ $n + m \neq 0$. (Recall Chapter 5, page 186.) Also a could not be equal to 0, for $n + 0 = n \neq 0$. Could $a = \,^-m$ where $m \neq n$? No, for if $n + \,^-m = 0$, then

$$m = 0 + m = (n + \,^-m) + m = n + (^-m + m) = n + 0 = n.$$

Thus ^-n is the unique additive inverse of n.

2. Suppose again that $n \in N$. Could there be an element $a \in I$, $a \neq n$, such that $^-n + a = 0$? Certainly such an a could not belong to $\{\ldots\,^-3, \,^-2, \,^-1\}$, for if $^-n + \,^-m = 0$, then

$$m + n = (m + n) + 0 - (m + n) + (^-n + \,^-m) = \cdots = 0,$$

contradicting Assumption 16 about W. Also a could not $= 0$, for if $^-n + 0 = 0$ then

$$n = n + 0 = n + (^-n + 0) = (n + \,^-n) + 0 = 0 + 0 = 0.$$

Finally, could $a = m$, where $m \in N$, $m \neq n$? No, for if $^-n + m = 0$, then

$$n = n + 0 = n + (^-n + m) = (n + \,^-n) + m = 0 + m = m.$$

3. Could $0 + a = 0$ for $a \neq 0$? Certainly not, since $a = 0 + a$.   Q.E.D.

This theorem allows us to define the negative of any element in I.

Definition   For any $a \in I$, the unique additive inverse of a will be called the *negative of* a and written $-a$. (In the language of equations, $-a$ denotes the unique solution to the equation $a + x = 0$; that is, $a + (-a) = 0$ and $a + b = 0 \Rightarrow b = -a$.) For example,

$$-6 = {}^-6, \qquad -{}^-3 = 3, \qquad -0 = 0.$$

More generally,

1. $-n = {}^-n, \qquad \forall n \in N$
2. $-{}^-n = n, \qquad \forall n \in N$
3. $-0 = 0$

The first of these equations allows us to replace all "raised minus signs" by "ordinary minus signs." Thus

I becomes $\{\ldots -3, -2, -1, 0, 1, 2, 3, \ldots\}$.
Assumption (7) becomes $n + (-n) = 0, \qquad \forall n \in N$,
The second equation above becomes $-(-n) = n, \qquad \forall n \in N$.
Now we define *subtraction* by

$$a - b = a + (-b), \qquad \forall a, b \in I.$$

For example,

$6 - 4 = 6 + (-4)$,
$4 - 6 = 4 + (-6)$,
$-2 - 3 = -2 + (-3)$,
$5 - (-3) = 5 + [-(-3)] = 5 + 3$,
$-1 - (-6) = -1 + [-(-6)] = -1 + 6$.

[*Note:* Subtraction is a binary operation on I because each $b \in I$ has a unique inverse, $-b$, and addition is a binary operation on I. Hence $a + (-b)$ is well defined, $\forall a, b \in I$. Subtraction is not a binary operation on W. That is what led us to consider the larger system I in the first place.]

Before we can move on to establish the rules for minus signs (Section 8–4), we need to prove a few easy but important results about I.

Theorem   (Cancel $+$) $a + b = a + c \Rightarrow b = c$.

Proof

$a + b = a + c$
$\qquad \Rightarrow -a + (a + b) = -a + (a + c)$
$\qquad \Rightarrow (-a + a) + b = (-a + a) + c$
$\qquad \Rightarrow 0 + b = 0 + c$
$\qquad \Rightarrow b = c$

Having proved this theorem, we now know that *all* the nine basic laws for W are also true of I. Hence their familiar consequences (Chapter 5, pages 160–161) also remain true in I. That is,

Theorem $0 \cdot a = 0, \qquad \forall a \in I$

Theorem $a \neq 0, b \neq 0 \Rightarrow ab \neq 0, \qquad \forall a, b \in I$
$(ab = 0 \Rightarrow a = 0 \text{ or } b = 0)$

EXERCISES 8–3

1. Do exercises of Section 8–3 numbered 3, 4, 5, 6, 7, 8, 10, 11, 12.
2. Prove the following statements:

   a) Every equation of the form $a + x = b$ $(a, b \in I)$ has a unique solution in I.

   b) Every element of I is the solution to some equation of the form

   $n + x = m$ $(n, m \in W)$.

   c) Conclude that the assumptions of Section 8–3a imply those of Section 8–3. (The theorem on page 249 of Section 8–3 shows that, conversely, the assumptions of Section 8–3 imply those of Section 8–3a. Thus you get the same results no matter which set of assumptions you choose to work with.)

8–4   rules for minus signs

The small amount of necessary theoretical work on I has now been completed. The rest is easy. We gather together in a single theorem all the usual "rules for minus signs." You should realize that all these rules are inevitable consequences of the few natural assumptions listed on page 248 (or on page 254 if you read Section 8–3a). They are forced on us. They are not conventions, or lucky accidents, or the result of the way trains run back and forth on tracks while a clock ticks.

Omnibus Theorem (*Rules for Minus Signs*)*

1. $-(-a) = a$
2. $-(a + b) = (-a) + (-b)$
3. $b - a = -(a - b)$
4. $-a = (-1) \cdot a$
5. $a(-b) = -(ab) = (-a)b$
6. $(-a)(-b) = ab$

---

* See Exercise 4, page 259, for more. Also see Aside 3.

▶ *Aside preceding proof*

1.   Although these rules are most often employed for $a, b \in W$, they are true for all $a, b \in I$, as the proofs show. Hence our choice of notation.

2.   The proofs rely primarily on just one thing: the definition of $-a$ as the unique solution to the equation $a + x = 0$ (or, if you prefer, the unique additive inverse of a).

3.   Which properties to list in an omnibus theorem of this sort is purely a matter of taste. Many people would like to see some of the properties of Exercise 4 (below) included. We have omitted them on the basis that they are all easy to prove using the omnibus theorem and the definition of subtraction. We have not been consistent, though.   Property 3 of the theorem certainly falls in this category. We chose to include it because, in a special case such as

$$3 - 7 = -(7 - 3),$$

it justifies the old familiar chant: "To subtract a larger (whole) number from a smaller (whole) number, subtract the smaller from the larger and affix a minus sign." (See also Exercise 8.)

Other people would prefer a much shorter list of rules for minus signs. See, for example, Exercises 7 and 2(b), (c). ◀

Proofs

1. $-(-a)$ denotes the unique solution to $-a + x = 0$. But $-a + a = 0$.

2. $-(a + b)$ denotes the unique solution to $(a + b) + x = 0$. But
$(a + b) + [(-a) + (-b)] = \cdots = 0$.

3. $-(a - b) = -[a + (-b)] = (-a) + [-(-b)] = -a + b = b + (-a) = b - a$.

4. $-a$ denotes the unique solution to $a + x = 0$.
But $a + [(-1)a] = 1 \cdot a + (-1) \cdot a = [1 + (-1)] \cdot a = 0 \cdot a = 0$.

5. $a(-b) = a[(-1)b] = (-1)[ab] = -(ab)$;
$(-a)b = [(-1)a]b = (-1)[ab] = -(ab)$.

6. $(-a)(-b) = -[a(-b)] = -[-(ab)] = ab$.

EXERCISES 8–4

1. Prove each of the following by referring to the omnibus theorem.

  a) $-9 = -4 + (-5)$ b) $-7 = -4 - 3$

  c) $(-4)5 = -20$ d) $-(-6) = 6$

  e) $-10 = 2(-5)$ f) $6 = (-1)(-6)$

  g) $-[-(-1)] = -1$ h) $(-1)(-1) = 1$

i) $10 = -(-7 - 3)$ j) $9 - 12 = -3$

k) $186 - 235 = -49$ l) $-156 \div 12 = -13$

m) $-60 \div -12 = 5$ n) $96 \div -16 = -6$

2. a) Look back at examples 2 and 3, page 244.

   i) Observe that they are special cases of the omnibus theorem.

   ii) Give a reason for each step in the *ad hoc* proofs on page 244.

   b) Supply a reason for each step in this *ad hoc* proof that $(-1)(-1) = 1$.
   $$0 = 0 \cdot (-1) = [1 + (-1)] \cdot (-1) = 1 \cdot (-1) + (-1) \cdot (-1)$$
   $$\|\hspace{6.5cm}\|$$
   $$(-1) + 1 \hspace{4cm} (-1) + (-1)(-1)$$

   $$\Downarrow$$
   $$1 = (-1)(-1)$$

   c) Prove $(-1)(-1) = 1$, using properties 1 and 4 of the omnibus theorem.

3. Fill in intermediate steps and reasons for each of the proofs 1 through 6 on page 258.

4. Prove these other formulas involving minus signs. [Use the omnibus theorem and the definition of subtraction, $a - b = a + (-b)$.]

   a) $a - (b + c) = (a - b) - c$ b) $a - (b - c) = (a - b) + c$

   c) $a(b - c) = ab - ac$ d) $-a(b - c) = ac - ab$

   e) $(a - b) + (c - d) = (a + c) - (b + d)$

   f) $(a - b) \cdot (c - d) = (ac + bd) - (ad + bc)$

   g) Any other formula you might recall

   [Formulas (e) and (f) have special theoretical importance, as will be seen when we investigate Stage 5 of the abstraction process in Chapter 11.]

5. Compute the following in at least two ways:

   a) $2 \cdot (5 - 3)$ b) $(3 - 6) \cdot (10 - 2)$

   c) $(1 - 7) + (9 - 4)$ d) $6 - (3 - 5)$

   e) $3 - (5 - 7)$ f) $(8 - 3) - [6 - (7 - 4)]$

   g) $6 - (8 + 4)$ h) $20 - (10 + 5)$

   i) $-6 \cdot (14 - 4)$ j) $(9 - 6) + (1 - 2)$

6. Solve the following equations:

   a) $(a + 6) + x = 13 + a$ b) $4 + x = -5$

   c) $x + (a + b) = b - 10$ d) $x + (14 - a) = 27 - a$

   e) $x - 5 = 6$ f) $x - (a + 7) = 21$

   g) $3 - x = 10$ h) $6 - (4 + x) = 10$

   i) $2x = -6$ j) $(-2)x = 6$

7. Derive properties 1, 2, 3, 5, 6 of the omnibus theorem from the two properties

$$-a = (-1) \cdot a, \qquad (-1)(-1) = 1.$$

8. a) What chant does property 5 of the omnibus theorem bring to mind? Is this all that property 5 implies, or does it say more?

b) Answer the same question for property 6.

9. Write down one equation whose (integral) solution is

a) $5 - 7$,   b) $3 - (6 + a)$,   c) $5 - (-7)$.

8–5   labeling the integers

You may have noted that we still do not know that

$$I = \{\ldots -3, -2, -1, 0, 1, 2, 3, \ldots\}.$$

We shall now prove this. More precisely, we shall prove that every integer bears one and only one of the standard labels: $\ldots -3, -2, -1, 0, 1, 2, 3, \ldots$ The converse, that each of these labels is a label for an integer, is trivial.

Assumption 11 tells us that each element of I is the solution to at least one equation of the form

$$n + x = m, \qquad (n, m \in W).$$

But our fundamental existence-uniqueness theorem (page 250) tells us that a label for that (unique) solution is $m + (-n)$, and the definition of subtraction simplifies that to $m - n$. Thus every element of I has a label of the form $m - n$, where $m, n \in W$.

Our labeling problem, however, is still not solved. The primary difficulty remaining is that a single element of I has many labels. For example,

$$2 - 0, \qquad 3 - 1, \qquad 4 - 2, \qquad 5 - 3$$

are all labels for 2. Thus we are led to two questions. The first is: When are two labels equal? The answer is entirely predictable.

Lemma $m - n = k - p \Leftrightarrow m + p = k + n$

Proof

$\Rightarrow$: $m - n = k - p$
$\Rightarrow m + (-n) = k + (-p)$
$\Rightarrow m + (-n) + (n + p) = k + (-p) + (n + p)$
$\Rightarrow m + p = k + n$
$\Leftarrow$: $m + p = k + n$
$\Rightarrow m + p + [(-p) + (-n)] = k + n + [(-p) + (-n)]$
$\Rightarrow m + (-n) = k + (-p)$
$\Rightarrow m - n = k - p$

▶ *Aside.*   We're interested now in this theorem only when $k, m, n, p \in W$. Observe, however, that the theorem is true $\forall k, m, n, p \in I$. ◀

The second question is: among the infinitely many labels for each element of I, is there exactly one from the list: $\ldots -3, -2, -1, 0, 1, 2, 3, \ldots$? The answer is yes.

Theorem   Every element of I is denoted by precisely one of the labels: $\ldots -3, -2, -1, 0, 1, 2, 3, \ldots$

Proof   *At least one:* Take an arbitrary element of I. It is expressible as $m - n = m + (-n)$. Now (exactly) one of $m > n$, $m = n$, $m < n$ holds. If $m > n$, write $m = n + k$ $(k \in N)$. Thus $m + (-n) = n + k + (-n) = k$, which is on the list. If $m = n$, then $m + (-n) = n + (-n) = 0$, which again is on the list. If $m < n$, write $n = m + p$ $(p \in N)$. Thus

$$m + (-n) = m + [-(m + p)] = m + [(-m) + (-p)] = -p,$$

which is also on the list.

At most one (inequality of the symbols on our list). We already know that no two of $0, 1, 2, 3, \ldots$ are equal. All that remains to be shown is (i) $k \in N \Rightarrow -k \neq 0$, (ii) $k, l \in N \Rightarrow -k \neq l$, (iii) $k, l \in N$ and $k \neq l \Rightarrow -k \neq -l$. All these follow easily from the preceding lemma and Exercise 8, page 252.

   i) $-k = 0 - k$; $0 = 0 - 0$,
      $0 - k \neq 0 - 0$,   since $0 + 0 = 0 \neq k = 0 + k$.

  ii) $-k = 0 - k$; $l = l - 0$,
      $0 - k \neq l - 0$,   since $0 + 0 = 0 \neq l + k$.

 iii) $-k = 0 - k$; $-l = 0 - l$,
      $0 - k \neq 0 - l$,   since $0 + l = l \neq k = 0 + k$.   Q.E.D.

We can thus give an explicit description of I:

$$I = \{\ldots -3, -2, -1, 0, 1, 2, 3, \ldots\}.$$

This is of course the set of symbols we ordinarily visualize when we think about the integers.

▶ *Aside.*   We wanted one standard label for each integer so that we could explicitly describe I in set notation. There are other good reasons too. Putting a standard label on each integer makes comparing them very easy. Consider the difficulty in comparing the profit (income minus expenses) of Company A with Company B if profits were reported as: Company A: $6{,}103{,}850 - 5{,}879{,}283$; Company B: $3{,}875{,}200 - 3{,}518{,}129$. ◀

EXERCISES 8–5

1. Prove the following, first without using the lemma on page 260, then using it.
   a) $11 - 8 = 6 - 3$ [*Hint:* $11 = 3 + 8$, $6 = 3 + 3$.]
   b) $6 - 2 = 5 - 1$
   c) $7 - 14 = 2 - 9$ [*Hint:* Use Rule 2 for minus signs.]
   d) $1 - 6 = 7 - 2$
   e) $-6 - 3 = -7 - 2$ f) $-3 - 8 = -9 - 2$
   g) $3 - (-4) = 5 - (-2)$ h) $10 - (-4) = 8 - (-6)$

2. Prove that for every whole number k, $-3 = k - (k + 3)$.   Does this remain true if k is any integer?

3. The proof of the theorem on page 261 may have seemed difficult. If so, that was because we proved a *general* result. In any *specific* case, it is easy to discover and prove which of ... -3, -2, -1, 0, 1, 2, 3, ... equals the difference between two given whole numbers. For example,

$$
\begin{aligned}
7 - 10 &= 7 + (-10)   &&\text{Defn subtr} \\
       &= 7 + [-(7 + 3)]   &&\text{Elem + Fact} \\
       &= 7 + [(-7) + (-3)]   &&\text{Rule 2 for } - \\
       &= [7 + (-7)] + (-3)   &&\text{Assoc } + \\
       &= 0 + (-3)   &&\text{Defn of } -7 \\
       &= -3   &&\text{Add 0}
\end{aligned}
$$

Perform an analysis similar to the above on each of the following.
   a) $3 - 8$ b) $4 - 11$ c) $10 - 4$
   d) $15 - 9$ e) $26 - 13$ f) $35 - 20$
   g) $18 - 35$ h) $19 - 47$ i) $0 - 17$
   j) $0 - 3$ k) $18 - 0$ l) $0 - 0$

4. Solve the equations
   a) $7 + x = 5$ b) $4 + x = 11$ c) $x + 7 = 3$
   d) $x + 6 = 5$ e) $x + 3 = 21$ f) $5 + x + 3 = 6$
   g) $8 + x = 0$

5. Prove that each of ... -3, -2, -1, 0, 1, 2, 3, ... denotes an integer. If you are not sure what must be proved, look back to page 248.

6. Consider this alternative proof of "at most one" which avoids the lemma:

   i) $k \in N$ and $-k = 0 \Rightarrow k + (-k) = k + 0 \Rightarrow 0 = k$ contradicting what?

   ii) $k, l \in N$ and $-k = l \Rightarrow k + (-k) = k + l \Rightarrow 0 = k + l$ contradicting what?

   iii) $k, l \in N$ and $k \neq l$ and $-k = -l \Rightarrow k + l + (-k) = k + l + (-l) \Rightarrow l = k$ contradicting what?

8–6   order in *I*

We need to establish one simple lemma before we can derive the familiar order properties of *I*.

Lemma   For any $a \in I$, exactly one of the following conditions holds:

$$a = 0, \qquad a \in N, \qquad -a \in N.$$

Proof $a \in I \Rightarrow$ exactly one of $a = 0$, $a \in N$, $a = -k$, where $k \in N$ (by the theorem on page 261). But $a = -k \Leftrightarrow -a = -(-k)$ and $-(-k) = k$.

Definition a is less than b, written $a < b$, means $b - a \in N$.

Theorem   *(Trichotomy)* For all $a, b \in I$, exactly one of $a < b$, $a = b$, $a > b$ holds.

Proof

$a < b \Leftrightarrow b - a \in N$,

$a = b \Leftrightarrow b - a = 0$,

$a > b \Leftrightarrow a - b = -(b - a) \in N$.

Now apply the lemma to the integer $b - a$.

Theorem   *(Transitivity)* For all $a, b, c \in I$, $a < b$ and $b < c \Rightarrow a < c$.

Proof $a < b$ and $b < c \Rightarrow b - a$ and $c - b \in N \Rightarrow$ (by fact 16 about W) $(c - b) + (b - a) \in N \Rightarrow c - a \in N \Rightarrow a < c$.

Theorem   *(Monotony)*

1. $a < b \Rightarrow a + c < b + c$
2. $a < b$ and $c > 0 \Rightarrow ac < bc$
3. $a < b$ and $c < 0 \Rightarrow ac > bc$

Proof

1. $a + c < b + c \Leftrightarrow (b + c) - (a + c) \in N$; but $(b + c) - (a + c) = b - a$ and $b - a \in N \Leftrightarrow a < b$
2. $a < b \Rightarrow b - a \in N$.   Also $c \in N$.   Thus $(b - a) \cdot c \in N$ by a theorem about W (page 160).   That is, $bc - ac \in N$ which $\Rightarrow ac < bc$.
3. $a < b \Rightarrow b - a \in N$. $c < 0 \Rightarrow -c > 0 \Rightarrow -c \in N$.   Therefore $-c(b - a) \in N$.   Now $-c(b - a) \in N \Rightarrow -cb + ca \in N \Rightarrow ac - bc \in N \Rightarrow bc < ac$.

▶ *Aside.* You will probably little note nor long remember the proofs of this section. You should, however, realize this: Except for one important change (part 3 of the monotony theorem) the same three fundamental order theorems are true of I as were true of W. These three theorems will also remain true in the larger systems Q (rationals) and R (reals). ◀

EXERCISES 8–6

1. a) $a \in N \Leftrightarrow a > 0$

   b) $a > 0 \Leftrightarrow -a < 0$

   [*Hint:* Use definition of $<$.]

2. Prove each of the following, using the definition of $<$.

   a) $7 < 10$ b) $-5 < 1$ c) $-36 < -20$

   d) $0 < 3$ e) $-1 < 0$ f) $-10 + a < -4 + a$

   g) $8 \cdot 7 < 8 \cdot 10$ [Do *not* reduce to $56 < 80$; use (a).]

   h) $8 \cdot (-5) < 8 \cdot 1$ [Do *not* reduce to $-40 < 8$.]

   i) $-3 \cdot 10 < -3 \cdot 7$ [Do *not* reduce to $-30 < -21$.]

3. Observe that we also proved the converse to part 1 of the monotony theorem: $a + c < b + c \Rightarrow a < b$. This is a cancellation law of a sort. Prove these further cancellation laws.

   a) $ac < bc$ and $c > 0 \Rightarrow a < b$.

   b) $ac < bc$ and $c < 0 \Rightarrow a > b$.

4. Prove $a^2 > 0$ for every nonzero integer a. [*Hint:* By the Lemma, either $a \in N$ or $-a \in N$. Also use Exercise 1.]

5. Are the following statements true or false?

   a) $5a < 6a$, $\forall a \in I$

   b) $0 \cdot a < 1 \cdot a$, $\forall a \in I$

   c) $a^2 \cdot (-4) < a^2 \cdot 7$, $\forall a \in I$

   d) $(a - b)^2 = 0 \Rightarrow a = b$, $\forall a, b \in I$

   e) $-(a^2) \leq 0$, $\forall a \in I$

6. Prove the following:

   a) $a > 0$ and $b > 0 \Rightarrow ab > 0$

   b) $a > 0$ and $b < 0 \Rightarrow ab < 0$

   c) $a < 0$ and $b < 0 \Rightarrow ab > 0$

   d) $ab > 0$ and $a > 0 \Rightarrow b > 0$

   e) $ab > 0$ and $a < 0 \Rightarrow b < 0$

   f) $a < b$ and $c < d \Rightarrow a + c < b + d$

   g) $a < b$ and $c \leq d \Rightarrow a + c < b + d$ ($\leq$ defined in the obvious way)

h) $a > 0$ and $b > 0 \Rightarrow a + b > 0$

i) $a < 0$ and $b < 0 \Rightarrow a + b < 0$

j) $a + a > 0 \Rightarrow a > 0$

8–7 the system of rationals

We saw that, in I, every equation of the form

$$b + x = a, \qquad a, b \in I,$$

has a unique solution; namely, $a - b$. Let us look now at another very simple sort of equation:

$$bx = a, \qquad a, b \in I.$$

Clearly not all such equations have solutions in I; for example,

$$0x = 1, \qquad 2x = 1, \qquad 2x = -3$$

do not. On the other hand, some do.

$$3x = 6, \qquad 2x = -8, \qquad (-7)x = 7.$$

Our intention now will be to assume the existence of a set Q (really a system $Q, +, \cdot$) just enough larger than I (really the system $I, +, \cdot$) so that *every* equation of the form

$$bx = a, \qquad a, b \in I; b \neq 0,$$

has a solution in Q. We impose the condition $b \neq 0$ on the equation $bx = a$ because no "reasonable" system could possibly contain a solution to $0 \cdot x = 1$.

Thus we assume the existence of a set $Q \supset I$ and binary operations $+$ and $\cdot$ on Q which satisfy

1) Assoc $+$ 2) Assoc $\cdot$

3) Comm $+$ 4) Comm $\cdot$

5) Add 0   6) Mult 1

7) Negatives exist   8) Cancel $\cdot$

9) Dist

[*Note:* Properties 1 through 9 are assumed to hold in Q, not just in I.]

10) Every equation of form $bx = a$ $(a, b \in I; b \neq 0)$ has a solution in Q.

11) Every element of Q is the solution to an equation of form $bx = a$

$(a, b \in I; b \neq 0)$.

The elements of Q are called *rational numbers*.

▶ *Aside*

1. We've replaced "Cancel +" by "Negatives exist," which means that for every $u \in Q$ there is a solution in Q to $u + x = 0$ called $-u$. We saw in Exercise 9, page 253, that Cancel + follows from this assumption, Assoc +, and Add 0.

2. Our assumptions 1 through 11 should strike you as modest and reasonable.

3. To be absolutely precise, we should have called the binary operations on Q $\oplus$ and $\odot$, and assumed that

$$a \oplus b = a + b, \qquad \forall a, b \in I,$$
$$a \odot b = a \cdot b, \qquad \forall a, b \in I.$$

Or, to be consistent with the precise approach to I, perhaps we'd have to call the operations on Q $\circledplus$ and $\circledcirc$, and assume that

$$a \circledplus b = a \oplus b, \qquad \forall a, b \in I,$$
$$a \circledcirc b = a \odot b, \qquad \forall a, b \in I.$$

(The drawbacks to a precise approach begin to appear!)

4. Again we have substitution, reflexivity, symmetry, and transitivity. ◀

Two immediate consequences of assumptions 1 through 9 are:

i) $0 \cdot u = 0, \qquad \forall u \in Q,$

ii) $u \neq 0, v \neq 0 \Rightarrow uv \neq 0, \qquad \forall u, v \in Q, \qquad (uv = 0 \Rightarrow u = 0 \text{ or } v = 0).$

(See page 249.) These will again be very important.

We would now like to establish the usual "rules for fractions." In order to do so, we first derive some important consequences of our assumptions and define some notation.

Theorem   There exists a unique solution to the equation $ux = 1$ for every nonzero $u \in Q$ (not just for every nonzero $u \in I$, which is a corollary to Assumption 10).

Proof

Existence $u \in Q \overset{(11)}{\Longrightarrow}$ there exist $a, b \in I$, $b \neq 0$, such that $bu = a$. Note that $a \neq 0$ by (ii) above. $a \in I$ and $a \neq 0 \Rightarrow$ there exists $v \in Q$ such that $av = 1$. Thus

$$buv = av = 1,$$

so that bv is a solution to $ux = 1$.

Uniqueness   Suppose v, w both denote solutions to $ux = 1$. Then

$$uv = 1 = uw,$$

but $u \neq 0$, so $v = w$ by Cancel $\cdot$. Thus v and w both had to denote a single solution.

It is now legitimate to make the following definition.

Definition   The unique solution (in Q) to

$$ux = 1, \qquad u \in Q; \; u \neq 0,$$

will be denoted by $\dfrac{1}{u}$ (read "one over u"), and will be called the *reciprocal of u* or the *multiplicative inverse of u*, or simply *u inverse* (not to be confused with the additive inverse of u). Thus, symbolically, for all nonzero $u \in Q$,

i) $u \cdot \dfrac{1}{u} = 1$,

ii) if $u \cdot v = 1$, then $v = \dfrac{1}{u}$.

If you prefer to memorize words rather than symbols, memorize this:

"*u inverse is that rational which when multiplied by u gives 1.*"

Examples   a) $\dfrac{1}{5}$ is that rational which when multiplied by 5 gives 1.

b) $\dfrac{1}{-7a}$ is that rational which when multiplied by $-7a$ gives 1.

c) $\dfrac{1}{4 + 3b}$ is that rational which when multiplied by $4 + 3b$ gives 1.

d) $\dfrac{1}{6 + \frac{1}{3}}$ is that rational which when multiplied by $6 + \frac{1}{3}$ gives 1.

Theorem   There exists a unique solution to the equation $ux = v$ for every $u, v \in Q$ ($u \neq 0$), namely $v \cdot \dfrac{1}{u}$.

Proof

Existence: $u(v \cdot \dfrac{1}{u}) = \cdots = v.$

Uniqueness: Follows from Cancel $\cdot$

▶ *Aside.*   Thus Q does not share the deficiency of I mentioned on page 265.◀

Definition   (*notational convention*)

$\dfrac{v}{u} = v \cdot \dfrac{1}{u}.$ $\dfrac{v}{u}$ is read "v over u."

The binary operation on Q which sends (v, u) to $\dfrac{v}{u}$ is called *division*.

"v over u means v times one over u."

Examples a) $\dfrac{8}{3} = 8 \cdot \dfrac{1}{3}$ b) $\dfrac{7 + 3}{-5} = (7 + 3) \cdot \dfrac{1}{-5}$

c) $\dfrac{u - 1}{u + 6} = (u - 1) \cdot \dfrac{1}{u + 6}$ d) $\dfrac{9}{\frac{3}{4}} = 9 \cdot \dfrac{1}{\frac{3}{4}} = 9 \cdot \dfrac{1}{3 \cdot \frac{1}{4}}$

EXERCISES 8–7

[*General hint:* Compare each problem with the corresponding problem about I (pages 251–254).]

1. a) Find integers a and b ($b \neq 0$) such that 5 is the solution to the equation $bx = a$.

   b) Repeat part (a), finding a different pair of values for a and b.

   c) Repeat parts (a) and (b), replacing 5 by c, where c can be *any* integer.

2. Assuming that 1 is the smallest positive integer (is this derivable from our other assumptions?), prove that there is no solution in I to the equation $2x = 1$.

   [*Hint:* Use problem 6(j), (g), page 264.]

3. Write the (multiplicative) inverse for each of the following.

   a) 4   b) $5u$ c) $\dfrac{1}{-3}$ d) $u - 6$ e) $\dfrac{1}{u + v}$ f) $\dfrac{1}{uv}$

4. Why does $5 \cdot \frac{1}{8} = \frac{5}{8}$?

5. Compute as in the example.

   Example

   $(-12) \cdot \frac{1}{-4}$
   $= [3 \cdot (-4)] \cdot \frac{1}{-4}$ Elem mult fact and rule 5 for $-$
   $= 3 \cdot [(-4) \cdot \frac{1}{-4}]$ Assoc $\cdot$
   $= 3 \cdot 1$ Defn of $\frac{1}{-4}$
   $= 3$ Mult 1

   a) $18 \cdot \frac{1}{6}$ b) $-24 \cdot \left(\dfrac{1}{-3} \cdot \dfrac{1}{4}\right)$ c) $\dfrac{1}{4} \cdot 72 \cdot \dfrac{1}{-3}$

   d) $\frac{1}{5} \cdot (-100)$ e) $\frac{1}{6} \cdot 36 \cdot 0$ f) $\dfrac{1}{8} \cdot \dfrac{1}{\frac{1}{8}}$

6. Prove the following, using the definition of "one over u."

a) $\dfrac{1}{u} \cdot u = 1$, $\quad \forall u \in Q$ such that $u \neq 0$ $\qquad$ b) $\dfrac{1}{6} \cdot \dfrac{1}{\frac{1}{6}} = 1$

c) $\frac{1}{6} \cdot 6 = 1$ $\qquad$ d) $\dfrac{1}{\frac{1}{u}} = u$, $\quad \forall u \in Q$ such that $u \neq 0$

e) $\dfrac{1}{4(-3)} = \dfrac{1}{4} \cdot \dfrac{1}{-3}$

$\left[\textit{Hint:} \text{ Compute } [4(-3)] \dfrac{1}{4(-3)} \text{ and } [4(-3)] \left[\dfrac{1}{4} \cdot \dfrac{1}{-3} \right] \text{ and compare.} \right]$

f) $\dfrac{1}{uv} = \dfrac{1}{u} \cdot \dfrac{1}{v}$, $\quad \forall u, v \in Q$ such that $u \neq 0, v \neq 0$

g) $\dfrac{1}{1} = 1$

7. Compute the following, using the definition of division and the results of Exercise 6 that are printed in color, as in the example.

Example

$\dfrac{2}{-9} \cdot \dfrac{3}{4} = \left(2 \cdot \dfrac{1}{-9} \right) \cdot \left(3 \cdot \dfrac{1}{4} \right)$ $\qquad$ Defn division

$= \left(2 \cdot \dfrac{1}{4} \right) \cdot \left(3 \cdot \dfrac{1}{-9} \right)$ $\qquad$ Comm · Assoc ·

$= \left(2 \cdot \dfrac{1}{2 \cdot 2} \right) \cdot \left(3 \cdot \dfrac{1}{3 \cdot (-3)} \right)$ $\qquad$ Elem mult fact, Rule 5 for −

$= \left(2 \cdot \dfrac{1}{2} \cdot \dfrac{1}{2} \right) \cdot \left(3 \cdot \dfrac{1}{3} \cdot \dfrac{1}{-3} \right)$ $\qquad$ 6 (f), Assoc ·

$= \left(1 \cdot \dfrac{1}{2} \right) \cdot \left(1 \cdot \dfrac{1}{-3} \right)$ $\qquad$ Defn of $\frac{1}{2}$, $\frac{1}{3}$

$= \dfrac{1}{2} \cdot \dfrac{1}{-3}$ $\qquad$ Mult 1

$= \dfrac{1}{2(-3)}$ $\qquad$ 6 (f)

$= \dfrac{1}{-6}$ $\qquad$ Mult fact, Rule 5 for −

a) $\dfrac{32}{4}$ $\qquad$ b) $\dfrac{25}{\frac{1}{5}}$ $\qquad$ c) $\dfrac{6u + 8}{2}$ $\qquad$ d) $\dfrac{7}{8} \cdot \dfrac{-6}{7}$ $\qquad$ e) $\dfrac{3}{8} \cdot \dfrac{7}{5}$

f) $\dfrac{1/u}{1/v}$ $\qquad$ g) $9 \cdot \dfrac{(4u - 8)}{3}$ $\qquad$ h) $\dfrac{4}{9} + \dfrac{1}{9}$ $\qquad$ i) $\dfrac{3}{15} + \dfrac{5}{15}$ $\qquad$ j) $\dfrac{1/-4}{1/8}$

8. Prove the following, using Exercise 6 and the definition of division.

a) $\dfrac{6}{-2} = -3$ b) $\dfrac{6}{8} = \dfrac{3}{4}$ c) $\dfrac{1}{\frac{5}{6}} = \dfrac{6}{5}$

d) $10 \cdot \dfrac{2}{5} = 4$ e) $\dfrac{2}{3} + \dfrac{4}{3} = 2$ f) $\dfrac{5}{5} = 1$

g) $1 + \dfrac{3}{5} = \dfrac{8}{5}$ h) $\dfrac{u}{u} = 1, \quad u \neq 0$

9. Suppose, in place of our Assumption 8, "Cancel ·," we had assumed "Inverses exist"; that is, every nonzero element $u \in Q$ has a multiplicative inverse, denoted by $\frac{1}{u}$, in the sense that $u \cdot \frac{1}{u} = 1$.

a) Prove that every nonzero element of Q has just one multiplicative inverse.

b) Prove "Cancel ·" as a theorem.

c) Prove there is a solution to $ux = v$ $(u \neq 0)$ without using Assumption 11.

10. Prove the following, using the definition of "u over v" (and Exercise 6).

a) $\dfrac{u}{1} = u$

b) $\dfrac{1}{u/v} = \dfrac{v}{u}, \quad u \neq 0, v \neq 0$

c) $\dfrac{0}{u} = 0, \quad u \neq 0$

d) $\frac{6}{-2}$ is the unique solution to the equation $(-2)x = 6$ and to these other equations: $2x = -6$, $x(-2) = 6$, $x \cdot 2 = -6$.

e) $\frac{u}{v}$ is the unique solution to $vx = u \, (v \neq 0)$.

f) The following equations are *equivalent*: $vx = u$, $xv = u$, $(-v)x = -u$, $x(-v) = -u$.

11. (*Discussion problem*) We defined

$$\dfrac{v}{u} \text{ to equal } v \cdot \dfrac{1}{u}$$

for all $v, u \in Q$ $(u \neq 0)$, in particular for all $v, u \in I$ $(u \neq 0)$. But when u and v are integers and u is a factor of v (cf. Chapter 5, page 185), the symbol $\frac{v}{u}$ already has a meaning. It denotes the (unique) solution in I to the equation $ux = v$. Does our new definition leave us in the embarrassing position of having a single symbol, $\frac{v}{u}$, denote two different elements of I?

These two different views of $\frac{v}{u}$ are exemplified in two different approaches to division. Consider the problem of dividing 85 by 17.

Viewpoint 1: Finding the unique solution in I to the equation $17x = 85$. "What must I multiply 17 by to get 85?" One needn't know of the existence of rational numbers to ask and answer this question. What is more, this interpretation is a natural one in real-life situations. "There are 17 of us present. How much must we each contribute to buy an 85¢ bag of coffee?"

Viewpoint 2: Finding the unique solution in Q to the equation $17x = 85$. "I know that the solution is expressible as $\frac{85}{17}$; the problem is to simplify this expression." To say this requires a knowledge of the rational numbers. Also the connection to real-life situations is not very clear. This viewpoint does, however, have the virtue of being conceptually neater. You multiply both sides of the equation by $\frac{1}{17}$ to isolate x. You *know* there is a solution.

Must the two viewpoints lead to the same solution (in this specific problem)? Does the person with Viewpoint 2 get by with any less work in obtaining an answer when he computes

$$\frac{85}{17} = 85 \cdot \frac{1}{17} = (5 \cdot 17) \cdot \frac{1}{17} = 5 \cdot (17 \cdot \frac{1}{17}) = 5 \cdot 1 = 5?$$

How would the person with Viewpoint 1 react to the problem: divide 85 by 16? How would the person with Viewpoint 2 react to it?

12. Check the binary operation (on Q), division, for associativity, commutativity, existence of neutral element, cancellation laws, distributivity with respect to $+$.

13. Prove that there is a unique solution in Q to any equation of the form

$$ux + v = w, \qquad u \neq 0;\ u, v, w \in Q.$$

8–8   rules for "fractions"

The theoretical groundwork has been laid. It is now an easy matter to establish the familiar computational rules.

Omnibus Theorem   (*Rules for "fractions"; all "denominators" are assumed nonzero*)

0. $u = \dfrac{u}{1}$

1. $\dfrac{1}{1/u} = u$

2. $\dfrac{1}{u} \cdot \dfrac{1}{v} = \dfrac{1}{uv}$

3. $\dfrac{1}{u/v} = \dfrac{v}{u}$

4. $\dfrac{uv}{uw} = \dfrac{v}{w} = \dfrac{vu}{wu}$ "Cancel common factors"

5. $\dfrac{u}{v} \cdot \dfrac{y}{w} = \dfrac{uy}{vw}$ "Numerator times numerator over denominator times denominator"

6. $\dfrac{u/v}{y/w} = \dfrac{u}{v} \cdot \dfrac{w}{y} = \dfrac{uw}{vy}$ "Invert and multiply"

7. $\dfrac{u}{v} + \dfrac{y}{v} = \dfrac{u+y}{v}$ "Add numerators when denominators are the same"

and its generalization $\dfrac{u}{v} + \dfrac{y}{w} = \dfrac{uw+vy}{vw}$

8. $-\left(\dfrac{u}{v}\right) = \dfrac{-u}{v} = \dfrac{u}{-v}$

9. $\dfrac{u}{v} - \dfrac{y}{v} = \dfrac{u-y}{v}$ "Subtract numerators when denominators are the same"

and its generalization $\dfrac{u}{v} - \dfrac{y}{w} = \dfrac{uw-vy}{vw}$

▶ *Aside preceding proof*

1. Although these rules are often applied in the special case $u, v, y, w \in I$, they are true for $u, v, y, w \in Q$. Hence our choice of notation.

2. Parts 0–3 you may have proved already (Exercises 6, 10, on pages 269–270). We prove them again in case you had trouble. Parts 4–7 are left to you (see Exercise 1). Before we can prove parts 8 and 9, we need to discuss subtraction in Q. Part 0 is thrown in because, in a special case, it says

$5 = \frac{5}{1}.$

Thus each integer can be transformed into a fraction and can then be combined with other fractions by means of rules 5, 6, 7, 8.

3. We put quotation marks around the words "fraction" and "denominator" because, in this section, they are to be interpreted in a very broad sense [cf. Exercise 2, parts (j) through (t)]. In Section 8–9 we shall use these terms in the usual more restricted sense. ◀

Proof of 0

$\dfrac{u}{1} = u \cdot \dfrac{1}{1}$ Defn division

$\phantom{\dfrac{u}{1}} = u \cdot 1$ Defn inverse

$\phantom{\dfrac{u}{1}} = u$ Mult 1

Proof of 1

$1/u \cdot \dfrac{1}{1/u} = 1$ Defn inverse

$1/u \cdot u = 1$ Defn inverse, Comm ·

Therefore $1/u \cdot u = 1/u \cdot \dfrac{1}{1/u}$ Tran $=$

Therefore $u = \dfrac{1}{1/u}$ Cancel $\cdot$ [*Note:* $1/u \neq 0$,   else

$$1 = 1/u \cdot u = 0 \cdot u = 0.]$$

Proof of 2

$uv \cdot \dfrac{1}{uv} = 1$ Defn inverse

$uv \left[\dfrac{1}{u} \cdot \dfrac{1}{v} \right] = \left(u \cdot \dfrac{1}{u} \right) \cdot \left(v \cdot \dfrac{1}{v} \right)$ Comm $\cdot$, Assoc $\cdot$

$\qquad\qquad = 1 \cdot 1$ Defn inverse

$\qquad\qquad = 1$ Mult 1

Therefore $uv \cdot \dfrac{1}{uv} = uv \cdot \left[\dfrac{1}{u} \cdot \dfrac{1}{v} \right]$ Tran $=$

Therefore $\dfrac{1}{uv} = \dfrac{1}{u} \cdot \dfrac{1}{v}$ Cancel $\cdot$ [*Note:* $uv \neq 0$, since $u \neq 0, v \neq 0$]

Proof of 3

$\dfrac{1}{u/v} = \dfrac{1}{u \cdot 1/v}$ Defn division

$\qquad = \dfrac{1}{u} \cdot \dfrac{1}{1/v}$ Property 2 of Omnibus theorem

$\qquad = \dfrac{1}{u} \cdot v$ Property 1 of Omnibus theorem

$\qquad = v \cdot \dfrac{1}{u}$ Comm $\cdot$

$\qquad = v/u$ Defn division

Before we can prove Properties 8 and 9 we have to make sure we know what all the symbols mean. The symbol $-w$ has meaning because of our assumption 7: "Every element $w \in Q$ has a negative (additive inverse) denoted by $-w$." The symbol $u - w$, however, does not have meaning yet. How should we define subtraction in Q? Obviously in the same way as we did in I; namely,

Definition $u - w = u + (-w)$, $\forall u, w \in Q$.

We now claim that

All the rules for minus signs (stated for I on page 257) *remain true in Q,*

and furthermore we need not prove them again! The reason is that since our assumptions about Q include all our assumptions about I (except that we have no analog of Assumption 11 about I), and since our definitions of negative and subtraction are the same as before, therefore we have at hand all the reasons we need to justify the rules for minus signs.

That we have no analog of Assumption 11 about I causes no difficulty because (a) Assumption 11 was only used once on the way to establishing the rules for minus signs; (b) the assumption, "negatives exist," makes even that brief appearance unnecessary [cf. Exercise 9(c), page 270].

▶ *Aside.* This, incidentally, is one very good reason for carefully deducing all results from a list of explicit assumptions. You may find yourself in a different situation, but with the same or a larger list of assumptions. If you do then you can immediately lay claim to all the results which you painfully established in the first situation. ◀

Proof of 8 $-(u/v)$ denotes the additive inverse of u/v which is unique [cf. Exercise 9(a), page 253]. But

$$\frac{u}{v} + \frac{-u}{v} = \frac{u + (-u)}{v} \qquad \text{Property 7 of Omnibus theorem}$$

$$= \frac{0}{v} \qquad \text{Defn negative}$$

$$= 0 \cdot \frac{1}{v} \qquad \text{Defn division}$$

$$= 0. \qquad \text{Mult prop of 0}$$

Thus

$$\frac{-u}{v} = -\left(\frac{u}{v}\right).$$

Also

$$\frac{u}{v} + \frac{u}{-v} = \frac{u(-v) + vu}{v(-v)} \qquad \text{Property 7 (generalization) of Omnibus theorem}$$

$$= \frac{-(uv) + uv}{-(vv)} \qquad \text{Rule 5 for } -, \text{ Comm } \cdot$$

$$= \frac{0}{-vv} \qquad \text{Defn negative}$$

$$= 0 \cdot \frac{1}{-vv} \qquad \text{Defn division}$$

$$= 0 \qquad \text{Mult prop 0}$$

Thus

$$\frac{u}{-v} = -\left(\frac{u}{v}\right).$$

Proof of 9

$$\frac{u}{v} - \frac{v}{v} = \frac{u}{v} + \left[-\left(\frac{y}{v}\right)\right] \qquad \text{Defn subtr}$$

$$= \frac{u}{v} + \frac{-y}{v} \qquad \text{Property 8 of Omnibus theorem}$$

$$= \frac{u + (-y)}{v} \qquad \text{Property 7 of Omnibus theorem}$$

$$= \frac{u - y}{v} \qquad \text{Defn subtr}$$

EXERCISES 8–8

1. Prove, using parts 0–3 of the Omnibus theorem, the definitions of inverse and division, and the 11 assumptions.

   a) $\dfrac{2}{3} \cdot \dfrac{7}{9} = \dfrac{2 \cdot 7}{3 \cdot 9}$

   b) $\dfrac{-5}{3} \cdot \dfrac{10}{7} = \dfrac{-5 \cdot 10}{3 \cdot 7}$

   c) $\dfrac{u}{v} \cdot \dfrac{y}{w} = \dfrac{u \cdot y}{v \cdot w}$, $v, w \neq 0$

   d) $\dfrac{\frac{2}{3}}{\frac{5}{7}} = \dfrac{2}{3} \cdot \dfrac{7}{5}$ $\left[\textit{Hint:} \ \dfrac{\frac{2}{3}}{\frac{5}{7}} = \dfrac{2}{3} \cdot \dfrac{1}{\frac{5}{7}}\right]$

   e) $\dfrac{\frac{1}{9}}{-\frac{6}{4}} = \dfrac{1}{9} \cdot \dfrac{4}{-6}$

   f) $\dfrac{u/v}{y/w} = \dfrac{u}{v} \cdot \dfrac{w}{y}$, $v, w, y \neq 0$

   g) $\dfrac{2}{7} + \dfrac{4}{7} = \dfrac{6}{7}$ $\left[\textit{Hint:} \ \dfrac{2}{7} = 2 \cdot \dfrac{1}{7}\right]$

   h) $\dfrac{5}{9} + \dfrac{1}{9} = \dfrac{6}{9}$

   i) $\dfrac{u}{v} + \dfrac{y}{v} = \dfrac{u + y}{v}$, $v \neq 0$

   j) $\dfrac{6 \cdot 3}{6 \cdot 7} = \dfrac{3}{7}$

   k) $\dfrac{2 \cdot 5}{1 \cdot 5} = \dfrac{2}{1}$

   l) $\dfrac{u \cdot v}{u \cdot w} = \dfrac{v}{w} = \dfrac{v \cdot u}{w \cdot u}$, $u, w = 0$

   m) $\dfrac{5}{3} + \dfrac{4}{7} = \dfrac{5 \cdot 7 + 3 \cdot 4}{3 \cdot 7}$

   n) $\dfrac{10}{6} + \dfrac{5}{8} = \dfrac{10 \cdot 8 + 6 \cdot 5}{6 \cdot 8}$

   o) $u/v + y/w = \dfrac{uw + vy}{vw}$, $v, w \neq 0$

2. Each of the following illustrates the application of one property in the Omnibus theorem. Decide which one.

   a) $\dfrac{6}{-4} = \dfrac{-6}{4}$

   b) $\dfrac{2}{3} \cdot \dfrac{-3}{4} = \dfrac{2 \cdot (-3)}{3 \cdot 4}$

   c) $\dfrac{1}{10} + \dfrac{9}{10} = \dfrac{1 + 9}{10}$

   d) $10 = \dfrac{10}{1}$

   e) $\dfrac{1}{\frac{1}{10}} = 10$

   f) $\dfrac{\frac{1}{10}}{\frac{9}{10}} = \dfrac{1 \cdot 10}{10 \cdot 9}$

g) $\dfrac{5 \cdot 3}{11 \cdot 3} = \dfrac{5}{11}$

h) $\dfrac{1}{8} \cdot \dfrac{1}{10} = \dfrac{1}{8 \cdot 10}$

i) $\dfrac{1}{\frac{4}{3}} = \dfrac{3}{4}$

j) $\dfrac{7}{8} - \dfrac{3}{8} = \dfrac{7 - 3}{8}$

k) $\dfrac{\frac{3}{2}}{6} \cdot \dfrac{-4}{\frac{1}{10}} \qquad \dfrac{\frac{3}{2} \cdot (-4)}{6 \cdot (\frac{1}{10})}$

l) $\dfrac{-(\frac{2}{3})}{7} = -\left[\dfrac{\frac{2}{3}}{7}\right]$

m) $\dfrac{\frac{1}{3}}{6} + \dfrac{\frac{5}{3}}{6} = \dfrac{\frac{1}{3} + \frac{5}{3}}{6}$

n) $\dfrac{2}{7} - \dfrac{3}{10} = \dfrac{2 \cdot 10 - 7 \cdot 3}{7 \cdot 10}$

o) $\dfrac{\frac{5}{1}}{1/\frac{6}{10}} = \dfrac{5}{1} \cdot \dfrac{\frac{6}{10}}{1}$

p) $\dfrac{2}{\frac{3}{5}} + \dfrac{\frac{7}{4}}{9} = \dfrac{2 \cdot 9 + (\frac{3}{5}) \cdot (\frac{7}{4})}{\frac{3}{5} \cdot 9}$

q) $\dfrac{1}{1 / \frac{1}{\frac{6}{7}}} = \dfrac{1}{\frac{6}{7}}$

r) $\dfrac{1}{\frac{5}{1}} = \dfrac{1}{5}$

s) $\dfrac{\frac{11}{9}}{1} = \dfrac{11}{9}$

t) $\dfrac{\frac{2}{3} \cdot \frac{3}{4}}{\frac{2}{3} \cdot 6} = \dfrac{\frac{3}{4}}{6}$

3. Prove each of the following, as in the example. (Use the Omnibus theorem!)

Example $6 \cdot (-\frac{3}{4}) = -(\frac{18}{4})$.

Proof

$6 \cdot (-\frac{3}{4}) = \frac{6}{1} \cdot -\frac{3}{4}$ Property 0

$\qquad = \dfrac{6 \cdot (-3)}{1 \cdot 4}$ Property 5

$\qquad = \dfrac{-18}{4}$ $\begin{cases} \text{Mult fact} \\ \text{Rule 5 for } - \\ \text{Mult 1} \end{cases}$

$\qquad = -(\frac{18}{4})$ Property 8

a) $\frac{2}{7} \cdot 6 = \frac{12}{7}$

b) $\frac{3}{4} \cdot (-12) = -9$

c) $\dfrac{\frac{1}{2}}{\frac{2}{3}} = \dfrac{1}{2}$

d) $\frac{2}{7} + \frac{4}{7} = \frac{6}{7}$

e) $\dfrac{1}{3} \cdot \dfrac{7}{-6} = \dfrac{-7}{18}$

f) $\dfrac{3}{16} - \dfrac{7}{16} = \dfrac{-1}{4}$

g) $\dfrac{\frac{1}{4}}{\frac{2}{9}} = \dfrac{9}{8}$

h) $\frac{3}{10} + \frac{3}{12} = \frac{11}{20}$

i) $19 - \frac{13}{4} = \frac{63}{4}$

j) $\frac{7}{8} + \frac{9}{8} = 2$

k) $\frac{2}{3} \cdot \frac{3}{11} = \frac{2}{11}$

l) $\dfrac{\frac{5}{6}}{7} = \dfrac{5}{42}$

m) $\dfrac{-3}{\frac{5}{6}} = \dfrac{-18}{5}$

n) $\dfrac{2}{3} - 5 = \dfrac{-13}{3}$

4. Compute and simplify as in the example.

Example

$$\left(9 + \frac{\frac{16}{3}}{7}\right) \cdot \frac{42}{13} = \left(9 + \frac{16}{21}\right) \cdot \frac{42}{13} = \left(\frac{9 \cdot 21 + 16}{21}\right) \cdot \frac{42}{13}$$

$$= \frac{189 + 16}{21} \cdot \frac{42}{13} = \frac{205}{21} \cdot \frac{42}{13} = \frac{205}{\cancel{21}} \cdot \frac{\cancel{21} \cdot 2}{13}$$

$$= \frac{410}{13}$$

You should feel that, if pressed, you could supply reasons for each equality
(rules for fractions, rules for minus signs, whole-number computation facts,
basic assumptions, . . .)

a) $\frac{1}{3} \cdot \left(\frac{5}{8} - \frac{1}{4}\right)$

b) $\dfrac{\frac{2}{3} + \frac{3}{4}}{\frac{5}{6}}$

c) $\dfrac{-2}{\frac{3}{4} - \frac{1}{2}}$

d) $\frac{5}{6} - \left(\frac{2}{9} - \frac{5}{2}\right)$

e) $\dfrac{\frac{15}{16}(1 + \frac{7}{8})}{2}$

f) $\dfrac{\frac{1}{2}}{\left(\dfrac{-\frac{3}{4}}{\frac{1}{6}}\right)}$

g) $(8 + \frac{1}{2}) - (6 + \frac{3}{4})$

5. Symbols such as $2\frac{1}{4}$, $7\frac{1}{2}$, $1\frac{3}{8}$, $99\frac{44}{100}$, $3\frac{1}{7}$ are often used to denote, respectively,

$$2 + \tfrac{1}{4} \qquad (= \tfrac{9}{4})$$
$$7 + \tfrac{1}{2} \qquad (= \tfrac{15}{2})$$
$$1 + \tfrac{3}{8} \qquad (= \tfrac{11}{8})$$
$$99 + \tfrac{44}{100} \qquad (= \tfrac{9944}{100})$$
$$3 + \tfrac{1}{7} \qquad (= \tfrac{22}{7})$$

Such symbols are called mixed numerals.   Compute and simplify the
following.

a) $2\frac{1}{4} + 5\frac{2}{4}$

b) $3\frac{1}{10} + 7\frac{3}{10} + 10\frac{1}{10}$

c) $6\frac{1}{3} + 5\frac{1}{4}$

d) $6\frac{1}{3} - 5\frac{1}{4}$ (What does $-5\frac{1}{4}$ denote?)

e) $6\frac{1}{4} - 5\frac{1}{3}$

f) $1\frac{7}{8} + 2\frac{1}{2}$

g) $5\frac{2}{3} \cdot 6\frac{1}{4}$

h) $\frac{1}{2} \cdot 6\frac{2}{3}$

i) $\frac{1}{2} \cdot 5\frac{1}{4}$

j) $9\frac{1}{4} + \frac{7}{8}$

k) $11\frac{1}{2} - \frac{2}{3}$

l) $\dfrac{6\frac{1}{2}}{2}$

m) $\dfrac{2\frac{1}{3}}{3}$

n) Think about and discuss advantages and dangers in using mixed numerals.

6. Prove the generalization in part 9 of the Omnibus theorem.

7. Assuming part 4 and the generalization in part 7 of the Omnibus theorem,
   prove 7 itself.

8. Look back at Examples 1 and 4 on pages 244 and 245.

   a) Observe that they are special cases of the Omnibus theorem.

   b) Give a reason or reasons for each step in their *ad hoc* proofs.

9. Solve the following equations.

   a) $\frac{2}{3}x = 5$ b) $\frac{1}{8}x + 7 = 10$ c) $x - \frac{2}{3} = \frac{5}{6}$

   d) $7x = \frac{3}{4}$ e) $5x - 6 = 1$ f) $3 - 2x = 11$

10. Write down one equation of form $ax = b$ $(a, b \in I)$ whose rational solution is:

   a) $\frac{2}{3}$ b) $-\frac{4}{5}$ c) $\dfrac{\frac{2}{3}}{-\frac{4}{5}}$ d) $\dfrac{6}{\frac{2}{3}}$

8–9   labeling the rationals; fractions

We still don't know what the rationals "look like." It is obviously of no help to say that a rational is of the form $\frac{u}{v}$, where u, v are rationals. We follow the example of Section 8–5 and explore the consequences of Assumption 11. Assumption 11 guarantees that each element of Q is the solution to at least one equation of the form

$$bx = a, \qquad a, b \in I;\ b \neq 0.$$

But our fundamental existence-uniqueness theorem tells us that a label for that (unique) solution is

$$a \cdot \frac{1}{b}$$

and the definition of division simplifies that to $\frac{a}{b}$. Thus every element of Q has a label of the form $\frac{a}{b}$, where $a, b \in I$ and $b \neq 0$.

Our labeling problem, however, is still not solved. Clearly all the labels

$$\frac{-8}{-4}, \frac{2}{1}, \frac{6}{3}$$

denote the same element, 2, of Q. Thus we are led again to the two questions: When are two labels the same? How ought we to choose a particularly nice label for each rational?

Before answering these questions, we introduce some standard terminology.

Definition   A label (for a rational number) of the form $\frac{a}{b}$, where $a, b \in I$ and $b \neq 0$ is called a *fraction*. The number a is called the *numerator* of the fraction $\frac{a}{b}$ and b the *denominator*.

Example

$$\frac{-6}{2}, \frac{3}{4}, \frac{286}{-2}, \frac{0}{11} \text{ are fractions, while } \frac{\frac{2}{3}}{1}, \frac{\frac{3}{4}}{\frac{6}{6}}, \frac{7}{\frac{-2}{3}} \text{ are not,}$$

although they are perfectly respectable labels for rational numbers; namely, the unique solutions to

$$1x = \tfrac{2}{3}, \tfrac{4}{6}x = \tfrac{3}{4}, \tfrac{-2}{3}x = 7,$$

respectively. (These latter three symbols are sometimes called *complex fractions*.)

The answer to the first question—when are two labels equal?—is the content of the following lemma.

Lemma

$$\frac{a}{b} = \frac{c}{d} \Leftrightarrow ad = bc, \qquad \forall a, b, c, d \in Q \text{ with } b, d \neq 0$$

Proof

$$\Rightarrow: \quad \frac{a}{b} = \frac{c}{d} \Rightarrow a \cdot \frac{1}{b} = c \cdot \frac{1}{d}$$

$$\Rightarrow a \cdot \frac{1}{b} \cdot (bd) = c \cdot \frac{1}{d} \cdot (bd) \Rightarrow ad = bc.$$

$$\Leftarrow: \quad ad = bc \Rightarrow ad \cdot \left(\frac{1}{b} \cdot \frac{1}{d}\right) = bc \cdot \left(\frac{1}{b} \cdot \frac{1}{d}\right) \Rightarrow \frac{a}{b} = \frac{c}{d}.$$

▶ *Aside.* The theorem is true for a, b, c, $d \in Q$. We have used the notation normally reserved for integers, however, to emphasize the special case we are presently concerned with: the case in which the labels are fractions. In this special case our theorem states, in words, that:

Two fractions are equal if and only if the numerator of the first times the denominator of the second equals the denominator of the first times the numerator of the second.

This is the familar "cross-multiplication" criterion for the equality of fractions. Our old (cancellation) Rule 4 for "fractions,"

$$\frac{ac}{bc} = \frac{a}{b}, \qquad a, b, c \in Q; \quad b, c \neq 0,$$

can be viewed as an immediate corollary to this lemma. We shall soon exploit this rule (in the special case of a, b, $c \in I$) when we "reduce a fraction to lowest terms." ◀

The second question—how do we choose a particularly nice standard label for each rational?—is the hard one. The answer, in short, is this: Each rational number has among its many labels exactly one fraction "in lowest terms." To explain what this means and to prove the result, we must return to the system of integers and discuss (rather superficially) the concepts of factorization and primes.

EXERCISES 8–9

1. From the list below pick out those which are fractions, and name the numerator and denominator for each fraction.

   a) $\frac{9}{4}$ b) $2\frac{1}{4}$ c) $\frac{1}{\frac{4}{9}}$ d) $\frac{\frac{9}{4}}{1}$ e) $\frac{8}{-20}$

   f) $\frac{0}{-5}$ g) $\frac{0}{0}$ h) $\frac{u}{v}$, $u, v \in Q$; $v \neq 0$

2. Prove the following, first without using the lemma on page 279, then using it.

   a) $\frac{6}{2} = \frac{-12}{-4}$ [*Hint*: $6 = 3 \cdot 2$; $-12 = 3(-4)$, and use cancellation rule number 4.]

   b) $\frac{3}{8} = \frac{375}{1000}$ c) $9 = \frac{27}{3}$ d) $\frac{1}{\frac{1}{3}} = \frac{12}{4}$

   e) $\frac{-6}{8} = \frac{3}{-4}$ f) $\frac{1}{4} = \frac{25}{100}$

3. Using the lemma on page 279, prove the following.

   a) Cancellation rule number 4   b) $\frac{\frac{3}{4}}{\frac{8}{7}} = \frac{21}{32}$

   c) $\frac{-\frac{2}{3}}{-6} = \frac{1}{9}$ d) $\frac{7}{\frac{7}{4}} = 4$

   e) $\frac{\frac{1}{8}}{\frac{5}{8}} = \frac{1}{5}$ f) $\frac{\frac{3}{4}}{9} = \frac{1}{12}$

   g) $\frac{8}{\frac{3}{4}} = \frac{32}{3}$,   h) $\frac{u}{3u} = \frac{1}{3}$, $\forall u \in Q$; $u \neq 0$

   i) $\frac{0}{u} = \frac{0}{v}$, $\forall u, v \in Q$ $(u, v \neq 0)$

4. Simplify (whatever that means) the following.

   a) $\frac{6 \cdot 13}{6 \cdot 8}$ b) $\frac{86}{10}$ c) $\frac{12}{60}$

   d) $\frac{-96}{256}$ e) $\frac{7 \cdot \frac{18}{45}}{3 \cdot \frac{18}{45}}$ f) $\frac{2 \cdot \frac{1}{3}}{4 \cdot \frac{1}{3}}$

8–10   factorization and primes (in *I*)

The concepts of factorization and primes are concepts about the system of integers, *not* about the system of rationals. We discuss these notions here, however, so that you will see their critical importance in the solution of the labeling problem for rationals.

Certain integers can be "factored"; i.e., written as products of *other* integers. For example,

$6 = 3 \cdot 2, \; -36 = (-9) \cdot 4, \; 88 = 8 \cdot 11.$

On the other hand,

$2, \; -3, \; -7, \; 11$

cannot be factored except in the trivial sense that

$2 = (-1) \cdot (-2), \; -3 = (-1) \cdot 3, \ldots$

Some people refer to these last two "factorizations" as "improper factorizations." We'll not even dignify them with that name. We'll say simply that 2 and -3 cannot be factored. The bothersome integers 1 and -1 we'll call *units*. A non-zero, non-unit integer which cannot be factored will be called a *prime*.

There is a subtle theorem which states that:

1. Every positive integer (except 1 and primes) can be factored into a product of positive primes, and

2. There is just one such factorization.

(Hence, also, any negative integer, except -1 and primes, can be factored into -1 times a product of positive primes, and this factorization is unique.)

This theorem is, no doubt, intuitively obvious. For example,

$$6 = 2 \cdot 3,$$
$$-36 = (-1)2 \cdot 2 \cdot 3 \cdot 3 = (-1)2^2 \cdot 3^2,$$
$$88 = 2 \cdot 2 \cdot 2 \cdot 11 = 2^3 \cdot 11.$$

When we take the rigorous approach, however, in which nothing is granted as intuitively obvious, this theorem requires a lengthy, painstaking proof involving, among other things, the notion of mathematical induction alluded to briefly in Chapter 5, pages 161–162. The importance attached to this theorem by mathematicians is apparent in the name usually given it: "The Fundamental Theorem of Arithmetic."

EXERCISES 8–10

1. Pick out primes from: $-10, \; -7, \; -4, \; 0, \; 1, \; 6, \; 7, \; 11, \; 15.$
2. List all positive primes <50.
3. Factor (into a product of positive primes and perhaps -1) the following:
    a) 28   b) 91   c) 64   d) -132 e) 174   f) 1716

4. Define "a is composite" so that I is the *disjoint* union of the following sets: $\{0\}$, $\{$units$\}$, $\{$primes$\}$, $\{$composites$\}$.

5. Which pairs of integers have some prime factor in common?

   a) 15, 36   b) 8, 52   c) 10, 21

   d) 105, 168   e) 1, 12   f) 17, $253 \cdot 186$

6. It is absurd to discuss factorization and primes in Q because everything (but 0) is a factor of everything else.

   a) Find a fraction such that $\frac{-6}{3} = \frac{17}{32} \cdot ($————$)$.   (Thus $\frac{17}{32}$ is a "factor" of $\frac{-6}{3}$.)

   b) Find a fraction such that $1 = \frac{19}{77} \cdot ($————$)$.   (Thus $\frac{19}{77}$ is a "factor" of 1.)

8–11 fractions in lowest terms; the labeling problem solved

A nonzero fraction $\frac{a}{b}$ $(a, b \in I; a, b \neq 0)$ is said to be *in lowest terms*, provided that

   i) $b > 0$,

   ii) a and b have no common prime factor.

By decree $\frac{0}{1}$ is in lowest terms, while $\frac{0}{c}$ is not, for all $c \neq 1$.

Example $\dfrac{7}{6}, \dfrac{-3}{4}, \dfrac{10}{21}, \dfrac{0}{1}, \dfrac{-8}{3}, \dfrac{4}{1}$ are in lowest terms,

while $\dfrac{8}{6}, \dfrac{3}{-4}, \dfrac{10}{15}, \dfrac{0}{2}, \dfrac{1}{-4}, \dfrac{4}{-1}, \dfrac{-1}{-5}$ are not.

We have all heard the expression, "two fourths reduced to lowest terms is one half." What is really being stated here is that $\frac{1}{2}$ is the fraction in lowest terms which names the same rational as does $\frac{2}{4}$. [*Note:* $\frac{1}{2} = \frac{2}{4}$ by our theorem, $a/b = c/d \Leftrightarrow ad = bc$, and an elementary multiplication fact.] We shall see how every fraction can be reduced to lowest terms in the course of proving the following more general theorem.

Theorem   Every rational number is named by exactly one fraction in lowest terms.

Proof

At least one.   We observed that an arbitrary rational number is named by a fraction (a symbol of form a/b, where $a, b \in I$ and $b \neq 0$). If $a = 0$, then $a/b = 0/1$, which is in lowest terms. If $a \neq 0$, we proceed in two steps, in which we successively satisfy the two conditions for "in lowest terms." (Performing this two-step is known as *reducing to lowest terms*.)

Step 1: If $b < 0$, we replace the label $\frac{a}{b}$ by the label $\frac{-a}{-b}$. [*Note:* $a/b = -a/-b$, since $a(-b) = b(-a)$.] For example, $60/-105$ is replaced by $-60/105$. If $b > 0$, we go directly to step 2.

Step 2: We factor both numerator and denominator (a positive integer) into products of positive primes (the factorization of the numerator may involve the factor -1 as well); then we successively cancel the common factors until the numerator and denominator have no prime factors in common; and finally we "multiply out" both numerator and denominator. For example:

$$\frac{-60}{105} = \frac{(-1) \cdot 2 \cdot 2 \cdot \cancel{3} \cdot \cancel{5}}{\cancel{3} \cdot \cancel{5} \cdot 7} = \frac{-4}{7}.$$

At most one. We must show that if a/b and c/d are both in lowest terms and if $a/b = c/d$, then they are, in fact, identical: $a = c$ and $b = d$. This is trivial if a or c is 0, so we suppose that a and c are not 0. But $a/b = c/d \Rightarrow ad = bc$, so if $b = d = 1$, we are done. Otherwise b and d have factorizations into positive primes, and by the Fundamental Theorem of Arithmetic the prime factorization of ad is identical to the prime factorization of bc. But no (positive) prime factors of d occur in c (why?), so they all must occur in b. Also no (positive) prime factors of b can occur in a, so they all must occur in d. Thus b and d have the very same positive prime factors. Since b and d are also both positive they must be equal. $ad = bc$ and $b = d \Rightarrow a = c$ by Cancel . (Why is $b \neq 0$?)
    This completes the proof.

    It is a consequence of the definition of fraction that, conversely, each fraction represents a rational number. Thus we have a 1–1 correspondence between rational numbers and fractions in lowest terms. This is the solution to the labeling problem.
    We are tempted to try to list explicitly the set of lowest-term fractions. We begin systematically:

$$Q = \left\{ \ldots \; \frac{-7}{1} \; \frac{-6}{1} \; \frac{-5}{1} \; \frac{-4}{1} \; \frac{-3}{1} \; \frac{-2}{1} \; \frac{-1}{1} \; \frac{0}{1} \; \frac{1}{1} \; \frac{2}{1} \; \frac{3}{1} \; \frac{4}{1} \; \frac{5}{1} \; \frac{6}{1} \; \frac{7}{1} \; \ldots \right.$$

$$\ldots \; \frac{-7}{2} \quad \frac{-5}{2} \quad \frac{-3}{2} \quad \frac{-1}{2} \quad \frac{1}{2} \quad \frac{3}{2} \quad \frac{5}{2} \quad \frac{7}{2} \; \ldots$$

$$\ldots \; \frac{-7}{3} \quad \frac{-5}{3} \; \frac{-4}{3} \quad \frac{-2}{3} \; \frac{-1}{3} \quad \frac{1}{3} \; \frac{2}{3} \quad \frac{4}{3} \; \frac{5}{3} \quad \frac{7}{3} \; \ldots$$

$$\ldots \; \frac{-7}{4} \quad \frac{-5}{4} \quad \frac{-3}{4} \quad \frac{-1}{4} \quad \frac{1}{4} \quad \frac{3}{4} \quad \frac{5}{4} \quad \frac{7}{4} \; \ldots$$

but realize very quickly that no neat pattern has emerged. It wouldn't be honest to put a row of dots across the bottom of this chart and consider it an explicit description of Q.

EXERCISES 8–11

1. Some of the fractions below are in lowest terms and some are not. Identify those that are, and reduce to lowest terms those that are not.

   a) $\dfrac{3}{45}$ b) $\dfrac{14}{6}$ c) $\dfrac{11}{91}$ d) $\dfrac{-8}{30}$

   e) $\dfrac{0}{5}$ f) $\dfrac{3}{-4}$ g) $\dfrac{12}{-39}$ h) $\dfrac{420}{-100}$

   i) $\dfrac{-86}{-1}$ j) $\dfrac{-86}{-6}$ k) $\dfrac{1}{1}$ l) $\dfrac{-7}{2}$

   m) $\dfrac{2^4 \cdot 3 \cdot 5^{10} \cdot 11}{2^2 \cdot 5^8 \cdot 7 \cdot 11^5}$ n) $\dfrac{6^3}{3 \cdot 6}$ o) $\dfrac{3^3}{2 \cdot 5^4}$ p) $\dfrac{-3 \cdot 5^4}{3^4 \cdot 5}$

   q) $\dfrac{0}{1}$ r) $\dfrac{144 \cdot 5}{144 \cdot 7}$ s) $\dfrac{18 \cdot 55}{18 \cdot 143}$ t) $\dfrac{2145 \cdot 24}{2145 \cdot 35}$

2. Remark about the advantages and dangers of canceling nonprime factors [parts (n), (r), (s), and (t) of Exercise 1].

3. Provide the argument dismissed by the phrase "This is trivial if a or c is 0" (page 283).

4. a) Extend the chart on page 283 four more lines (down).

   b) Look for patterns in the chart, draw conclusions, and prove some of your conclusions.

5. Reduce the following to lowest terms.

   a) $\dfrac{\frac{17}{6}}{8}$ b) $\dfrac{\frac{2}{3}}{\frac{4}{3}}$ c) $\dfrac{\frac{7}{10}}{\frac{3}{10}}$ d) $\dfrac{6}{-\frac{3}{2}}$

6. Denote by a fraction in lowest terms the rational solution to the following equations.

   a) $8x = 4$ b) $\frac{2}{3}x = 10$ c) $\frac{4}{5}x - \frac{1}{8} = \frac{9}{10}$

   d) $3 - \frac{2}{3}x = 7$ e) $1 = (-5)x$

7. Given that a/b and c/d are fractions in lowest terms, answer the following questions:

   a) Must $\dfrac{ad + bc}{bd}$ be in lowest terms?

   b) Must $\dfrac{ad - bc}{bd}$ be in lowest terms?

   c) Must $\dfrac{ac}{bd}$ be in lowest terms?

   d) Must $\dfrac{ad}{bc}$ be in lowest terms?

   e) Illustrate your answers with examples.

8–12   order in Q

When we discussed I, we defined $<$ by

$$a < b \Leftrightarrow b - a \in N.$$

N originally denoted the natural numbers, but when we viewed N as a subset of I we began to refer to it as the set of "positive" integers. Thus our definition was

$$a < b \Leftrightarrow b - a \text{ is a "positive" integer.}$$

Our intention now is to define what it means to call a rational number "positive," and then to define $<$ on Q by

$$u < v \Leftrightarrow v - u \text{ is a "positive" rational.}$$

Definition   The rational number denoted by the fraction a/b will be called "positive" if and only if $ab > 0$. [*Note:* a/b a fraction $\Rightarrow a, b \in I \Rightarrow ab \in I \Rightarrow$ we can decide whether or not $ab > 0$. The $<$ is our good old $<$ on I. See Exercise 1 below.] Nonzero, nonpositive rationals are called "negative."

Example $\dfrac{1}{10}, \dfrac{9}{4}, \dfrac{-3}{-8}, \dfrac{-12}{-3}$ are positive, while $\dfrac{0}{1}, \dfrac{3}{-1}, \dfrac{-4}{2}, \dfrac{-3}{75}$ are not.

Definition $\dfrac{a}{b} < \dfrac{c}{d} \Leftrightarrow \dfrac{c}{d} - \dfrac{a}{b}$ is "positive."

The familiar theorems of Trichotomy, Transitivity, and Monotony (cf. page 263) are consequences of these definitions, but the proofs are most neatly accomplished by first establishing certain analogous properties for the set of all positive rationals. We leave this as an exercise for the interested reader (see Exercises 2 and 3).

EXERCISES 8–12

1. Suppose that a rational number is named by both fractions a/b and c/d. If the label a/b proclaims the rational number to be positive, must the label c/d do the same? (That is, does $a/b = c/d$ and $ab > 0 \Rightarrow cd > 0$?) Unless the answer to this question is yes, our definition of positive is ambiguous.

2. Let Q^+ denote the set of all positive rationals. Prove the following.

   a) For each $r \in Q$, exactly one of $r \in Q^+, r = 0, -r \in Q^+$ holds.

   (Use the theorem on page 282 and the Lemma on page 263.)

   b) $r, s \in Q^+ \Rightarrow r + s \in Q^+$

   c) $r, s \in Q^+ \Rightarrow rs \in Q^+$

Now state and prove the following.

    d) Trichotomy theorem for Q.

    e) Transitivity theorem for Q.

    f) Monotony theorems for Q.

3. State and prove the "cancellation laws" for $<$.

4. Classify as positive or negative the following (use definition!).

    a) $\frac{1}{7}$ b) $\frac{2}{9}$ c) $\dfrac{-6}{10}$

    d) $\frac{a}{b}$, where a and b are positive integers

    e) $-\frac{a}{b}$, where a and b are positive integers

5. Prove the following, using the definitions of $<$ and *positive*.

    a) $\frac{3}{7} < \frac{4}{7}$

    b) $\frac{5}{9} < \frac{7}{9}$

    c) $\dfrac{a}{5} < \dfrac{b}{5}$, where $a < b$, $a, b \in I$

    d) $\dfrac{3}{c} < \dfrac{7}{c}$, where c is a positive integer

    e) $\dfrac{a}{c} < \dfrac{b}{c}$, given that a, b, c are positive integers and $a < b$. (Is it necessary that we assume that a and b are positive?)

    f) $0 < \frac{1}{7}$

    g) $0 < \frac{2}{9}$

    h) $0 < \dfrac{a}{b}$, given that a, b are positive integers

    i) $\dfrac{-a}{b} < 0$, given that a, b are positive integers

    j) $\frac{2}{9} < \frac{86}{13}$

    k) $\dfrac{-86}{13} < \dfrac{-2}{9}$

    l) $\dfrac{a}{b} < \dfrac{c}{d} \Rightarrow -\left(\dfrac{c}{d}\right) < \left(\dfrac{-a}{b}\right)$

    m) $\frac{1}{3} < \frac{9}{10}$

    n) $\frac{10}{9} < \frac{3}{1}$

    o) Given that a, b, c, d are positive integers, $\dfrac{a}{b} < \dfrac{c}{d} \Rightarrow \dfrac{b}{a} > \dfrac{d}{c}$

6. Between any two rationals there is another rational. In fact, if $u < v$, then

$$u < \frac{u + v}{2} < v. \text{ Prove this. } \left[Hint: v = \frac{2v}{2} = \frac{(1 + 1)v}{2} = \frac{v + v}{2}. \right]$$

7. (A problem for the entire chapter) List as many "cancellation" rules as you can for Q. Be careful to accompany each with the conditions which must be satisfied before the rule can be applied.

8. Comment on the following "cancellations."

a) $6 + \not{2} \cdot 3 = 8 + \not{2} \cdot 2$

b) $\dfrac{5 + \not{4} \cdot 3}{6 + \not{4} \cdot 5}$

c) $5 - \not{3} = a - \not{3}$

d) $a^{\not{2}} = 3^{\not{2}}$

e) $\dfrac{3}{\not{4}} = \dfrac{a}{\not{4}}$

f) $\dfrac{6 - \not{3}}{10 - \not{3}}$

g) $(-\not{2}) \cdot 5 < (-\not{2}) \cdot 3$

h) $\not{5}(7 - 3) = \not{5}(10 - 6)$

i) $6 - \not{x} < 10 - \not{x}$

SUMMARY

Parallel developments of the integers I and rationals Q are presented in this chapter. Each development is motivated by the desire to invent enough new numbers to have solutions to certain equations. The two-column arrangement below calls attention to similarities in the two developments.

In I

Besides the 9 basic axioms, Comm $+$, Assoc $+$, ..., we assume that in I every equation $n + x = m$, $n, m \in W$, has a solution in I; moreover, the only numbers in I are those which satisfy such an equation.

Now we can prove that every equation $b + x = a$, $a, b \in I$, has a unique solution in I. We do this by first proving that each equation $b + x = 0$, $b \in I$, has a unique solution in I. We denote this solution by $-b$ and call it the *negative* of b. Hence

$$b + (-b) = 0, \qquad \forall b \in I.$$

Now we note that the integer $a + (-b)$ is the unique solution of the equation $b + x = a$. We abbreviate $a + (-b)$ as $a - b$ and call

In Q

Besides the 9 basic axioms, we assume that in Q every equation $b \cdot x = a$, $b, a \in I$, $b \neq 0$, has a solution in Q; moreover, the only numbers in Q are those which satisfy such an equation.

Now we can prove that every equation $v \cdot x = u$, $u, v \in Q$, $v \neq 0$, has a unique solution in Q. We do this by first proving that each equation $v \cdot x = 1$, $v \in Q$, $v \neq 0$, has a unique solution in Q. We denote this solution by $\frac{1}{v}$ and call it the *reciprocal* of v. Hence

$$v \cdot \frac{1}{v} = 1, \qquad \forall v \in Q, \qquad v \neq 0.$$

Now we note that the rational number $u \cdot \frac{1}{v}$ is the unique solution of the equation $v \cdot x = u$. We abbreviate this number a *minus* b, the *difference* of a and b, or b *subtracted* from a.

It follows that for all a, b, c, $d \in I$,

1) $a - 0 = a$

2) $-(-a) = a$

(The negative of the negative of a is a.)

3) $(-a) + (-b) = -(a + b)$

(The sum of the negatives of two integers is the negative of their sum.)

4) $-(a - b) = b - a$

(The negative of the difference of two integers is their difference in the reverse order.)

5) $(a + b) - (a + c) = b - c$

6) $(a - b) + (c - d) = (a + c) - (b + d)$

7) $(a - b) - (c - d) = (a - b) + (d - c) = (a + d) - (b + c)$

8) $(-1) \cdot a = -a;$
   $a \cdot (-b) = -(ab)$
   $(-a)(-b) = ab$

9) $(a - b) \cdot (c - d) = (ac + bd) - (ad + bc)$

In particular the rules above hold if a, b, c, d are whole numbers. These rules tell us how to handle minus signs in I. But we have not yet agreed on names for our integers. We should be able to name integers with whole-number symbols.

Each integer a satisfies an equation

$$n + x = m, \qquad m, n \in W,$$

so a possible name is $m - n$. But each integer has many such names.

$u \cdot \frac{1}{v}$ as $\frac{u}{v}$ and call this number u *over* v, the *quotient* of u and v, or v *divided into* u.

It follows that for all u, v, w, $y \in Q$ (provided no denominators are zero)

1') $\dfrac{u}{1} = u$

2') $\dfrac{1}{1/u} = u$

(The reciprocal of the reciprocal of u is u.)

3') $\dfrac{1}{u} \cdot \dfrac{1}{v} = \dfrac{1}{uv}$

(The product of the reciprocals of two rational numbers is the reciprocal of their product.)

4') $\dfrac{1}{u/v} = \dfrac{v}{u}$

(The reciprocal of the quotient of two rational numbers is their quotient taken in the reverse order.)

5') $\dfrac{u \cdot v}{u \cdot w} = \dfrac{v}{w}$

6') $\dfrac{u}{v} \cdot \dfrac{y}{w} = \dfrac{u \cdot y}{v \cdot w}$

7') $\dfrac{u/v}{y/w} = \dfrac{u}{v} \cdot \dfrac{w}{y} = \dfrac{u \cdot w}{v \cdot y}$

8') $(-1) \cdot u = -u;$
   $u \cdot (-v) = -(u \cdot v)$
   $(-u)(-v) = uv$

9') $\dfrac{u}{v} + \dfrac{y}{w} = \dfrac{uw + yv}{vw}$

In particular the rules above hold if u, v, w, y are integers. These rules tell us how to handle fractions in Q. But we have not yet agreed on names for our rational numbers. We should be able to name rational numbers with integer symbols.

For example,

if $8 + a = 3$, then $18 + a = 13$,

and the integer a has both $3 - 8$ and $13 - 18$ for names.

We would like to choose unique names for integers. In order to do this, we prove the following theorem:

Each nonzero integer has a unique name m or $-m$, where $m \in W$. (That is, each integer is either a whole number or the negative of a whole number.)

The nonzero whole numbers are called *positive integers* and those integers not whole numbers are called *negative integers*.

We define $a < b$ to mean that $b - a$ is a positive integer.

Trichotomy, Transitivity, and Monotony hold as described below:

i) $\forall a, b \in I$, exactly one of $a < b$, $a = b$, $b < a$ holds.

ii) $\forall a, b, c \in I, a < b$ and $b < c \Rightarrow a < c$.

iii) $\forall a, b, c \in I$,

$a < b \Rightarrow a + c < b + c$,
$a < b$ and $0 < c \Rightarrow ac < bc$,
$a < b$ and $c < 0 \Rightarrow ac > bc$.

Each rational u satisfies an equation $b \cdot x = a$, $a, b \in I$, so a possible name is $\frac{a}{b}$. But each rational number has many such names. For example, if $8 \cdot u = 3$, then $80 \cdot u = 30$, and the rational u has both $\frac{3}{8}$ and $\frac{30}{80}$ for names.

We would like to choose unique names for rationals. In order to do this we prove the following theorem:

Each rational number has a unique name $\frac{a}{b}$, where a and b are integers, b is positive, and the greatest common factor of a and b is 1.

A nonzero rational number $\frac{a}{b}$ is called *positive* if the integer $a \cdot b$ is positive, *negative* if $a \cdot b$ is negative.

We define $u < v$ to mean that $v - u$ is a positive rational number.

Trichotomy, Transitivity, and Monotony hold as described below:

i) $\forall u, v \in Q$, exactly one of $u < v$, $u = v$, $v < u$ holds.

ii) $\forall u, v, w \in Q, u < v$ and $v < w \Rightarrow u < w$

iii) $\forall u, v, w \in Q$,

$u < v \Rightarrow u + w < v + w$,
$u < v$ and $0 < w \Rightarrow u \cdot w < v \cdot w$,
$u < v$ and $w < 0 \Rightarrow u \cdot w > v \cdot w$.

9 decimals

9–1 introduction

We have two purposes in mind in discussing decimals at this time. One is that the concept is an extremely *practical* one. The society we live in transacts most of its quantitative business in the efficient language of decimals, and consequently much school time is devoted to their study. The other is that decimals provide a bridge from the relatively concrete system of rational numbers to the highly abstract system of real numbers.

In this chapter we develop the concept of decimal and explore some of its practical applications. In the next chapter we use it to lend substance to the apparitional real numbers.

9–2 why decimals?

Fractions in lowest terms are not the most pleasant symbols with which to compute. Consider the problem of computing

$$\frac{45}{68} + \frac{13}{19}.$$

By our rule for adding fractions, this is

$$\frac{45 \cdot 19 + 68 \cdot 13}{68 \cdot 19}.$$

Simplifying involves finding three products and one sum

$$45 \cdot 19 = 855, \qquad 68 \cdot 13 = 884, \qquad 68 \cdot 19 = 1292;$$
$$855 + 884 = 1739.$$

The answer is $\frac{1739}{1292}$. It would have been much easier had we been asked to compute

$$\frac{855}{1292} + \frac{884}{1292}.$$

Then we would only have had to add numerators.

Consider another problem. Which is greater, $\frac{45}{68}$ or $\frac{13}{19}$? To answer this, we would perform two multiplications,

$$45 \cdot 19 = 855, \qquad 68 \cdot 13 = 884,$$

rewrite,

$$\frac{45}{68} = \frac{45 \cdot 19}{68 \cdot 19} = \frac{855}{68 \cdot 19}, \qquad \frac{13}{19} = \frac{68 \cdot 13}{68 \cdot 19} = \frac{884}{68 \cdot 19},$$

and deduce that $\frac{45}{68} < \frac{13}{19}$ because

$$\frac{855}{68 \cdot 19} < \frac{884}{68 \cdot 19}.$$

[cf. Exercise 5(e), page 286, Chapter 8]. A much easier problem would have been: Which is greater, $\frac{855}{1292}$ or $\frac{884}{1292}$?

The point of these examples is that adding and comparing fractions is much harder than adding and comparing integers, unless the fractions happen to have a *common denominator*. The same is of course true for subtraction.

For multiplication, even having common denominators is no help. For example, to compute the product of fractions, $\frac{19}{32} \cdot \frac{15}{32}$, we must compute two products of integers,

$$19 \cdot 15 = 285, \qquad 32 \cdot 32 = 1024,$$

to get the answer, $\frac{285}{1024}$.

An example of an easier type of multiplication problem is $\frac{19}{32} \cdot \frac{15}{100}$, the reason being that one of the denominators is so nice that we can compute the product of the denominators mentally.

If one chooses to work only with fractions having denominators that are powers of ten, then these denominators are so nice that finding products and common denominators is child's play. Computational difficulties disappear; it is as easy to work with these fractions as it is to work with integers.

Example 1   Compute $\frac{869}{1000} + \frac{17}{10}$.

$$\frac{17}{10} = \frac{1700}{1000} \quad \text{(child's play)}.$$

Therefore, we have

$$\frac{869}{1000} + \frac{17}{10} = \frac{869}{1000} + \frac{1700}{1000} = \frac{869 + 1700}{1000} = \frac{2569}{1000}.$$

(As easy as adding 869 and 1700.)

Example 2   Which is larger, $\frac{365}{1000}$ or $\frac{8}{100}$?

$$\frac{8}{100} = \frac{80}{1000} \text{ (child's play)} \qquad \text{and} \qquad \frac{80}{1000} < \frac{365}{1000}.$$

(As easy as comparing 365 and 80.)

Example 3   Compute $\frac{17}{10} \cdot \frac{96}{100}$.

$$10 \cdot 100 = 1000 \text{ (child's play)} \qquad \text{and so} \qquad \frac{17}{10} \cdot \frac{96}{100} = \frac{17 \cdot 96}{10 \cdot 100} = \frac{1632}{1000}.$$

(As easy as finding 17 times 96.)

When we work with decimals we are working with precisely this special collection of fractions. The answer to the question "Why decimals?" is "They are so nice to work with."

Perhaps all this reminds you of the simpleton who lost his watch in a dark alley and looked for it under the street lamp because the light was better there. To begin with, we worked with fractions because they denote rational numbers. Then we began to bemoan the difficulties associated with fractions. Now we've seen that these difficulties can be avoided by simply throwing out all but the nicest fractions. The trouble is that this throws out all but a special kind of rational as well. For example, none of the rationals denoted by

$$\frac{1}{3}, \frac{5}{6}, \frac{2}{7}, \frac{1}{11}$$

can be denoted by decimals.

So what is the point of working with decimals? The answer is that *every* rational number is represented by something very much like a decimal. We shall elaborate on this in Section 9–6, but right now let us define decimals carefully and review the way they are used.

EXERCISES 9–1

1. Compute

    a) $\dfrac{175}{10,000} + \dfrac{350}{1,000}$

    b) $\dfrac{86}{100} + \dfrac{75}{1000}$

    c) $\frac{12}{10} + 6$

    d) $5 - \frac{35}{100}$

e) $\frac{9}{10} \cdot \frac{176}{10}$ f) $\frac{-18}{1,000} \cdot \frac{35}{1,000}$ i) $\dfrac{\frac{3}{100}}{\frac{6}{10,000}}$

g) $\frac{-63}{100} - \frac{3}{10,000}$ h) $\dfrac{\frac{24}{10}}{\frac{16}{100}}$

2. Compare: a) $\frac{97}{1000}$ and $\frac{11}{100}$;   b) $\frac{5675}{100,000}$ and $\frac{437}{10,000}$.

3. a) Prove that there is no whole number n such that $\frac{1}{3} = \frac{n}{10}$.

   [*Hint.*   Use the Fundamental Theorem of Arithmetic.]

   b) Prove that there are no whole numbers n and m such that

$$\frac{1}{3} = \frac{n}{10^m}.$$

4. Perform the analysis of Exercise 3 on   a) $\frac{5}{6}$,   b) $\frac{2}{7}$,   c) $\frac{1}{11}$.

5. Consider the calculation

$$\frac{3}{8} = \frac{3}{2 \cdot 2 \cdot 2} = \frac{3 \cdot \overset{5}{\cancel{10}} \cdot \overset{5}{\cancel{10}} \cdot \overset{5}{\cancel{10}}}{\cancel{2} \cdot \cancel{2} \cdot \cancel{2} \cdot 10 \cdot 10 \cdot 10} = \frac{375}{1000}.$$

   a) Write $\frac{3}{4}$ as a fraction with denominator a power of 10.

   b) Write $\frac{3}{16}$ as a fraction with denominator a power of 10.

   c) Write $\frac{7}{125}$ as a fraction with denominator a power of 10.

   d) Write $\frac{97}{400}$ as a fraction with denominator a power of 10.

6. Why don't sports pages report batting proficiency using fractions of the form

$$\frac{\text{Base hits}}{\text{Official times at bat}} ?$$

   This certainly conveys a lot of information.

7. Give a few objections to the following proposal for simplifying computations with fractions: "Let's agree on a universal common denominator, say 1,000,000, and work only with fractions having that denominator."

9–3   decimals defined

In order to define decimal we must extend the concept of exponent discussed in Chapter 5 (pages 165–166).

For any nonzero rational r, we define the powers of r: $r^0, r^1, r^2, r^3, \ldots$, successively by

$$r^0 = 1, \quad r^1 = r, \quad r^2 = r \cdot r, \quad r^3 = r \cdot r \cdot r, \quad \ldots$$

Observe that this agrees with our earlier definition of powers of a natural number when r belongs to the subset N of Q. As a consequence of this definition we have the following familiar theorem.

Theorem   (Laws of Exponents)

$$r^m \cdot r^n = r^{m+n}, \qquad (r^m)^n = r^{mn}, \qquad \forall m, n \in W.$$

You may recall that we defined $r^0 = 1$ precisely so that this theorem would be true for all $m, n \in W$ (not just N). We now intend to define negative exponents in such a way that this theorem remains true for all $m, n \in I$ (not just W). Consider the following example:

$$1 = \frac{36}{36} = \frac{6^2}{6^2} = 6^2 \cdot \frac{1}{6^2}.$$

Thus if we were to define 6^{-2} as $\dfrac{1}{6^2}$, we would have

$$6^2 \cdot 6^{-2} = 6^2 \cdot \frac{1}{6^2} = 1 = 6^0 = 6^{2+(-2)}.$$

The exponents would have "added up."

Considerations of this sort lead us to the following.

Definition $r^{-1} = 1/r, \ r^{-2} = 1/r^2, \ \ldots,$ or, more concisely, $r^{-n} = 1/r^n$, $\forall n \in N$. We have thus defined r^a for all nonzero $r \in Q$ and for all $a \in I$. And this definition does lead to the theorem we want.

Theorem   1. $r^a \cdot r^b = r^{a+b}$ $\begin{cases} \forall a, b \in I \\ \forall r \in Q; \ r \neq 0 \end{cases}$

  2. $(r^a)^b = r^{ab}$

Proof   A careful proof requires induction and a recursive definition of exponentiation; a semicareful proof requires the investigation of many cases ($a > 0$ and $b > 0$; $a > 0$ and $b < 0$ and $a > -b$; $\ldots$). We examine only a few special cases.

1–1 $r^5 \cdot r^{-7} = r^5 \cdot \dfrac{1}{r^7} = r^5 \cdot \left(\dfrac{1}{r}\right)^7$ (cf. Exercise 1 following)

$$= \left(r \cdot \left(r \cdot \left(r \cdot \left(r \cdot \left(r \cdot \frac{1}{r}\right) \cdot \frac{1}{r}\right) \cdot \frac{1}{r}\right) \cdot \frac{1}{r}\right) \cdot \frac{1}{r}\right) \cdot \frac{1}{r} \cdot \frac{1}{r}$$

$$= \frac{1}{r} \cdot \frac{1}{r} = \left(\frac{1}{r}\right)^2 = \frac{1}{r^2} \quad \text{(cf. Exercise 1)}$$

$$= r^{-2} = r^{5+(-7)}.$$

1–2 $r^0 \cdot r^3 = 1 \cdot r^3 = r^3 = r^{0+3}$.

2–1 $(r^2)^{-3} = \dfrac{1}{(r^2)^3} = \left(\dfrac{1}{r^2}\right)^3$ (cf. Exercise 1)

$\qquad = \left[\left(\dfrac{1}{r}\right)^2\right]^3$ (cf. Exercise 1)

$\qquad = \left(\dfrac{1}{r} \cdot \dfrac{1}{r}\right)^3 = \left(\dfrac{1}{r} \cdot \dfrac{1}{r}\right) \cdot \left(\dfrac{1}{r} \cdot \dfrac{1}{r}\right) \cdot \left(\dfrac{1}{r} \cdot \dfrac{1}{r}\right)$

$\qquad = \left(\dfrac{1}{r}\right)^6 = \dfrac{1}{r^6}$ (cf. Exercise 1)

$\qquad = r^{-6} = r^{2(-3)}$.

2–2 $(r^0)^{-4} = 1^{-4} = \dfrac{1}{1^4} = \left(\dfrac{1}{1}\right)^4$ (cf. Exercise 1)

$\qquad = 1^4 = 1 = r^0 = r^{0(-4)}$.

We can now extend our early notion of expanded form. Recall that the decimal numeral 10,457 equals

$$1 \cdot 10^4 + 0 \cdot 10^3 + 4 \cdot 10^2 + 5 \cdot 10^1 + 7 \cdot 10^0.$$

We now make the further convention that (for example)

$.23 = 2 \cdot 10^{-1} + 3 \cdot 10^{-2} \left(= \dfrac{2}{10} + \dfrac{3}{10^2} = \dfrac{2}{10} + \dfrac{3}{100} \right);$

$5.101 = 5 + 1 \cdot 10^{-1} + 0 \cdot 10^{-2} + 1 \cdot 10^{-3}$

$\left(= 5 + \dfrac{1}{10} + \dfrac{0}{10^2} + \dfrac{1}{10^3} = 5 + \dfrac{1}{10} + \dfrac{1}{1000} \right);$

$276.95 = 2 \cdot 10^2 + 7 \cdot 10 + 6 + 9 \cdot 10^{-1} + 5 \cdot 10^{-2}$

$\left(= 2 \cdot 10^2 + 7 \cdot 10 + 6 + \dfrac{9}{10} + \dfrac{5}{10^2} = 2 \cdot 100 + 7 \cdot 10 + 6 + \dfrac{9}{10} + \dfrac{5}{100} \right.$

$\left. = 200 + 70 + 6 + \dfrac{9}{10} + \dfrac{5}{100} \right).$

Or, somewhat more suggestively,

$276.95 = 2 \cdot 10^2 + 7 \cdot 10^1 + 6 \cdot 10^0 + 9 \cdot 10^{-1} + 5 \cdot 10^{-2}.$

Any symbol of the form exemplified by 276.95 is called a *decimal numeral*. This term implies that the symbol is to be interpreted using the base-ten-exponential-positional convention (i.e., the interpretation in color). [*Note:* The symbol need not have a decimal point to qualify as a decimal numeral; 10,457 is as much a decimal numeral as is 5.75. The word "decimal" comes from the Latin *decem*, meaning ten, and refers to the base of our numeration system.]

Often we refer to symbols of the form

11.34, -1.025, .75

simply as *decimals* to distinguish them from integers. We'll not try to make such distinctions. We'll use the word "decimal" to refer to any of the broad class of decimal numerals. (Thus we won't be forced to distinguish between 17 and 17.0.) We shall need one more bit of terminology. The number 23.1475 is called a "four-place decimal" because there are four digits to the right of the decimal point.

EXERCISES 9–2

1. Prove that $r^{-6} = (r^{-1})^6$; that is, that

$$\frac{1}{r^6} = \left(\frac{1}{r}\right)^6, \qquad r \neq 0, r \in Q. \qquad \text{Generalize.}$$

   [*Hint:* Use rule 2 for fractions.]

2. Simplify the following. (There are two ways to do most of them.)
   a) 2^{-5} b) $(2^3)^{-2}$ c) $2^2 \cdot 2^3$
   d) $2^2 \cdot 3^2$ e) $2^2 \cdot 3^{-2}$ f) $2^2 \cdot 3^3$

   g) $(2^{-1})^4$ h) $\dfrac{2^{-2}}{2^3}$ i) $\dfrac{2}{2^{-4}}$

   j) $\left(\dfrac{2^2}{3^{-2}}\right)^{-1}$ k) $\dfrac{2^{-2}}{3^2}$ l) $2^2 \cdot 2^{-2}$

   m) $(2^5)^0$ n) 10^2 o) 10^4
   p) 10^{10} q) $10^{15} \cdot 10^{11}$

3. Verify the following as we did on pages 294–295.
   a) $r^{-3} \cdot r^{-2} = r^{(-3)+(-2)}$
   b) $(r^{-3})^{-2} = r^{(-3) \cdot (-2)}$

4. How ought one to define 0^a ($a \in I$) so that the laws of exponents continue to hold?

5. Express each of the following decimals in expanded form.
   a) 17.15   b) 223.1   c) 728
   d) .003   e) 10652.037   f) 54,000
   g) .23   h) 5.101   i) 12.71828

6. Verify the following.
   a) $17.15 = 10 + 7 + .1 + .05$
   b) $5.101 = 5 + .1 + .001$
   c) $10652.037 = 10{,}000 + 600 + 50 + 2 + .03 + .007$

7. Verify the following.
   a) $17.15 = 10 + 7 + \frac{1}{10} + \frac{5}{100}$
   b) $5.101 = 5 + \frac{1}{10} + \frac{1}{1000}$
   c) $10652.037 = 10,000 + 600 + 50 + 2 + \frac{3}{100} + \frac{7}{1000}$

8. Verify the following.
   a) $17.15 = \frac{1715}{100}$
   b) $5.101 = \frac{5101}{1000}$
   c) $10652.037 = \frac{10652037}{1000}$
   d) Does every decimal denote a rational number?
   e) Does every decimal equal a fraction whose denominator is a power of 10?
   f) Does every fraction whose denominator is a power of 10 equal a decimal?
   g) Is every rational number labeled by a fraction whose denominator is a power of 10?

9. Write each of the following (1) as a fraction, (2) as an integer (as small as possible) times a power of 10.
   a) 2.03   b) 1.725   c) 2.3
   d) .00465   e) 211.5   f) 21.7308
   g) 2.718281828459045

10. Comment on the illusory nature of the property "four decimal places" by comparing: 23.1475, 23.14750, 23.147500000.

11. a) Write as fractions: 1080.891, 81.7.
    b) Add the fractions in (a) and convert the answer to a decimal.
    c) Subtract the fractions in (a) and convert the answer to a decimal.
    d) Multiply the fractions in (a) and convert the answer to a decimal.
    e) Divide the fractions in (a) and convert the answer to a decimal.

12. a) Express 1080.891 in expanded form.
    b) Multiply the expanded form in (a) by 10 and rewrite as a decimal. Repeat this process, using as a multiplier 10^{-2}, 10^5, 10^{-6}. What is the effect on the decimal point of multiplying by positive and negative powers of 10?
    c) Multiply each of 1080.891 and 81.7 by 10^3, add the resulting whole numbers, and multiply the sum by 10^{-3}. Compare with Exercise 11(b).
    d) Multiply each of 1080.891 and 81.7 by 10^3, subtract, and multiply the difference by 10^{-3}. Compare with Exercise 11(c).
    e) Multiply 1080.891 by 10^3, 81.7 by 10^1, multiply the resulting numbers, and multiply the product by 10^{-4} $(=10^{-(3+1)})$. Compare with Exercise 11(d).
    f) Multiply 1080.891 by 10^3, divide the resulting number by the product of 81.7 and 10^1. Multiply the quotient by 10^{-2} $(= 10^{1-3})$. Compare with Exercise 11(e).

9–4   the algorithms for decimals

The addition algorithm.   To add two decimals, write them down so that the decimal point of one is directly below the decimal point of the other. If necessary supply 0's so that both have the same number of decimal places. Add them as though there were no decimal points. Insert a decimal point in the sum directly below the decimal points of the summands.

$$
\begin{array}{r}
1080.891 \\
81.700 \\
\hline
1162.591
\end{array}
$$

To see why the rule works, let $a = 1080.891$ and $b = 81.7$. We want to find $a + b$.

$$
\begin{aligned}
10^3 a &= 1080891 \\
10^3 b &= 81700
\end{aligned}
$$

Thus $10^3 a + 10^3 b = 1162591$.

This corresponds to lining up decimal points, supplying any necessary 0's, and adding as though there were no decimal points.

By the distributive law, $10^3 (a + b) = 1162591$.

Therefore

$$10^{-3} 10^3 (a + b) = 10^{-3}(1162591).$$

That is,

$$10^0 (a + b) = 1162.591$$

This corresponds to inserting decimal point in sum directly below decimal points of summands.

or

$$a + b = 1162.591.$$

You may prefer to justify the rule by working with fractions rather than exponents.

$$1080.891 + 81.7 = \frac{1080891}{1000} + \frac{817}{10}$$

$$= \frac{1080891}{1000} + \frac{81700}{1000}$$

Lining up decimal points and supplying necessary 0's.

$$= \frac{1080891 + 81700}{1000}$$

Adding, ignoring decimal points.

$$= \frac{1162591}{1000}$$

$$= 1162.591.$$

Inserting decimal point in sum below decimal points of summands.

The multiplication algorithm. To multiply two decimals multiply them as though there were no decimal points. Then add the number of decimal places of one of them to the number of decimal places of the other and insert a decimal point in the product, so that it has this number (the sum) of decimal places.

$$\begin{array}{ll} 1080.891 & \text{(3 decimal places)} \\ \underline{\times\ 81.7} & \text{(1 decimal place)} \\ 88308.7947 & \text{(3 + 1 = 4 decimal places)} \end{array}$$

To see why the rule works, let $a = 1080.891$ and $b = 81.7$. We want to find ab.

$10^3a = 1080891$ $10^1b = 817$	This corresponds to counting decimal places in each factor, then

Thus

$10^3a \cdot 10^1b = 883087947$	ignoring decimal point and multiplying as usual.
That is, $\quad 10^3 \cdot 10^1(ab) = 883087947$	This corresponds to adding up the number of decimal places of the factors.
That is, $\quad\quad 10^{3+1}(ab) = 883087947$	
That is, $\quad\quad\quad 10^4(ab) = 883087947$	

Thus

$10^{-4}10^4(ab) = 10^{-4}(883087947)$ or $ab = 88308.7947$	This corresponds to "pointing off" the proper number of places in the product.

If you prefer to think in terms of fractions,

$$1080.891 \times 81.7 = \frac{1080891}{1000} \times \frac{817}{10} = \frac{1080891 \times 817}{1000 \times 10} = \frac{883087947}{10000}$$
$$= 88308.7947.$$

The division algorithm. The situation for division is much more involved. If we begin with a simple problem, "Divide 1.56 by 1.2," a simple chant suffices.

Simple chant. Ignore decimal points and divide as usual. Then insert a decimal point in the quotient so that its number of decimal places = (number of decimal places in dividend) − (number of decimal places in divisor).

$$\begin{array}{r} 1.3 \ (2 - 1 = 1 \text{ decimal place}) \\ 1.2\,\overline{\smash)\,1.56} \ (2 \text{ decimal places}) \\ \longrightarrow (1 \text{ decimal place}) \end{array}$$

This chant can be justified immediately by looking at the example as a multiplication problem: $1.2 \times 1.3 = 1.56$. We give a more detailed analysis as well, to illustrate how the subtraction of decimal places is related to the law of exponents.

Let $a = 1.2$, $b = 1.56$. Find b/a.

$10^1 a = 12$, $10^2 b = 156$ Counting decimal places of divisor and dividend.

Thus

$$13 = \frac{156}{12} = \frac{10^2 b}{10^1 a} = 10^2 \cdot 10^{-1} \frac{b}{a} = 10^{2-1} \frac{b}{a} = 10^1 \frac{b}{a}$$

↑

Dividing
as usual

Subtracting decimal places of divisor from decimal places of dividend.

Thus

$$10^{-1} 10^1 \frac{b}{a} = 10^{-1} (13)$$

Pointing off proper number of places in quotient.

That is, $\dfrac{b}{a} = 1.3$.

For those who prefer fractions,

$$\frac{1.56}{1.2} = \frac{\frac{156}{100}}{\frac{12}{10}} = \frac{156}{100} \times \frac{10}{12} = \frac{156}{12} \times \frac{10}{100} = 13 \times \tfrac{1}{10} = 1.3.$$

In a problem such as "Divide 36 by 1.2," the chant doesn't quite work. We cannot have a quotient boasting $0 - 1 = -1$ decimal places. We have to prefix our chant with this warning. If dividend has fewer decimal places than does divisor, then annex enough 0's to the dividend so that it has as many.

           30 ← quotient has $1 - 1 = 0$ decimal places

1.2 | 36.0 ← annex 0 to get 1 decimal place

       ↖ 1 decimal place

To justify this, let $a = 1.2$ and $b = 36$ and find b/a:

$10^1 a = 12$, $b = 36$.

Thus

$$3 = \frac{36}{12} = \frac{b}{10^1 a} = 10^{-1} \left(\frac{b}{a}\right).$$

Thus

$$10^1 10^{-1} \frac{b}{a} = 10^1 \cdot 3 \quad \text{or} \quad \frac{b}{a} = 30.$$

In terms of fractions,

$$\frac{36}{1.2} = \frac{36}{\frac{12}{10}} = 36 \times \frac{10}{12} = \frac{36}{12} \times 10 = 3 \times 10 = 30.$$

Consider another example: Divide .6 by 1.2. The dividend has as many decimal places as the divisor, so it seems we should go directly to our simple chant. But when we ignore decimal points and try to divide as usual, we find that 12 does not divide 6 evenly (i.e., the quotient is not an integer). We, of course, get around this difficulty by annexing another 0 to the dividend.

$$.5 \leftarrow 2 - 1 = 1 \text{ decimal place}$$

$$1.2 \overline{\smash{)}\,.60} \leftarrow 2 \text{ decimal places; } 0$$

$$\uparrow \qquad \text{annexed so that division comes out even.}$$

1 decimal place

So we patch up our chant again.

Revised chant. Annex enough 0's to the dividend so that both the following conditions are satisfied:

a) Number of decimal places in dividend ≥ number of decimal places in divisor.

b) When decimal points are ignored, the division comes out even (yields integral quotient).

Then, as in the simple chant, divide, ignoring decimal points and point off in quotient so that (number of decimal places in quotient) = (number of decimal places in dividend) − (number of decimal places in divisor).

Fortunately, once we have annexed enough 0's to satisfy (a), we have a systematic method of determining how many more are needed to satisfy (b). Consider the following example: Divide 17.5 by .56.

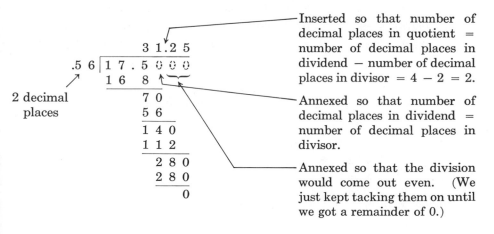

Inserted so that number of decimal places in quotient = number of decimal places in dividend − number of decimal places in divisor = 4 − 2 = 2.

Annexed so that number of decimal places in dividend = number of decimal places in divisor.

Annexed so that the division would come out even. (We just kept tacking them on until we got a remainder of 0.)

Justification: Let $a = .56$ and $b = 17.5$. Find b/a.

$10^2 a = 56$ Exponent 2 chosen to purge decimal point

$10^4 b = 175000$ Exponent 4 chosen experimentally; all we knew for sure was that it had to be ≥ 2.

$3125 = \dfrac{175000}{56} = \dfrac{10^4 b}{10^2 a} = 10^4 \cdot 10^{-2}(b/a)$ Even division occurred after annexation of third 0.

$\quad = 10^{4-2}(b/a) = 10^2(b/a)$ Exponent 2 represents decimal places in dividend minus decimal places in divisor.

Thus

$b/a = 10^{-2} 10^2 (b/a) = 10^{-2}(3125) = 31.25$ Pointing off proper number of places in quotient.

In case the detailed analyses given for the algorithms have obscured the important point we have been trying to make, we repeat it. Computations with decimals are almost as easy as computations with integers. The only new procedures are the quickly accomplished ones of "annexing zeros" and "pointing off."

EXERCISES 9–3

1. Compute the following.
   a) $17.5 + 8.362$ b) $1.004 + 21.099$ c) $9.6 + .088 + 13.452$
   d) $11 + 3.41$ e) $.004 + 5 + 6.5$ f) 10.5×14.6
   g) $.004 \times .6$ h) 15×3.17 i) $6.1 \times 2 \times 10.0$
   j) $12.25 \times .335$ k) $86.76 \div 3.6$ l) $.8676 \div .36$
   m) $.08676 \div 36$ n) $867600 \div .36$ o) $.0693 \div .36$
   p) $.0693 \div 36$ q) $6.93 \div .00036$ r) $5.143 - 2.7$
   s) $6 - 4.56$ t) $3.46 - 7$ u) $9.742 - 11.5$
   v) $100 - .005$

2. Fill in whole numbers for x, y, z and a decimal for D.

   a) $13 \cdot 7.5 = \dfrac{13}{x} \cdot \dfrac{75}{y} = \dfrac{z}{1000} = D$

   b) $.4 \cdot .02 = \dfrac{4}{x} \cdot \dfrac{2}{y} = \dfrac{8}{z} = D$

   c) $6.3 \div .7 = \dfrac{63}{x} \div \dfrac{7}{y} = \dfrac{63}{x} \cdot \dfrac{y}{7} = D$

d) $.0025 \div .5 = \dfrac{25}{x} \div \dfrac{5}{y} = \dfrac{25}{x} \cdot \dfrac{y}{5} = D$

e) $6 \cdot .025 = \dfrac{6}{x} \cdot \dfrac{25}{y} = \dfrac{150}{z} = D$

f) $.81 \div 90 = \dfrac{81}{x} \div \dfrac{90}{y} = \dfrac{81}{x} \cdot \dfrac{y}{90} = D$

3. Supply a reason at each equals sign in the justifications of (a) the addition algorithm (page 298), (b) the multiplication algorithm (page 299).

4. State and justify the subtraction algorithm for decimals just as we did the addition algorithm. Use the numerical example, $1080.891 - 81.7 = 999.191$.

5. Analyze the following (as in the text) in two ways, using exponents and using fractions: (a) $1.925 + .36$, (b) $1.925 \times .36$, and (c) $693 \div 3.6$.

6. The following examples illustrate a mechanical technique for correctly positioning the decimal point in the quotient. Explain what the technique is and why it works.

$$
\begin{array}{ccc}
1.925 & .1925 & 1925. \\
.36\,\overline{).693} & 36\,\overline{)6.93} & .036\,\overline{)69.300} \\
\end{array}
\quad,
$$

7. In discussing division we found it convenient to rewrite

$$\dfrac{a}{100} \times \dfrac{10}{b} \qquad \text{as} \qquad \dfrac{a}{b} \times \dfrac{10}{100}\,.$$

Prove that these two expressions are equal for all integers a and b ($b \ne 0$). Is it also true for all rationals a and b ($b \ne 0$)?

8. One can easily check whether the decimal point has been correctly placed by *estimating* the answer. Pick the correct solution to each of the following.

a) $.35 \times .18 = .63$ or $.063$ or $.0063$ [*Answer:* $.063$ because $.35 \approx \frac{3}{10}$, $.18 \approx \frac{2}{10}$.   Therefore $.35 \times .18 \approx \frac{6}{100}$.]

b) $18.75 \times 1.12 = 21$ or 210 or 2100

c) $21 \div .4375 = 4.8$ or 48 or 480

d) $.012 \times 125 = .15$ or 1.5 or 15

e) $.6 \div .5 = .12$ or 1.2 or 12

f) $.0096 \div 16 = .006$ or $.0006$ or $.00006$

9–5 rounding off, scientific notation, and percent

There are three special topics connected with decimals which deserve at least brief mention because of their widespread use and their consequent inclusion in the school mathematics curriculum. They are: *rounding off, scientific notation, and percent.*

Rounding off. In many situations exact information is neither available nor desirable. When someone asks you your weight the reply expected and given is probably an approximation to the nearest pound. The weight of a newborn baby, on the other hand, may be reported to the nearest half ounce. The population of a large city may be given to the nearest 100,000, while that of a small town may be given to the nearest 10.

When you are asked to round 16,586 to the nearest hundred, you are really being asked to find the integral multiple of 100 which is nearest to 16,586. Clearly,

$$165 \times 100 = 16{,}500 < 16{,}586 < 16{,}600 = 166 \times 100,$$

and the nearer of the two is 16,600, since

$$16{,}600 - 16{,}586 = 14, \qquad \text{while} \qquad 16{,}586 - 16{,}500 = 86.$$

When you are asked to round off 21.325 to the nearest tenth, you are really being asked to find the integral multiple of $\frac{1}{10}$ which is nearest to 21.325. Clearly,

$$213 \times \tfrac{1}{10} = 21.3 < 21.325 < 21.4 = 214 \times \tfrac{1}{10},$$

and the nearer of the two is 21.3, since

$$21.325 - 21.3 = .025, \qquad \text{while} \qquad 21.4 - 21.325 = .075.$$

Consider the following chart.

The number 4519.8361
rounded to the nearest hundred is 4500
rounded to the nearest   ten   is 4520
rounded to the nearest   unit   is 4520
rounded to the nearest tenth is 4519.8.

The same number, 4520, appears twice, but the second appearance conveys more information than the first because it is accompanied by the phrase "rounded to the nearest unit." We would like a less clumsy way of reporting the accuracy of an approximate figure. The way this is usually done is through the use of "scientific notation."

Scientific notation. Every positive decimal is expressible as a power of ten times a decimal between zero and ten. For example,

$$967.28 = 9.6728 \times 10^2, \qquad .00361 = 3.61 \times 10^{-3}.$$

When a number is expressed as a power of ten times a decimal between 0 and 10, we say that it is *expressed in scientifiic notation.*

The connection between scientific notation and rounding off is best illustrated with examples. If the population of Maine is reported (in scientific notation) as 9.69×10^5, then you are expected to interpret this as meaning that the population is nearer to 969,000 than to either 968,000 or 970,000; that is, it is between 968,500 and 969,500. If the population of Maine is reported (in scientific notation) as 1.0×10^6, you are to interpret this as meaning that the population is nearer to 1.0×10^6 than to $.9 \times 10^6$ or to 1.1×10^6; that is, it is nearer to 1,000,000 than to 900,000 or to 1,100,000. If it is reported as 1×10^6, all you are expected to conclude is that it is nearer to 1×10^6 than to 0×10^6 or to 2×10^6; that is, it is somewhere between 500,000 and 1,500,000.

We expand our earlier chart.

The number 4519.8361

rounded to the nearest hundred is 4500, in scientific notation 4.5×10^3
rounded to the nearest   ten   is 4520, in scientific notation 4.52×10^3
rounded to the nearest   unit   is 4520, in scientific notation 4.520×10^3
rounded to the nearest   tenth is 4519.8, in scientific notation 4.5198×10^3.

The digits reported in the decimal factor in scientific notation are called the "significant digits." They provide the measure of accuracy of the approximation.

Percent. We have seen that fractions having a common denominator are very easy to add, subtract, and compare. The invention of the concept of percent can probably be traced to a longing for a universal common denominator, the choice in the case of percent being one hundred. (*Per centum* is a Latin phrase meaning "out of a hundred.")

A special sort of shorthand has grown up about the notion of percent.

25% is shorthand for $\frac{25}{100}$,

$4\frac{3}{4}\%$ is shorthand for $\dfrac{4\frac{3}{4}}{100} = \left(\dfrac{4 + \frac{3}{4}}{100}\right)$,

5.39% is shorthand for $\dfrac{5.39}{100} = \left(\dfrac{\frac{539}{100}}{100}\right)$.

In general, if r is any rational number

$$r\% = \frac{r}{100}.$$

Since we tolerate symbols like $4\frac{3}{4}\%$, it is an easy matter to write *any* fraction as a percent. For example,

$$\frac{17}{37} = \frac{17 \times 100}{37 \times 100} = \frac{\frac{1700}{37}}{100} = \frac{1700}{37}\%.$$

When dealing with percents, however, it is standard practice to convert to a mixed number any fraction greater than 1. That is,

$45\frac{35}{37}\%$ is preferable to $\frac{1700}{37}\%$ and $46\frac{1}{11}\%$ is preferable to $\frac{507}{11}\%$.

(To see why, try comparing $\frac{1700}{37}\%$ and $\frac{507}{11}\%$. Then try comparing $45\frac{35}{37}\%$ and $46\frac{1}{11}\%$.)

Another standard practice is to express numbers to the nearest percent or to the nearest tenth of a percent. For example,

$\frac{17}{37}$ expressed to the nearest whole percent is 46%,

$\frac{17}{37}$ expressed to the nearest tenth of a percent is 45.9%,

because

$$
\begin{array}{r}
.459 \\
37\overline{\smash{\big)}\ 17.000} \\
14\ 8 \\
\hline
220 \\
185 \\
\hline
350 \\
333 \\
\hline
17 \ < \ \tfrac{1}{2}(37)
\end{array}
$$

EXERCISES 9–4

1. Round to the nearest hundred*th*. Report answer first as just a decimal, and second in scientific notation.

   a) 22.7182   b) 108.354

   c) 7.11932   d) .0657

   e) .699   f) 2.9951

   g) 5   h) 11.6

2. There are reported to be 2.32×10^5 acres of national forest in Vermont. This tells us that the precise number of acres is between what two numbers?

3. a) How do people usually "round off" their age?

   b) How does a grocer "round off" $\frac{79}{3}$?

4. Complete the following chart.

Official U.S. Population in 1810: 7,239,881

		Scientific notation
To the nearest million:	_____ or	_____
To the nearest 100,000:	_____ or	_____
To the nearest 10,000:	_____ or	_____
To the nearest 1,000:	_____ or	_____
To the nearest 100:	_____ or	_____

5. If a number x is approximated by 7.46×10^3, then we know that

   $$7.455 \times 10^3 \le x \le 7.465 \times 10^3,$$

and hence x differs from its approximation, 7.46×10^3, by at most $.005 \times 10^3$. The maximum difference ($.005 \times 10^3$) between x and the approximation to x (7.46×10^3) is called the *greatest possible error* in the approximation. Find upper and lower limits for x and the greatest possible error for the following approximations to x.

a) 3.5×10^7 b) 9.5×10^{-3}

c) 7×10^5 d) 7.0×10^5

e) 7.00×10^5 f) 1.795×10^{-10}

g) 4.0×10^{-8} h) 4.0000×10^{-8}

6. Scientific notation is useful in solving problems involving very large and very small numbers. If a large bacterium has diameter 1×10^{-5} feet and the earth has circumference 1.3×10^9 feet, how many large bacteria must be laid side by side to form a chain about the earth?

7. Round the following to the nearest tenth.

a) $\frac{1}{3}$ b) $\frac{1}{6}$

c) $\frac{1}{9}$ d) $\frac{1}{11}$

e) $\frac{5}{13}$ f) $-\frac{2}{3}$

g) $-\frac{17}{64}$ h) $\frac{1}{37}$

8. If we make some convention about ambiguous cases (such as "when in doubt round up": $\frac{1}{2} \to 1$, $-\frac{7}{2} \to -3$) then "round to the nearest unit" is a *function* with domain Q. Is it 1–1? What is its range? What numbers are sent to 3?

9. There is another notational convention in common use. The following are illustrations.

12.37   denotes approximation to the nearest hundredth.
 1.3456 denotes approximation to the nearest ten-thousandth.
 7.300   denotes approximation to the nearest thousandth.
10.0   denotes approximation to the nearest tenth.
 3.   denotes approximation to the nearest unit.

The limitations of this convention are obvious. There is no way of indicating that the figure 1200 is only correct to the nearest hundred. The symbol 1200. implies accuracy to the nearest unit. The symbol 12 is misleading. Perhaps 12__ should be used. How does one express this approximation in scientific notation?

10. Suppose that x is approximated by 9.6×10^4 and y is approximated by 3×10^2.

a) Find upper and lower limits for x.

b) Find upper and lower limits for y.

c) Find upper and lower limits for $x + y$.

d) Find upper and lower limits for xy.

e) Compare (c) with 9.63×10^4 (sum of approximations).

f) Compare (d) with 2.88×10^7 (product of approximations).

11. Write the following as a percent.

a) $\frac{3}{25}$ [*Hint:* Multiply numerator and denominator by 4. Why is this legitimate?]

b) $\frac{11}{4}$

c) $\frac{1}{200}$

d) $\frac{5}{300}$ [*Hint:* Divide numerator and denominator by 3. Why is this legitimate?]

e) $\frac{11}{900}$ f) $\frac{9}{16}$ g) .42

h) 3.57   i) .633   j) .0225

k) $\frac{64}{9}$ l) $\frac{235}{11}$ m) $\frac{765}{3}$

12. Write each of the following as a percent (i) rounded to the nearest tenth of a percent, (ii) rounded to the nearest whole percent.

a) .0537   b) .2794   c) .2796

d) .9956   e) $\frac{13}{16}$ f) $\frac{7}{11}$

g) $\frac{18}{7}$ h) $\frac{1}{3}$

13. Express (i) to the nearest percent, (ii) to the nearest tenth of a percent, the number x approximated by:

a) 3.3×10^{-2} b) 2.763×10^{-1}

c) 5.7×10^{-3} d) 9.74161×10^2

Could you do this for 6.327×10?

9–6   terminating and repeating decimals; labeling the rationals

We return now to the discussion of Sections 9–2 through 9–4. Recall two of the points made about decimals.

1.   Decimals are much nicer to compute with than fractions. (That's good.)

2.   Many fractions are not equal to decimals. (That's too bad.)

In this section we shall make a third point which ought to mitigate the gloom engendered by point 2:

3.   If we are willing to abuse (slightly) the definition of decimal, then every fraction *is* equal to a decimal.

To clarify point 3, let us begin by making an observation that you probably made back in Section 9–4: Even the revised form of the division algorithm usually doesn't work! Except in very carefully contrived problems, it is impossible to annex enough zeros to the dividend to make it evenly divisible by the divisor. For example,

$$
\begin{array}{r}
2.727\ldots \\
11\overline{\smash{\big)}\,30.000\ldots} \\
\underline{22} \\
80 \\
\underline{77} \\
30 \\
\underline{22} \\
80 \\
\underline{77} \\
3\ldots
\end{array}
$$

The trouble is that none of the fractions

$$\frac{30}{11}, \frac{300}{11}, \frac{3000}{11}, \frac{30{,}000}{11}, \ldots$$

is an integer. [As a matter of fact, almost any pair of integers, a and b, has the property that none of

$$\frac{a}{b}, \frac{10a}{b}, \frac{100a}{b}, \frac{1000a}{b}, \ldots$$

is an integer. See Exercise 3.]

If, however, we blunder blindly along in the division algorithm, we arrive at the curious assertion that

$$\tfrac{30}{11} = 2.72\overline{72}7\ldots$$

and we call this strange symbol a *repeating decimal*. (The bar over the 27 indicates that it is this pair of digits which continues to repeat.)

Strictly speaking, of course, this is nonsense. A "repeating decimal" is not a decimal. The word decimal implies that

$$2.72\overline{72}7\ldots = 2 + 7\cdot10^{-1} + 2\cdot10^{-2} + 7\cdot10^{-3} + 2\cdot10^{-4} + 7\cdot10^{-5} + \ldots$$

but the symbol on the right-hand side is meaningless. We have no concept of an "infinite sum." Addition, we recall, is a *binary* operation. We can only add *two* numbers at a time. We can, of course, add three numbers by adding two of them and then adding the third to this sum. Proceeding in this fashion we could add up 150 terms. But infinitely many? Never! Justification for writing

$$2 + \frac{7}{10} + \frac{2}{100} + \frac{7}{1{,}000} + \frac{2}{10{,}000} + \frac{7}{100{,}000} + \cdots$$

requires the concepts of sequence, series, and convergence, concepts distinctly beyond the boundaries of elementary mathematics.

But if we are willing to be a little careless we can "prove" that every fraction is equal to either a repeating or a "terminating" decimal. The adjective "terminating" refers to an ordinary (finite sum type) decimal such as 7.34. Incidentally, we shall also consider $7.34\overline{000}$ ... to be a terminating rather than a repeating decimal.

Theorem 1. Every fraction is equal to either a terminating or a repeating decimal. 2. Conversely every terminating or repeating decimal is equal to a fraction.

"Proof"   (You don't *prove* a theorem by showing that it is true in a few specific instances, especially when those instances involve computations with nonsense symbols.) Indication of why Theorem 1 ought to be true:

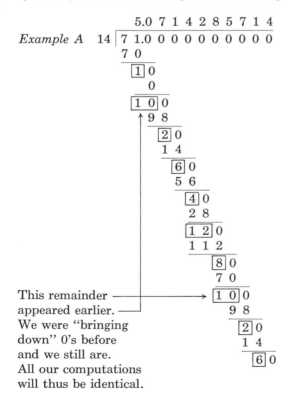

Example A

[*Note:* The boxed numbers are our successive remainders. They are all < 14. (Why?)]

This remainder appeared earlier. We were "bringing down" 0's before and we still are. All our computations will thus be identical.

Is it inevitable that sooner or later you will get a remainder you saw before?

Therefore $\frac{71}{14} = 5.0714285\ \overline{714285}$ ...

Example B

$$\begin{array}{r} 3.375 \\ 8\,\overline{\smash{)}\,27.000} \\ \underline{24} \\ 30 \\ \underline{24} \\ 60 \\ \underline{56} \\ 40 \\ \underline{40} \\ 0 \end{array}$$ ◄——— Remainder 0; decimal quotient terminates

Therefore $\frac{27}{8} = 3.375$

Summarizing the "proof" of Theorem 1, when you divide b into a, the remainders you obtain are all found among $0, 1, 2, \ldots, b - 1$. Thus, after you begin bringing down zeros, sooner or later you either get a remainder of 0 or else you get a remainder you had before. In the first case the decimal (quotient) terminates; in the second it repeats.

Indication of why Theorem 2, ought to be true:

Example A The terminating decimal 17.305 is easily seen to equal the fraction $\frac{17305}{1000}$ (cf. Exercise 8, page 297).

Example B Consider the repeating decimal $5.0714285\ \overline{714285}\ldots$ For the moment let

$r = 5.0714285\ \overline{714285}\ldots$

Then $10r = 50.\ 714285\ \overline{714285}\ldots$

and $10^7 r = 50\ 714285.\ 714285\ \overline{714285}\ldots$

Thus $10^7 r - 10r = 50714235$. That is,

$(10{,}000{,}000 - 10)r = 50{,}714{,}235$

That is,

$r = \dfrac{50{,}714{,}235}{9{,}999{,}990}$, a fraction.

(We know, from Example A of Theorem 1, that this fraction equals the lowest-terms fraction $\frac{71}{14}$.)

Q.E.D.

We have just "proved" that every fraction is equal to either a repeating or a terminating decimal, and conversely, every repeating or terminating decimal is equal to a fraction. But we know that every fraction labels a rational number, and conversely, every rational number is labeled by a fraction. Thus every rational number is labeled by either a repeating or a terminating decimal, and conversely, every repeating or terminating decimal labels a rational.

We are led once again to two familiar questions. When are two decimals (in the set of repeating and terminating decimals) equal? When more than one decimal labels a single rational number, how do we choose a particular nice one?

The answer to the first question might be surprising. Different-looking decimals can be equal. For example, .999 . . . = 1. The following "proof" may or may not convince you of this.

Let r = .99\overline{9} . . . Then

$10r - r = (9.99\overline{9} . . .) - (.99\overline{9} . . .) \Rightarrow 9r = 9 \Rightarrow r = 1.$

It is true, however, that the only cases of double labeling are ones involving repeating 9's.

.99\overline{9} . . . = 1
2.76142 = 2.76141\overline{999} . . .
13.899\overline{9} . . . = 13.9.

Thus the answer to the second question is obvious: Throw out decimals ending in repeating 9's.

In summary:

If we exclude from the set of all repeating and terminating decimals those which end in repeating 9's, then each rational number is labeled by precisely one of the decimals remaining.

EXERCISES 9–5

1. Express each of the following fractions as a decimal.
   a) $\frac{1379}{40}$ b) $\frac{97}{125}$
   c) $\frac{33}{6}$ d) $\frac{-91}{35}$
   e) $\frac{1}{3}$ f) $\frac{-1}{6}$
   g) $\frac{92}{17}$

2. Express each of the following decimals as a fraction.
   a) 13.765   b) .00059
   c) $-.3204$ d) .713713\overline{713} . . .
   e) 29.5454\overline{54} . . .   f) 365.731642\overline{1642} . . .
   g) $-.1248\ \overline{1248}$ . . .

3. a) Prove: The lowest-terms fraction, $\frac{a}{b}$, is equal to a terminating decimal if and only if the only distinct prime factors in b are 2's and 5's.

[*Hint:* Look at your work in Exercise 1. Did you reduce (c) and (d) to lowest terms to save some labor?]

b) Write as decimals the "useful household fractions" $\frac{1}{2}$, $\frac{1}{3}$, $\frac{2}{3}$, $\frac{1}{4}$ $\frac{3}{4}$, $\frac{1}{6}$, $\frac{5}{6}$, $\frac{1}{8}$, $\frac{3}{8}$, $\frac{5}{8}$, $\frac{7}{8}$.

4. When one works in base 12, a symbol such as $7\,E\,1.\,3\,T\,4$ is called a duo-decimal (*duodecem* is the Latin word for twelve), and denotes

$$7 \cdot (10)^2 + E \cdot (10) + 1 + \frac{3}{10} + \frac{T}{(10)^2} + \frac{4}{(10)^3} \,.$$

(Remember that 10 is read "one-zero" and means "one twelve and zero units," or simply "twelve.")

a) Express the useful household fractions from Exercise 3(b) as duodeci-mals. What advantage do you see in the duodecimal system?

b) What duodecimal theorem corresponds to the decimal theorem of Exercise 3(a)?

c) Is there a theorem relating rationals to repeating and terminating duodecimals?

5. Decimals were introduced originally because they are easy to compute with. The original class of decimals was expanded to include repeating decimals so that each rational would have a decimal label. Much of the original computational advantage is lost in this expansion. Try computing

a) $.1666\overline{6}\ldots + .666\overline{6}\ldots$ b) $.1666\overline{6}\ldots \times .666\overline{6}\ldots$

c) $.1666\overline{6}\ldots \div .666\overline{6}\ldots$

6. The phrase "after you begin bringing down 0's" in the summary on page 311 is necessary, as the following computation illustrates. Explain why *this* didn't force termination, whereas *these* forced repetition.

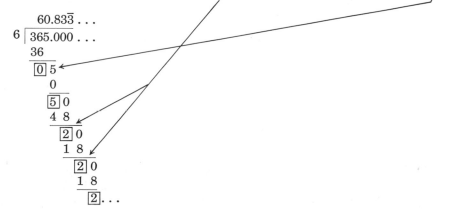

7. (Test your mind-reading ability.) Write out the first 40 digits in the infinite decimal

.21121111211111121 . . .

Does this infinite decimal represent a rational number? If so, which one (name it with a fraction)? If not, what does it represent?

SUMMARY

Decimal symbols denote those rational numbers with fraction representations of the form

$\dfrac{a}{10^n}$, where $a \in I, n \in W$.

For example,

$32.1 = \dfrac{321}{10}$, $-4.037 = \dfrac{-4037}{10^3}$.

A rational number has a decimal representation if and only if its lowest-terms fraction has a denominator whose only prime factors are 2 and 5.

$$\frac{7}{2^2 \cdot 5^3} = \frac{7 \cdot 10^3}{2^2 \cdot 5^3 \cdot 10^3} = \frac{7 \cdot 2}{10^3} ; \qquad \frac{317}{2^6 \cdot 5^4} = \frac{317 \cdot 10^6}{2^6 \cdot 5^4 \cdot 10^6} = \frac{317 \cdot 5^2}{10^6}$$

By suitably defining the use of negative exponents, one gets an expanded form:

$$23.154 = 2 \cdot 10^1 + 3 \cdot 10^0 + 1 \cdot 10^{-1} + 5 \cdot 10^{-2} + 4 \cdot 10^{-3}.$$

The rules for locating decimal points in calculations with decimals may be explained as multiplying and dividing the numbers involved by suitable powers of ten. For example,

$$\begin{array}{r} 2.13 \xrightarrow{\times 10^2} 213 \\ \times .036 \xrightarrow{\times 10^3} \times 36 \\ \hline .07668 \xleftarrow{\div 10^5} 7668 \end{array}$$

When one is giving explanations to school children, it is well to utilize fraction notation:

$.3 \times .12 = \frac{3}{10} \times \frac{12}{100} = \frac{36}{1000} = .036,$

$.3 + .12 = \frac{3}{10} + \frac{12}{100} = \frac{30}{100} + \frac{12}{100} = \frac{42}{100} = .42.$

Scientific notation is employed principally to indicate the accuracy with which measurements have been made. A measurement reported as 9.2×10^{-3} is said to have two significant digits (the 9 and 2). The true value is expected to lie between 9.15×10^{-3} and 9.25×10^{-3}. The greatest possible error is said to be $.05 \times 10^{-3}$. A measurement reported as 9.20×10^{-3} has 3 significant digits (9, 2, and 0). The true value is expected to fall between 9.195×10^{-3} and 9.205×10^{-3}, with a greatest possible error of $.005 \times 10^{-3}$.

For each rational number r, the symbol $r\%$ means $\frac{r}{100}$.

Using the division process, one obtains for each rational number a terminating or a repeating decimal. If we exclude repeating decimals which repeat 9's, then each rational has exactly one decimal representation as a terminating or repeating decimal, and each such decimal denotes a rational number.

10 real numbers

10–1 introduction

We begin our discussion of the real numbers, R, in the spirit of Chapter 8. (Compare the following discussion with Sections 8–3 and 8–7.)

The system of rational numbers, Q, has the property that "any first-degree equation with coefficients in Q has a unique solution in Q." That is, any equation of the form

$$ux + v = w, \qquad u, v, w \in Q; \ u \neq 0,$$

has a unique solution in Q; namely,

$$x = \frac{w - v}{u}.$$

For example, the equation

$$\tfrac{2}{3}x + 6 = \tfrac{19}{7}$$

has the unique solution

$$x = \frac{\tfrac{19}{7} - 6}{\tfrac{2}{3}} \in Q.$$

"Second-degree" equations are another matter, as are equations of degree three, four, etc. For example, there is no solution in Q to any of the equations

$$x^2 = 2, \quad x^2 = 6, \quad x^3 = 4, \quad x^4 = 8, \quad x^2 + 2x = 4.$$

We shall prove only that the equation $x^2 = 2$ has no solution in Q, and leave the others as exercises.

If there were a solution in Q to $x^2 = 2$, then there would be a fraction $\dfrac{a}{b}$ such that

$$\left(\frac{a}{b}\right)^2 = 2.$$

Now

$$\left(\frac{a}{b}\right)^2 = 2 \Longrightarrow \frac{a}{b} \cdot \frac{a}{b} = 2 \Longrightarrow a \cdot a = 2b \cdot b$$

By the Fundamental Theorem of Arithmetic, the prime factorization of $a \cdot a$ must be identical to the prime factorization of $2b \cdot b$. But 2 appears an even number of times in the factorization of $a \cdot a$ (why?), and an odd number of times in the factorization of $2 \cdot b \cdot b$ (why?). Hence the prime factorizations of $a \cdot a$ and $2 \cdot b \cdot b$ are not identical, and our assumption that there exists a solution in Q to $x^2 = 2$ is untenable.

Thus the system of rational numbers is inadequate for solving various simple (and natural; see Exercise 3 below) equations. Again we need a larger system, but now the old tricks of Chapter 8 are not going to work. The equations we want to be able to solve $(x^2 = 2, x^3 = 4, x^2 + 2x = 4, \ldots)$ do not all have the same neat form as was the case when we moved from W to I and from I to Q. We want a system of numbers which contains a solution to every "reasonable" equation.

The equation

$$x^2 = -1$$

is unreasonable because we shall want our system, R, to have the familiar order properties, and we have seen [Exercise 2(e) and Exercise 4 page 264] that these order properties imply that $-1 < 0$ while $a^2 \geq 0$ for every a.

▶ *Aside.* If, however, we are willing to get along without the familiar order properties, then it is no longer unreasonable to hope for a solution to an equation such as $x^2 = -1$.

As a matter of fact there is a system of numbers, called the *complex number system*, which (1) includes R (and thus Q and I and W), (2) contains a solution to $x^2 = -1$, and (3) enjoys all the nice properties of Q *except* the order properties. ◀

It is possible to simply assume the existence of a set R (really a system $R, +, \cdot, <$) containing Q (really $Q, +, \cdot, <$) and satisfying all the usual properties (associativity, commutativity, etc.), all the order properties, and one additional property, and then to proceed with an analysis similar to the analyses of Chapter 8. The difference is that now the analysis is much more difficult. Rather than try to follow this clean but difficult path, we shall take a less precise but more concrete and visual approach, the approach via infinite decimals.

EXERCISES 10-1

1. Prove that there is no solution in Q to the following equations.

   a) $x^2 = 3$ b) $x^2 = 6$ c) $x^3 = 4$ d) $x^4 = 8$ e) $x^2 + 2x = 4$

   [*Hint:* Rewrite as $x^2 + 2x + 1 = 5$. Note that $(x + 1)^2 = x^2 + 2x + 1$, and observe that $x \in Q \Rightarrow x + 1 \in Q$.]

2. Some equations of degree more than one do have solutions in Q. Find all solutions in Q to each of the following equations.

a) $x^2 = 9$ b) $x^3 = 1$

c) $x^2 - 5x + 6 = 0$ d) $4x^2 = 9$

e) $27x^3 = -8$

3. What equations need to be solved to answer the following "real-life" questions?

a) It is known that an object falls $16 \cdot t^2$ feet in t seconds. How long does it take to fall 96 feet?

b) What should the dimensions of a cubical tank be if it is to hold 4 cubic feet of water?

10–2 infinite decimals revisited

Let us re-examine somewhat more closely our loose treatment of infinite decimals. We shall indicate a more reasonable sort of interpretation than the "infinite-sum" interpretation for symbols such as .333 . . . This will lead us to the real number system.

Symbols such as .333 . . . arise in computations of the sort

$$
\begin{array}{r}
.333\ldots \\
3\,\overline{\smash{\big)}\,1.000\ldots} \\
\underline{9} \\
10 \\
\underline{9} \\
10 \\
\underline{9} \\
1\ldots
\end{array}
$$

The ellipsis marks are, of course, the problem. When we write

$$
\begin{array}{r}
.3 \\
3\,\overline{\smash{\big)}\,1.0} \\
\underline{9} \\
1
\end{array}
$$

we really mean that $1 = (.3)3 + .1$, which, when it is multiplied by $\frac{1}{3}$, becomes

$$\tfrac{1}{3} = .3 + \tfrac{1}{3}(.1)$$

or

$$\tfrac{1}{3} - .3 = \tfrac{1}{3} \cdot \tfrac{1}{10}.$$

When we write

```
      .33
3 | 1.00
      9
    ─────
     10
      9
    ─────
      1
```

we really mean that $1 = (.33)3 + .01$, which, when it is multiplied by $\frac{1}{3}$, becomes

$$\tfrac{1}{3} = .33 + \tfrac{1}{3}(.01)$$

or

$$\tfrac{1}{3} - .33 = \tfrac{1}{3} \cdot \tfrac{1}{100}.$$

At the next step we get

$$\tfrac{1}{3} - .333 = \tfrac{1}{3} \cdot \tfrac{1}{1000}.$$

Thus .3, .33, .333, are successively "closer" to $\frac{1}{3}$. (The differences between $\frac{1}{3}$ and .3, .33, .333, get successively smaller.) In fact it is clear that "you can get as close as you please to $\frac{1}{3}$ if you go out far enough in the sequence .3, .33, .333, . . . ," or, in technical terminology, "the sequence, .3, .33, .333, . . . , *converges to* $\frac{1}{3}$." This is what we really mean when we write

$$\tfrac{1}{3} = . 333\overline{3}. . .$$

To the mathematically pure of heart, the expressions in quotation marks cry out for explanation. Unfortunately the formal definitions required are very difficult to understand and would draw us out of the realm of elementary mathematics (cf. Exercise 8 below). We rely on your intuitive feelings for what the expressions in quotation marks ought to mean.

Let us consider a slightly more complicated computation:

```
       2.727 . . .
11 | 30.000 . . .
     22
    ─────
      80
      77
    ─────
       30
       22
    ─────
        80
        77
    ─────
         3 . . .
```

This time

$$
11 \overline{\smash{\big)}\ 30} \\
\quad \underline{22} \\
\qquad 8
$$

means $30 = 2 \cdot 11 + 8$ or $\quad \frac{30}{11} - 2 = \frac{8}{11}$.

The computation

$$
\begin{array}{r}
2.7 \\
11 \overline{\smash{\big)}\ 30.0} \\
22 \\
\hline
80 \\
77 \\
\hline
3
\end{array}
$$

means $30 = (2.7) \cdot 11 + .3$ or $\quad \frac{30}{11} - 2.7 = \frac{3}{11} \cdot \frac{1}{10}$.

The computation

$$
\begin{array}{r}
2.72 \\
11 \overline{\smash{\big)}\ 30.00} \\
22 \\
\hline
80 \\
77 \\
\hline
30 \\
22 \\
\hline
8
\end{array}
$$

means $30 = (2.72) \cdot 11 + .08$ or $\quad \frac{30}{11} - 2.72 = \frac{8}{11} \cdot \frac{1}{100}$.

The next equation will be

$$\frac{30}{11} - 2.727 = \frac{3}{11} \cdot \frac{1}{1000}$$

and the next

$$\frac{30}{11} - 2.7272 = \frac{8}{11} \cdot \frac{1}{10000}, \quad \text{etc.}$$

It is again clear that "the sequence 2, 2.7, 2.72, 2.727, 2.7272, . . . converges to (approaches) $\frac{30}{11}$" or that "you can get as close as you please to $\frac{30}{11}$ by going out far enough in the sequence 2, 2.7, 2.72, 2.727, 2.7272, . . ." *This* is what we mean when we write $\frac{30}{11} = 2.727272 \ldots$. That is:

The infinite decimal $2.727272 \ldots$ stands for the number $\frac{30}{11}$ approached by the sequence of rational numbers:

$$2, 2.7, 2.72, 2.727, \ldots$$

We pause to summarize our progress. Until now, $2.727272 \ldots$ was a nonsense symbol (infinite sums are nonsense). On the other hand, each of the symbols 2, 2.7, 2.72, 2.727, . . . , when looked at individually, makes perfectly good sense. Each represents a certain *finite* sum of rationals. Thus we legitimize the original symbol by letting it denote the number approached by the sequence of bona-fide numbers: 2, 2.7, 2.72, 2.727, . . .

This suggests that we ought to interpret the symbol

.21121111211111121 . . .

similarly, as the number approached by the sequence of rationals

.2, .21, .211, .2112, .21121, . . .

The trouble is *there is no such rational number.*

Sketch of proof   Our big theorem from Section 9–6 tells us that each rational is represented by either a terminating or a repeating decimal. (We now know that this theorem is to be interpreted in terms of sequences approaching things.) But you know (cf. Exercise 7, page 314) that the symbol, .21121111211111121 . . . neither repeats nor terminates. Finally, if you are willing to grant that two distinct infinite decimals can be equal only if one ends in repeating 9's and the other in 0's, then we are finished, for .21121 . . . does not end in 0's or 9's.

EXERCISES 10–2

1. When we write $\frac{2}{3} = .6\overline{66}$ . . . , we mean that the sequence .6, .66, .666, . . . approaches $\frac{2}{3}$. What do we mean when we write

   a) $\dfrac{11}{15} = .7333\overline{3}$ . . .?

   b) $\dfrac{1}{11} = .0909\overline{09}$ . . .?

   c) $\dfrac{11}{7} = 1.571428\overline{571428}$ . . .?

   d) $\dfrac{-1}{6} = -.166\overline{6}$ . . .?

2. a) Express each of the differences as a fraction:

   $\frac{2}{3} - .6$, $\frac{2}{3} - .66$, $\frac{2}{3} - .666$, $\frac{2}{3} - .6666$.

   Does the sequence of differences approach 0?
   b) Analyze $\frac{4}{9}$ and .44$\overline{4}$ . . . as in (a).
   c) Analyze $\frac{26}{99}$ and .2626$\overline{26}$ . . . as in (a).
   d) Analyze $\frac{1}{11}$ and .0909$\overline{09}$ . . . as in (a).
   e) Analyze $\frac{11}{15}$ and .7333$\overline{3}$ . . . as in (a).

3. Complete in 25 words or less. "If a number x is represented by an infinite decimal (and hence is approached by a sequence of finite decimals), then x differs from the 1-place decimal in the sequence by at most ———, from the 2-place decimal in the sequence by at most ———, from the 3-place decimal in the sequence by at most ———, and in general . . ."

4. What number is being approached by each of the following sequences (cf. Exercise 2, page 312)? Corroborate your answer by computing some differences and noting that they approach 0.

   a) .1, .12, .121, .1212, .12121, .121212, . . .

   b) $\frac{7}{10}$, $\frac{77}{100}$, $\frac{777}{1000}$, $\frac{7777}{10000}$, . . .

   c) .1, .12, .123, .1231, .12312, .123123, . . .

5. It is easy to go from the infinite-decimal representation for a number to its successive decimal approximations. For example, $\frac{2}{3} = .66\overline{6}$ . . . implies that

   $\frac{2}{3}$ rounded to the nearest tenth is .7

   $\frac{2}{3}$ rounded to the nearest hundredth is .67

   $\frac{2}{3}$ rounded to the nearest thousandth is .667 . . .

   a) Find the first 6 approximations to .123123$\overline{123}$ . . .

   b) Same as (a) for .369369$\overline{369}$ . . .

   c) Same as (a) for .199199$\overline{199}$ . . .

6. a) Show that if the infinite decimals a and b begin $a = .34690512$ . . . , $b = .34690514$ . . . , then they cannot be equal (represent the same number).

   [*Hint:* What is the largest number that could be approached by any sequence of rationals (which comes from an infinite decimal) beginning as the sequence for a begins (be careful). What is the smallest number that could be approached by any sequence of rationals beginning as the sequence for b begins (be careless).]

   b) If the infinite decimals a and b begin

   $$a = .34690512 \ldots, \qquad b = .34690513 \ldots,$$

   could they be equal?

7. It wasn't necessary to write out .21121111211111121 . . . and have you guess at its further entries. We could have said, "Consider the infinite decimal which has in its Rth position the digit $F(R)$, where the function F is defined by

   $$F(R) = 2 \qquad \text{if } R \text{ is a perfect square,}$$
   $$F(R) = 1 \qquad \text{if } R \text{ is not a perfect square.}$$

   Invent some more infinite decimals which do not represent rational numbers. Describe them by means of a function as well as by writing out the first several entries.

8. Ponder the following precise definitions.

   a) A *sequence* of rational numbers is a function from N into Q.

   b) A *sequence* F of rationals *converges to* the rational number R if and only if corresponding to each positive rational number S is a natural number L

with the property that if M is any other natural number $> L$ then

$$-S < F(M) - R < S.$$

This second definition ought to say to you, "You can get (and stay) as close as you please to R by going out far enough in the sequence."

9. The sequence of rationals associated with the decimal of Exercise 7, .2, .21, .211, .2112, .21121, .211211, does not get arbitrarily close to (converge to, approach) any rational. "The terms of the sequence do, however, get arbitrarily close to each other if you go out far enough." Verify that:

a) Any two terms of the sequence differ by less than $\frac{1}{10}$. Give two numbers differing by a tenth between which they all lie.

b) Any two terms of the sequence, beyond the first, differ by less than $\frac{1}{100} = (\frac{1}{10})^2$. Give two numbers differing by a hundredth between which lie all terms other than the first.

c) Any two terms of the sequence, beyond the second, differ by less than $\frac{1}{1000} = (\frac{1}{10})^3$.

It should be clear that beyond the Rth term any two terms differ by less than $(\frac{1}{10})^{R+1}$. When R is large $(\frac{1}{10})^{R+1}$ is very small. Thus "the terms of the sequence get arbitrarily close to each other if you go out far enough." A sequence with this property is said to be "Cauchy" (after the French mathematician Augustin Cauchy, 1789–1857). We have seen, then, that *there is a Cauchy sequence of rationals which does not converge to a rational.*

10–3   the reals as infinite decimals; the number line

The result of pages 320–321 suggests not only that the system of rationals is full of "holes" (that was recognized earlier when we saw that the equation $x^2 = 2$ had no rational solution), but also suggests a way to plug the holes. Define the set of real numbers to be the set of *all* decimals, both repeating and nonrepeating.

▶ *Aside.* This is not exactly how it is done. Infinite decimals are too closely connected with the base ten numeration system to please the pure mathematician (who treats all numeration systems equally by ignoring them all). Instead he defines a real number to be an equivalence class of Cauchy sequences of rationals. Note that he is forced to talk about the sequences themselves rather than their limits because, having only rational numbers as candidates, many Cauchy sequences do not have limits (cf. Exercise 9 above). ◀

The expression, "The system of rationals is full of holes," results from visualizing the rationals as labels for points on a line (see the figure at the top of next page). (Do you recall a straightedge-and-compass construction for dividing a segment into any number of equal parts?)

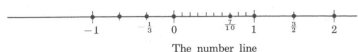

The number line

Suppose that we now draw two of these number lines to intersect as shown.

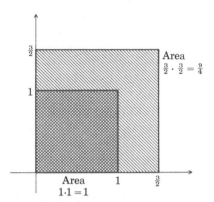

Then we are led to assign rational numbers to certain square regions in the plane, and to say that this number is the area of the region. Now "between" the squares of areas 1 and $\frac{9}{4}$ there should be one of area 2. But we have seen that there is no rational number r such that $r \cdot r = 2$. In this sense there is a "hole." There is a point on the line to which *no* rational number has been assigned.

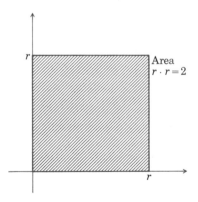

Let us see whether our admission of all infinite decimals has plugged this hole. We claim it has. That is, we are claiming that there is an infinite decimal whose square is 2. We only claim that there is one; we do not claim that we can produce it. That kind of claim would make a carnival barker blush. It is absurd to hope to write out an infinite list of digits. What is more, since $\sqrt{2}$

is not rational, the list is not repeating, and so ellipsis marks are not justified. (One could perhaps nurse the wistful hope that there would be some sort of pattern, as there is in .2112111121 . . . , but chances for this appear slim.)

From the abstract point of view one can hope for a proof of existence of a real number whose square is 2 and a proof that every real number (in particular $\sqrt{2}$) is expressible as an infinite decimal. Such proofs exist, but all are too deep to be given here.

From a computational point of view the best "answer" one can hope for is a process (or method or algorithm) by means of which one can produce as many entries in the infinite decimal as one has the need or time or patience for. Our next order of business will be to describe and justify such an algorithm.

EXERCISES 10-3

1. Plot on the number line the points corresponding to:

   $0, -\frac{2}{3}, \frac{2}{3}, .6, .66, .67, .7$

2. Shade on the number line
   a) $\{x \in R \mid 1 \le x \le 3\}$
   b) $\{x \in R \mid x = 1 \text{ or } x = 3\}$
   c) $\{x \in R \mid x^2 - 4x + 3 = 0\}$
   [*Hint:* For a product to be zero, at least one factor must be zero.]

   d) $\{x \in R \mid x \ge 1 \text{ and } x \le 3\}$
   e) $\{x \in R \mid x \ge 1 \text{ and } x \ge 2\}$
   f) $\{x \in R \mid x^2 - 4x + 3 > 0\}$
   [*Hint:* In order for a product to be positive, both factors must be positive or both factors must be negative.]

   g) $\{x \in R \mid x^2 - 3x + 2 \le 0\}$
   h) $\{x \in R \mid x^2 - 3x + 2 \ge 0\}$
   i) $\{x \in R \mid x^2 = -1\}$
   j) $\{x \in R \mid 2x = 3\}$

10–4 a square-root algorithm

We can compute as many entries in the infinite decimal for $\sqrt{2}$ as we have patience for by simply grinding through "the square-root algorithm." Before doing so, however, let's rehearse the chant in the simpler case of a perfect square, and also see why the chant works.

The chant. To compute $\sqrt{133{,}225}$, first group the digits by pairs from the right. Write down above the first pair, 13, the largest digit, 3, whose square is less than 13. Subtract its square, 9, from 13 and bring down the next pair, 32. Double the 3 (to get 6) and write down 6__. Find the largest digit x (to fill in the blank) so that $x \cdot 6x \le 432$.* Write that digit, 6, above the second pair and subtract $6 \cdot 66$ ($= 396$) from 432. Bring down the third pair, 25. Double 36 (to get 72) and write down 72__. Find digit y (to fill in the blank) so that $y \cdot 72y = 3625$. Write that digit, 5, above the third pair. Before reading further, we suggest that you do Exercises 1, 2, 3.

$$
\begin{array}{r|rrr}
 & 3 & 6 & 5 \\
\hline
\sqrt{} & 13 & 32 & 25 \\
 & -9 & & \\
\hline
 & 4 & 32 & \\
66 & -3 & 96 & \\
\hline
 & 36 & 25 & \\
725 & -36 & 25 & \\
\hline
 & & 0 &
\end{array}
$$

The justification. Any 1-digit number, when squared, gives either a 1- or a 2-digit number:

$$1 \le a \le 9 < 10 \Rightarrow 1 = 1^2 \le a^2 < 10^2 = 100.$$

Any 2-digit number, when squared, yields either a 3- or a 4-digit number:

$$10 \le a \le 99 < 100 \Rightarrow 100 = 10^2 \le a^2 < 100^2 = 100{,}000$$

Similarly squaring a 3-digit number leads to a 5- or a 6-digit number. Thus when one is asked to find $\sqrt{729}$, the first thing one does is to pair off the digits, from the right, 7 29, and conclude immediately that the answer will be a 2-digit number. If one is asked to compute $\sqrt{133225}$, one pairs off, 13 32 25, and knows the answer must be a 3-digit number.

Consider the problem of computing $\sqrt{729}$. We know not only that the answer is a 2-digit number, but we also know that its first digit must be 2 because

$$(20)^2 = 400 < 729 \qquad \text{while} \qquad (30)^2 = 900 > 729.$$

Thus the problem is reduced to finding a digit x such that

$$(2x)^2 = (20 + x)^2 = 729.$$

Now

$$(20 + x)^2 = 729 \iff (20)^2 + 2 \cdot 20 \cdot x + x^2 = 729$$
$$\iff x \cdot (2 \cdot 20 + x) = 729 - (20)^2 \iff x(40 + x) = 329.$$

We might try $x = 8$ first, but find it is too large. We then try $x = 7$ and it works: $7 \cdot 47 = 329$.

Consider next the problem of finding $\sqrt{133225}$. We know, by pairing, that the answer is a 3-digit number. Furthermore, we know its first digit is 3, since

---

* The symbol $6x$ denotes $6 \cdot 10 + x$, not 6 times x. In *this* section we shall follow the convention that ab always means $a \cdot 10 + b$. If we want to write "a times b" we shall use the dot notation, $a \cdot b$.

$(300)^2 = 9\ 00\ 00 < 13\ 32\ 25$, while $(400)^2 = 16\ 00\ 00 > 13\ 32\ 25$. Thus:

Write down above the first pair, 13, the largest digit, 3, whose square is less than 13.

The second digit, x is to be chosen as large as possible, but such that

$$(3x0)^2 = (300 + 10 \cdot x)^2 < 13\ 32\ 25.$$

Of course,

$$(300 + 10 \cdot x)^2 = (30 + x)^2 \cdot 100$$

(why?) so that the largest x such that

$$(30 + x)^2 \leq 13\ 32$$

will also be the largest x such that

$$(300 + 10 \cdot x)^2 \leq 13\ 32\ 25.$$

We find this x just as we found it in the previous problem, the only difference being that now we are solving an inequality rather than an equation.

$$(30 + x)^2 \leq 13\ 32 \quad \Leftrightarrow \quad (30)^2 + 2 \cdot 30 \cdot x + x^2 \leq 1332$$
$$\Leftrightarrow \quad x \cdot (2 \cdot 30 + x) \leq 1332 - (30)^2 \quad \Leftrightarrow \quad x \cdot 6x \leq 1332 - 900 = 432.$$

Subtract 3^2 from 13 and bring down the next pair, 32. Double the 3 (to get 6) and write down 6__. Find the largest digit x (to fill in the blank) such that

$$x \cdot 6x \leq 432.$$

We might try $x = 7$ first. It fails, but $x = 6$ works. The second digit must be 6.

Write that digit, 6, above the second pair.

Note that

$$13\ 32\ 25 - (360)^2 = 13\ 32\ 25 - (300 + 60)^2$$
$$= 13\ 32\ 25 - [(300)^2 + 60 \cdot (2 \cdot 300 + 60)]$$
$$= (13\ 32\ 25 - [90000 + 60 \cdot 660] = 4\ 32\ 25 - 39600 = 36\ 25.$$

Subtract $6 \cdot 66 \ (= 396)$ from 432. Bring down the third pair, 25.

Now we want y such that

$$(36y)^2 = 13\ 32\ 25.$$

This will be true

$$\Leftrightarrow \quad (360)^2 + 2 \cdot 360 \cdot y + y^2 = 13\ 32\ 25$$
$$\Leftrightarrow \quad y \cdot (2 \cdot 360 + y) = 13\ 32\ 25 - (360)^2 \quad \Leftrightarrow \quad y \cdot (72y) = 36\ 25.$$

Double 36 (to get 72) and write down 72__. Find digit y (to fill in the blank) so that $y \cdot 72y = 3625$.

The value of y that works is 5, so the third digit must be 5.

Write down that digit 5 above the third pair.

Postscript. There are other methods for approximating square roots by decimals. In fact there are very general methods which are suitable for computing decimal approximations to not only square roots, cube roots, fourth roots, etc., but also to roots of many other kinds of equations. Some of these methods have the added virtue that they lend themselves to programming on electronic computers. The justifications of these algorithms, however, require concepts from advanced mathematics.

EXERCISES 10–4

1. Compute (a) $\sqrt{729}$, (b) $\sqrt{10,349,089}$.
2. Prove that $(a \cdot b)^2 = a^2 \cdot b^2$.
3. a) Prove that $(a + b)^2 = a^2 + b \cdot (2 \cdot a + b)$.

   b) Substitute $a = 300$ and $b = 60$ in the above formula, write as the sum of two simplified terms, and compare with the computations on page 326.

   c) Now substitute $a = 360$ and $b = 5$ into the formula in (a), write as the sum of two simplified terms, and compare with the computations on page 326.

   d) Substitute the results of (b) into the result of (c) and draw conclusions.
4. a) Prove that $\sqrt{1332.25} = 36.5$.

   b) Prove that $\sqrt{13.3225} = 3.65$.

   c) Prove that $\sqrt{.0000133225} = .00365$.
5. Compute the first 5 digits in the infinite decimal for $\sqrt{2}$.
6. If a machine is available for computation, the divide-and-average technique is convenient for computing approximate square roots. For example, 1.4 is a one-place approximation to $\sqrt{2}$. We divide as below.

4-digit quotient ⟶ 1.428 ⟵

2-digit divisor ⟶ 1.4 | 2.0000   Round this to nearest *even* digit so that
                        1 4   averaging comes out evenly
                       ————
                         60
                         56
                       ————
                         40
                         28
                       ————
                        120
                        112
                       ————
                          8

The average of 1.4 and 1.428 is

$$\frac{1.4 + 1.428}{2} = 1.414,$$

which is correct to 3 decimal places. Dividing 2 by 1.414, carrying out the quotient to 8 digits (7 decimal places), and averaging gives a decimal correct to 6 decimal places, 1.414214.

a) Find $\sqrt{3}$ correct to 6 decimal places.

b) Find $\sqrt{5}$ correct to 6 decimal places.

c) Find $\sqrt{200}$ correct to 5 decimal places.

10–5   irrational numbers

Those real numbers which are not rational numbers, i.e., the reals represented by nonrepeating, nonterminating decimals, are known as *irrational numbers*. We have already encounted several irrationals; for example, $\sqrt{2}$, $\sqrt{3}$, and .2112111121 ... There are many more. Here, for example, is an infinite collection. No number in the set below is rational.

$$\{r\sqrt{2} \mid r \in Q; \ r \neq 0\}.$$

Proof   If $r\sqrt{2} = s$, where $s \in Q$, then $\sqrt{2} = s/r$, since $r \neq 0$. But $r, s \in Q$ and $r \neq 0 \Rightarrow s/r \in Q \Rightarrow \sqrt{2} \in Q$, which we know is impossible.

     Now consider the union of the two sets below.

$$\{r\sqrt{2} \mid r \in Q, \ r \neq 0\} \cup \{\sqrt{3}\}.$$

     This is a *subset* of the irrationals which can be placed in 1–1 correspondence with the set of *all* rationals:

$$\sqrt{3} \leftrightarrow 0,$$
$$r\sqrt{2} \leftrightarrow r, \qquad r \neq 0, \ r \in Q.$$

In this sense there are "at least as many" irrationals as rationals. It is a rather deep theorem (see Exercise 5 below) that *there are more irrationals than rationals*, in the sense that the set of rationals cannot be put in 1–1 correspondence with the set of *all* irrationals.

     Two of the most important numbers in all mathematics, π and e (the base for "natural" logarithms, and a ubiquitous number in calculus), are also irrational. The number π was proved to be irrational in 1767 by Lambert, but not until several men had spent years in vain search for a repeating pattern in the decimal representation for π. The irrationality of π illustrates again the (theoretical) inadequacy of the system of rationals. Anyone who would want to get by with only the rational numbers would have to agree that a circle of diameter 1 had no circumference! The irrationality of e can be proved by a calculus student. The decimal approximation for π, correct to four decimal places is 3.1416; for e it is 2.7183.

The theoretical importance of irrational numbers is undeniable. In computations, however, rational approximations are invariably used. Depending on the accuracy desired, we might use 3 or 3.14 or $\frac{22}{7}$ or 3.1416 as an approximate value for π. Note that all these numbers are rationals. We round off real numbers just as we did rationals in Chapter 9.

EXERCISES 10–5

1. a) Prove that $r \cdot \pi$ is irrational for any nonzero rational number r.

   b) Prove that there is no rational number r such that $r\sqrt{2} = \sqrt{3}$.

   c) Prove that $2 + \sqrt{3}$ is irrational.

   d) Prove that if a is rational and $a + b$ is irrational, then b is irrational.

2. a) Find the repeating decimal equal to $\frac{22}{7}$. What is its decimal approximation to the nearest tenth? hundredth? thousandth? ten-thousandth?

   b) $\frac{22}{7}$ and π have the same decimal approximations correct to _____ decimal places.

3. Find a rational number between (not necessarily *strictly* between)

   8.1628356745 . . .   and   8.1628356744 . . .   (Interpret the dots however you please.)

   Is it clear that between any two real numbers there is a rational? This property is usually expressed in the words "the rationals are dense in the reals." Does it seem paradoxical to you that, although between any two reals there is a rational, still there are "more" irrationals than rationals?

4. Two sets, A and B, are said to have "the same number of elements" if there exists a 1–1, onto function from A to B. For each pair of sets below, prove that the two sets have the same number of elements.

   a) $\{1, 2, 3, 4, 5, \ldots\}$ and $\{1, 4, 9, 16, 25, \ldots\}$

   b) $\{1, 2, 3, 4, 5, \ldots\}$ and $\{2, 4, 6, 8, 10, \ldots\}$

   c) $\{1, 2, 3, 4, 5, \ldots\}$ and $\{1, 2, 3, \ldots\} \cup \{-1, -2, -3, \ldots\}$

   d) $\{1, 2, 3, 4, 5, \ldots\}$ and $\{0, 1, 2, 3, 4, 5, \ldots\}$

   e) $\{1, 2, 3, 4, 5, \ldots\}$ and $\{\ldots -3, -2, -1, 0, 1, 2, 3, \ldots\}$

5. The accompanying diagram may convince you that N and Q^+ have the same number of elements. Explain.

$$Q^+: \quad \frac{1}{1} \quad \frac{1}{2} \quad \frac{2}{1} \quad \frac{1}{3} \quad \frac{3}{1} \quad \frac{1}{4} \quad \frac{2}{3} \quad \frac{3}{2} \quad \frac{4}{1} \quad \frac{1}{5} \quad \frac{5}{1} \quad \frac{1}{6} \quad \frac{2}{5} \quad \frac{3}{4} \cdots$$

$$\uparrow \uparrow \uparrow \uparrow \uparrow \uparrow \uparrow \uparrow \uparrow \quad \uparrow \quad \uparrow \quad \uparrow \quad \uparrow \quad \uparrow$$

$$N: \quad 1 \ 2 \ 3 \ 4 \ 5 \ 6 \ 7 \ 8 \ 9 \ 10 \ 11 \ 12 \ 13 \ 14 \cdots$$

Consider the following proof that there is *no* 1–1, onto function from N to R^+ (the positive reals).

We suppose that f is a 1–1 function from N into R^+, and we shall prove that f cannot be onto by exhibiting a positive real number, p, not in its range. Let p be the infinite decimal

$$p = .a_1a_2a_3a_4 \ldots,$$

where

$$a_1 = \begin{cases} 5 \text{ if } f(1) \text{ has a 6 in its first decimal place} \\ 6 \text{ otherwise} \end{cases}$$

$$a_2 = \begin{cases} 5 \text{ if } f(2) \text{ has a 6 in its second decimal place} \\ 6 \text{ otherwise} \end{cases}$$

$$a_3 = \begin{cases} 5 \text{ if } f(3) \text{ has a 6 in its third decimal place} \\ 6 \text{ otherwise} \end{cases}$$
$$\vdots$$

In general,

$$a_n = \begin{cases} 5 \text{ if } f(n) \text{ has a 6 in its } n\text{th decimal place} \\ 6 \text{ otherwise} \end{cases}$$

For example, if

$$f(1) = 12.3649827 \ldots$$
$$f(2) = -8.1645301 \ldots$$
$$f(3) = .1175286 \ldots$$
$$f(4) = 157.3004561 \ldots$$
$$f(5) = -.0055552 \ldots$$
$$f(6) = .1392465 \ldots$$
$$f(7) = 3.0429175 \ldots$$
$$\vdots$$

Then $p = .6566656 \ldots$ We claim that $p \neq f(1)$, $p \neq f(2)$, $p \neq f(3)$, $\ldots$ and thus p is not in the range of f, so f is not onto.

a) Why is this claim true?

b) Using the three facts,

    i) there is a 1–1, onto function: $N \to Q^+$,

    ii) there is *no* 1–1, onto function: $N \to R^+$,

    iii) $R^+ = Q^+ \cup \{\text{positive irrationals}\}$,

prove that there is no 1–1, onto function: $Q^+ \to \{\text{positive irrationals}\}$.

[*Hints:* The composition of 1–1, onto functions is 1–1, onto. Use technique of Exercise 4(c).]

10–6   the real numbers as a
complete ordered field; summary of properties

The rigorous algebraic approach to the system of real numbers is beyond the level of this book. Consequently we were forced to speak of real numbers in terms of a system of labels for them, the set of all (finite and infinite) decimals.

Number system	Standard labels	Other labels
N: Natural numbers	1, 2, 3, . . .	$3 + 6$, $\frac{12}{3}$, $9 \cdot 2$, . . .
W: Whole numbers	0, 1, 2, 3, . . .	$6 - 6$, $0 + 7$, . . .
I: Integers	. . ., -3, -2, -1, 0, 1, 2, 3, . . .	$3 \cdot (-2)$, $5 - 8$, $(-3)^3$, . . .
Q: Rationals	Lowest-terms fractions Terminating and repeating decimals	$\frac{6}{8}$, $\frac{17}{3}$, $\frac{3}{-5}$, . . .
R: Reals	All decimals	$\sqrt{2}$, π, $\sqrt{11}$, . . .

This approach leaves the common algebraic properties of the system of real numbers unspoken. We correct that here.

The real number system consists of a set $R \supset Q$ and binary operations $+$ and $\cdot$ on R which satisfy:

1. Assoc $+$
2. Assoc $\cdot$
3. Comm $+$
4. Comm $\cdot$
5. Add 0
6. Mult 1
7. Negatives exist (i.e., each element of R has a unique additive inverse, or negative)
8. Reciprocals exist (i.e., each non-zero element of R has a unique multiplicative inverse, or reciprocal)

9. Dist

Furthermore there is an order relation, $<$, on R which satisfies the Trichotomy, Transitivity, and Monotony theorems.

▶ *Aside.* 1) $+$, $\cdot$, $<$ are used rather than $\oplus$ $\odot$ $\otimes$ to signify that on the subset Q these are the old familiar binary operations and order relation.
2) Any system, consisting of a set and two binary operations, which satisfies Properties 1 through 9 (with $1 \neq 0$) is called a *field*. If it also has an order relation, $<$, such that Trichotomy, Transitivity, and Monotony hold, then it is called an *ordered field*. Thus the system of real numbers is an ordered field. But so also was the system of rational numbers. However, the real number system has one additional property that sets it apart: the completeness property (see

Exercise 1 below). This makes the system of real numbers a *complete ordered field.* ◀

Since this list of assumptions contains or implies all the assumptions about Q (except for the analog of Assumption 11, page 265):

All the rules for fractions and all the rules for minus signs remain true for real numbers.

[*Note.* Assumption 11 on page 265 was used only once in establishing the rules for fractions. The assumption "Reciprocals exist" makes even that single occurrence unnecessary; cf. Exercise 9(c), page 270.]

EXERCISES 10–6

1. The extra property of the real number system, the *completeness* property, states that:

   Any (nonempty) subset of real numbers which has an upper bound (u.b.) has a least upper bound (l.u.b.).

   The definitions which give this meaning are:
   1) r is an u.b. for S ⟺ $s \leq r$, $\forall s \in S$.
   2) r is a l.u.b. for S ⟺   (a) r is an u.b. for S, and (b) if l is an u.b. for S, then $r \leq l$.

   a) Is 5 an u.b. for the set of all negative numbers?

   b) Is 5 a l.u.b. for the set of all negative real numbers?

   c) Prove that if a set has a l.u.b., then that l.u.b. is unique.

   d) Give an example of a set which has no l.u.b.

   e) Give an example of a set which contains its l.u.b.

   f) Give an example of a set which has a l.u.b. but does not contain it.

   g) Assuming that there is neither a greatest rational $< \sqrt{2}$ nor a least rational $> \sqrt{2}$, prove that among the rational upper bounds for

   $$\{u \in Q \mid u < \sqrt{2}\}$$

   there is no least one. (Thus Q is not complete.)

   h) Define lower bound; greatest lower bound.

   i) Prove that any subset of R with a lower bound has a greatest lower bound.

2. A "hole" in the rational line divides Q into two subsets, B (*below*) and A (*above*), with the following properties: (1) $A \cup B = Q$, (2) $A \neq \varnothing$ and $B \neq \varnothing$, (3) $A \cap B = \varnothing$, (4) $b < a$ $\forall b \in B$, $\forall a \in A$, (5) A contains no least element and B contains no greatest element.

Prove that there cannot be a pair of subsets of R, A and B, such that (1) $A \cup B = R$, and (2), (3), (4), (5) hold as above. Thus there are no holes in the real line.

[*Hint:* Assume that there is such a pair and prove that B has no l.u.b.]

3. A consequence (not at all easy to establish) of the completeness property is that any equation of the form

$$x^n = r$$

(where r is a positive real and n is a positive integer) has a *unique positive* (real) solution. (Some equations of this form, for example, $x^2 = 4$, also have a negative solution.) This unique positive solution is denoted by $\sqrt[n]{r}$ and is called the *principal nth root of r*. Thus all the equations we listed on page 316 do have real solutions. Also the familiar terms square root, cube root, fourth root, etc., make sense.

Prove the following:

a) $\sqrt{2}\,\sqrt{3} = \sqrt{6}$

b) $\sqrt{a}\,\sqrt{b} = \sqrt{ab}$, $\forall a, b > 0$

c) $\sqrt{9} = 3$

d) $\sqrt{(-3)^2} = 3$

e) $\sqrt{a^2} = a$ if $a \geq 0$; $-a$ if $a < 0$

f) $\sqrt[q]{t^q} = t$, $t > 0$

g) $\sqrt[m]{a^n} = (\sqrt[m]{a})^n$, $m, n \in N;\ a > 0$

SUMMARY

The rational number system Q is incomplete in the sense that simple equations like $x^2 = 2$ have no solution in Q. However, by a square-root algorithm one can produce a sequence of rational numbers

1, 1.4, 1.41, 1.414, 1.4142, . . .

whose squares "approach" 2 as closely as we please. Thus we recognize the existence of an "infinite" decimal whose square should be exactly 2. This decimal certainly is not terminating or repeating, for if so it would represent a rational number.

The above considerations suggest that we think of all decimals, repeating or nonrepeating, as representing numbers. This seems the simplest way to envision the real number system. Each repeating decimal can be viewed as a sequence of decimal approximations to a rational number. For example, the repeating decimal for $\frac{1}{3}$ is $.33\overline{3}$ . . . and

$\frac{1}{3} - .3 < .1$; $\frac{1}{3} - .33 < .01$; $\frac{1}{3} - .333 < .001$.

In the same way we think of a nonrepeating decimal as furnishing a sequence of decimal approximations to a real number which is not rational (i.e., it is irrational):

$$\sqrt{2} - 1.4 < .1; \quad \sqrt{2} - 1.41 < .01; \quad \sqrt{2} - 1.414 < .001, \ldots$$

When we think of real numbers as labeled by infinite decimals some properties are clear, others are not. For example, it is not difficult to see that between any two real numbers there are many rationals and between any two rationals there are many irrationals. However, it is quite difficult to formulate rules for computing with real numbers. In Chapter 8 we were able to assign labels to rational numbers in such a way that we could explain all computational rules for rationals in terms of computing with integers. And rules for computing with integers are described in terms of computing with whole numbers (and manipulating minus signs). But we have no such simple approach to the arithmetic of real numbers. It is not easy to calculate with infinite decimals. This computational difficulty poses no practical problem because in real life we use rational approximations to real numbers. But any complete theoretical treatment of the real number system must face up to the task of describing addition and multiplication of real numbers in terms of these operations on rationals. Because of the complexity of this procedure we forgo it and state without proof a few of the important properties of the real number system R.

1) Each nonzero real number has a unique reciprocal.

2) An order relation $<$ in R satisfies the Trichotomy, Transitivity, and Monotony theorems.

3) The real number system is *complete*. That is, each nonempty set of real numbers which has an upper bound has a least upper bound.

When one is computing with "radicals," it is necessary to know that each equation

$$x^n = r$$

where n is a natural number and r is a positive real number, has *exactly one positive* real number solution. This fact gives us the right to write symbols like $\sqrt{7}$ and $\sqrt[4]{9}$, for these are, respectively, names for the unique positive solutions of

$$x^2 = 7 \quad \text{and} \quad x^4 = 9.$$

This knowledge enables us to prove things like $\sqrt{2} \cdot \sqrt{3} = \sqrt{6}$ and justifies the computational techniques with radicals taught in school algebra.

11 set-theoretic constructions: the fifth stage of abstraction

11–1 introduction

Let us review, in the context of the whole number system, the four stages of the abstraction process that we have studied so far.

1. We learn the conventions (verbal and symbolic) of a numeration system. The numbers have no meaning except in relation to each other: "precedes," "follows."

2. We learn to count sets of tangible objects (i.e., to assign numbers to various physical sets in a prescribed fashion), and we invent operations (+ and ·) on the numbers which correspond to the set operations of (disjoint) union and cartesian product. The numbers now have a meaning in relation to physical sets: "how many."

3. We work to increase our skill in using the operations + and · on the numbers. The connection between these operations and the set operations fades. Patterns emerge; shortcuts and tricks are discovered. Arithmetic becomes a game with nearly meaningless symbols.

4. We purify, simplify, and codify the game. We divest the numbers and the operations + and · of all lingering connotations from stages 1 and 2, and then we list explicitly a small number of rules governing their behavior. Nothing else is assumed. The symbols have no intrinsic meaning.

In the fifth stage of the abstraction process the mathematician restores a "meaning" to each of the symbols. Every number, every operation, and even the order relation becomes a set. The sets, to be sure, are no longer sets of tangible objects. They are mathematical sets, defined in accordance with the axioms of mathematical set theory. Still they are conceptually rather concrete to the mathematician. What is more, he feels that the axioms of mathematical set theory provide a more satisfactory and unifying foundation for his work than do the assumptions of Stage Four.

Problem   To see how binary operations and relations can be viewed as sets, see pages 43 and 144.

a) Since $+$ is a binary operation on W, it is a set. List a few of its members.

b) List a few elements in the set $<$ ($<$ viewed as a relation on W).

11–2   construction of W

We give only a flavor of the set-theoretic construction of W. You may recall that our Stage-4 treatment of W was less clean than the corresponding treatments for I and Q. We have the same contrast at Stage 5. The reason should be obvious: W is the *basic* number system. It stands closest to the axioms, whatever ones might be chosen. Once we have deduced the properties of W, it is relatively easy to derive analogous ones for I and Q.

What follows is a brief outline of the construction of W. No axioms of set theory are listed; no justifications are given for statements made. Fuller treatments are provided in the books of Halmos and Suppes (see references on pages 39 and 12, respectively). The definitions below are of *ordinal numbers*. The *cardinal numbers* of sets are defined in terms of ordinal numbers.

The empty set is denoted by $\varnothing$. The whole numbers are defined by:

$$0 = \varnothing$$
$$1 = 0 \cup \{0\} = \{0\} = \{\varnothing\}$$
$$2 = 1 \cup \{1\} = \{0, 1\} = \{\varnothing, \{\varnothing\}\}$$
$$3 = 2 \cup \{2\} = \{0, 1, 2\} = \{\varnothing, \{\varnothing\}, \{\varnothing, \{\varnothing\}\}\}$$
$$\vdots$$

The binary operations, $+$ and $\cdot$, are defined ($\forall m, n \in W$) by

$$\begin{cases} m + 0 = m \\ m + 1 = m \cup \{m\} \\ m + (n + 1) = (m + n) + 1 \end{cases} \qquad \begin{cases} m \cdot 0 = 0 \\ m \cdot 1 = m \\ m \cdot (n + 1) = m \cdot n + m \end{cases}$$

For example,

a) $1 + 1 = 2$ because
$\quad\ 1 + 1 = 1 \cup \{1\}$ 2nd clause of defn of $+$
$\qquad\quad = 2$ defn of 2

b) $1 + 2 = 3$ because
$\quad\ 1 + 2 = 1 + (1 + 1)$ by (a)
$\qquad\quad = (1 + 1) + 1$ 3rd clause of defn of $+$
$\qquad\quad = 2 + 1$ by (a)
$\qquad\quad = 2 \cup \{2\}$ 2nd clause of defn of $+$
$\qquad\quad = 3$ defn of 3

c) $1 \cdot 1 = 1$ by clause 2 of definition of $\cdot$

d) $1 \cdot 2 = 2$ because
       $1 \cdot 2 = 1 \cdot (1 + 1)$ by (a)
       $ = 1 \cdot 1 + 1$ 3rd clause of defn of $\cdot$
       $ = 1 + 1$ by (c)
       $ = 2$ by (a)

The order relation $<$ on W is defined by $m < n$ if $m \in n$. For example, $1 < 3$ because $1 \in 3$ because $3 = \{0, 1, 2\}$.

   One then *proves* that the system $(W, +, \cdot, <)$ has all the familiar properties.

EXERCISES 11–1

   1. Write out the definition of 4.
      a) In terms of 3 only.
      b) In terms of 0, 1, 2, 3.
      c) In terms of only the empty set.
   2. Prove that $3 < 4$.
   3. Prove (in order). (Use the results of the example on page 337.)
      a) $2 + 1 = 3$ b) $2 + 2 = 4$ c) $2 + 3 = 5$
      d) $2 \cdot 1 = 2$ e) $2 \cdot 2 = 4$ f) $1 \cdot 3 = 3$

11–3   construction of *I*

The clue to the construction of I from W is found in two results of Chapter 8.

1) Every integer is of the form $m - n$, where $m, n \in W$ (page 260).

2) $m - n = p - q$ if and only if $m + q = p + n$ ($\forall m, n, p, q \in W$) (page 260).

The first result tells us that the integers are closely connected with pairs of whole numbers. The second tells us when two pairs of whole numbers determine the same integer.

   The first result leads us to consider

$$W \times W = \{(m, n) \mid m, n \in W\};$$

the second result leads us to the following:

Definition   If (m, n) and $(p, q) \in W \times W$, then we say that (m, n) and (p, q) are related, and write $(m, n) \sim (p, q)$, if

$$m + q = p + n.$$

[*Note:* Although we are writing ordered pairs, we have in the back of our minds that these pairs ought to behave as differences do.] For example,

$(8, 3) \sim (10,5)$ because $8 + 5 = 10 + 3$;
$(2, 9) \sim (8, 15)$ because $2 + 15 = 8 + 9$.

It is not hard to prove that $\sim$ is an equivalence relation on $W \times W$ (a reflexive, symmetric, and transitive relation). Although we ought to denote the equivalence class of (m, n) by $[(m, n)]$, we denote it by $[m, n]$ for notational simplicity. Thus

$$[m, n] = \{(p, q) \mid (p, q) \sim (m, n)\}.$$

We define I to be the set of all such equivalence classes. Three typical elements of I are

$\{(3, 0), (4, 1), (5, 2), (6, 3), \ldots\}$,
$\{(0, 0), (1, 1), (2, 2), (3, 3), \ldots\}$,
$\{(0, 5), (1, 6), (2, 7), (3, 8), \ldots\}$.

We then define operations of addition and multiplication on I by

$C_1 + C_2 = [m_1 + m_2, n_1 + n_2]$,
$C_1 \cdot C_2 = [m_1 m_2 + n_1 n_2, m_1 n_2 + m_2 n_1]$,

where (m_1, n_1) is any element in the equivalence class $C_1 \in I$ and (m_2, n_2) is any element in the equivalence class $C_2 \in I$. For example, if

$C_1 = \{(3, 0), (4, 1), (5, 2), (6, 3), \ldots\}$,
$C_2 = \{(0, 5), (1, 6), (2, 7), (3, 8), \ldots\}$,

then we choose an element from C_1, say $(6, 3)$, and an element from C_2, say $(2, 7)$, and we compute:

$C_1 + C_2 = [6 + 2, 3 + 7] = [8, 10]$
$\qquad\quad = \{(0, 2), (1, 3), (2, 4), \ldots, (8, 10), \ldots\}$,
$C_1 \cdot C_2 = [6 \cdot 2 + 3 \cdot 7, 6 \cdot 7 + 2 \cdot 3] = [33, 48]$
$\qquad\quad = \{(0, 15), (1, 16), (2, 17), \ldots, (33, 48), \ldots\}$.

We must still verify that the operations $+$ and $\cdot$ are binary operations. That is, we must show that:

1) $(m_1 + m_2, n_1 + n_2)$ and $(m_1 m_2 + n_1 n_2, m_1 n_2 + m_2 n_1)$ do in fact belong to $W \times W$. (This is easy.)

2) The sum (product) of C_1 and C_2 is uniquely determined: You end up with the same equivalence class no matter which elements of C_1 and C_2 you choose to compute with. (This is a little harder.)

For example, suppose that C_1 and C_2 are as above, but that we decide to compute with the pairs $(3, 0) \in C_1$ and $(1, 6) \in C_2$. Then

$C_1 + C_2 = [3 + 1, 0 + 6] = [4, 6]$
$\qquad = \{(0, 2), (1, 3), \ldots, (4, 6), \ldots, (8, 10), \ldots\}$ the same as before;
$C_1 \cdot C_2 = [3 \cdot 1 + 0 \cdot 6, 3 \cdot 6 + 0 \cdot 1] = [3, 18]$
$\qquad = \{(0, 15), (1, 16), \ldots, (3, 18), \ldots, (33, 48), \ldots\}$ the same as before.

"Why *must* the classes be the same as before?" is the question that needs to be answered to establish (2).

Now that we have verified that $+$ and $\cdot$ are binary operations, the next step is to *prove* the familiar properties of I (the 11 properties listed on page 248). But before we can even begin to do this, we must face and overcome one difficulty: $I \not\supseteq W$. No whole number is an integer! The elements of I are equivalence classes of ordered pairs of whole numbers, so clearly no whole number is an element of I. Fortunately, however, there is a subset of I which "behaves just like W under addition and multiplication," namely

$\{(0, 0), (1, 1), (2, 2), \ldots\}$ which acts like 0,
$\{(1, 0), (2, 1), (3, 2), \ldots\}$ which acts like 1,
$\{(2, 0), (3, 1), (4, 2), \ldots\}$ which acts like 2,
$\qquad \cdot \cdot \cdot$

Once we have made the "identification" of W with this subset, verification of the eleven properties is routine.

EXERCISES 11-2

1. Verify the following:
   a) $(11, 6) \sim (6, 1)$ b) $(12, 10) \sim (5, 3)$ c) $(3, 8) \sim (9, 14)$
   d) $(6, 6) \sim (0, 0)$ e) $(5, 10) \sim (0, 5)$ f) $(3, 0) \sim (8, 5)$

2. Find a whole number k such that
   a) $(k, 8) = (3, 0)$ b) $(7, 10) = (0, k)$ c) $(5, 1) = (k, 0)$
   d) $(k, 3) = (7, k)$ e) $(k, k) = (0, 0)$ f) $(9, 10) = (k, 0)$

3. Prove that $\sim$ is an equivalence relation on $W \times W$.

4. Are the following pairs of equivalence classes the same or different?
   a) $[8, 5]$ and $[3, 0]$ b) $[7, 10]$ and $[3, 0]$ c) $[k, 5 + k]$ and $[0, 5]$
   d) $[3, 18]$ and $[33, 48]$ e) $[4, 6]$ and $[8, 10]$

5. Compute the following:
   a) $[6, 2] + [3, 6]$ b) $[4, 0] + [0, 3]$ c) $[6, 2] \cdot [3, 6]$ d) $[4, 0] \cdot [0, 3]$

6. a) Compare $[6, 2]$ and $[4, 0]$.   b) Compare $[3, 6]$ and $[0, 3]$.
   c) Compare answers to 5(a), 5(b).   d) Compare answers to 5(c), 5(d).

e) Prove that if $[m, n] = [6, 2]$ and $[p, q] = [3, 6]$, then

    i) $[m + p, n + q] = [6 + 3, 2 + 6]$

    ii) $[mp + nq, mq + np] = [6 \cdot 3 + 2 \cdot 6, 6 \cdot 6 + 2 \cdot 3]$

7. Complete the statement of the following general theorem analogous to 6(e):
   If $[m_1, n_1] = [m_2, n_2]$ and $[p_1, q_1] = [p_2, q_2]$, then

   i) ———

   ii) ———

   Prove it if you can.

8. a) Which sum was easier to compute, 5(a) or 5(b)?

   b) Which product was easier to compute, 5(c) or 5(d)?

   c) A pair of whole numbers (m, n) will be called "nice" if $m = 0$ or $n = 0$. Prove that every equivalence class $(\in I)$ contains exactly one "nice" pair. [*Hint:* Compare with the proof in Chapter 8 on page 261.]

   Since every class contains a nice pair, and since it doesn't matter what pairs one uses to compute with, it is to your advantage to compute with nice pairs. Compute the following by choosing nice pairs.

   d) $[12, 17] + [9, 2]$ e) $[18, 14] \cdot [11, 14]$ f) $[17, 19]^2$

   g) Graph $[8, 5]$ in the plane; i.e., plot $\{(x, y) \in W \times W \mid (x, y) \sim (8, 5)\}$. Where does the nice pair appear?

   h) Repeat (g) for $[2, 5]$.

   i) Describe, in general, what the equivalence classes look like and where the nice pairs appear.

9. Verify the following:

   a) $[n, n] = [0, 0]$ b) $[n, n] + [8, 5] = [8, 5]$

   c) $[5, 8] + [n, n] = [5, 8]$ d) $[n, n] + [p, q] = [p, q]$

   e) $\{[3, 4] + [2, 8]\} + [5, 1] = [3, 4] + \{[2, 8] + [5, 1]\}$

   f) $[9, 6] + [1, 5] = [1, 5] + [9, 6]$ g) $[8, 3] + [3, 8] = [0, 0]$

   h) $[p, q] + [q, p] = [0, 0]$

   i) $\{[3, 4] \cdot [2, 8]\} \cdot [5, 1] = [3, 4] \cdot \{[2, 8] \cdot [5, 1]\}$

   j) $[9, 6] \cdot [1, 5] = [1, 5] \cdot [9, 6]$ k) $[2, 1] \cdot [6, 3] = [6, 3]$

   l) $[n + 1, n] \cdot [6, 3] = [6, 3]$ m) $[n + 1, n] \cdot [p, q] = [p, q]$

   n) $[3, 6] \cdot [m, n] = [3, 6] \cdot [5, 11] \Rightarrow [m, n] = [5, 11]$

10. Find a solution (the equivalence class of a pair of whole numbers) to each of the following.

    a) $[5, 0] + x = [3, 0]$ b) $[9, 6] + x = [2, 1]$

    c) $[0, 3] + x = [1, 0]$ d) $[10, 15] + x = [1, 25]$

11. Verify that $[m, 0] + [n, m] = [n, 0]$. Which of the 11 properties of I (on page 248) does this establish?

12. Prove that the function $f: W \to I$ defined by $f(n) = [n, 0]$
    a) is 1–1   b) satisfies $f(m + n) = f(m) + f(n)$
    c) satisfies $f(m \cdot n) = f(m) \cdot f(n)$

    This is the "identification" function mentioned on page 340.

11–4   construction of Q

The construction of Q from I is similar to the construction of I from W. The clues from Chapter 8 are:

 1. Every rational number is of the form a/b, where $a, b \in I$; $b \neq 0$ (page 278).
 2. $a/b = c/d$ if and only if $ad = bc$ ($\forall a, b, c, d \in I$; $b \neq 0$; $d \neq 0$) (page 279).

The first result leads us to consider the set,

$\{(a, b) \mid b \neq 0; \ a, b \in I\}$.

The second result leads us to the following:

Definition   If (a, b) and (c, d) are pairs of integers (with $b, d \neq 0$), then we say that (a, b) and (c, d) are related, and write $(a, b) \sim (c, d)$, if $ad = bc$.

[*Note*: Although we are writing ordered pairs, we have in the back of our minds that these pairs ought to behave as quotients.]

Example

$(9, 3) \sim (-12, -4)$ because $9(-4) = 3(-12)$
$(2, 6) \sim (8, 24)$ because $2(24) = 6(8)$

It is not hard to prove that $\sim$ is an equivalence relation and we agree to denote the equivalence class of (a, b) by $[a, b]$. Thus

$[a, b] = \{(c, d) \mid (c, d) \sim (a, b)\}$

We define Q to be the set of all such equivalence classes. Three typical elements of Q are

$\{(2, 3), (-2, -3), (4, 6), (-4, -6), (6, 9), \ldots\}$,
$\{(-3, 4), (3, -4), (-6, 8), (6, -8), (-9, 12), \ldots\}$,
$\{(0, 1), (0, -1), (0, 2), (0, -2), (0, 3), \ldots\}$.

We then define operations of addition and multiplication on Q by

$C_1 + C_2 = [a_1 b_2 + b_1 a_2, b_1 b_2]$,
$C_1 \cdot C_2 = [a_1 a_2, b_1 b_2]$,

where (a_1, b_1) is any element in the equivalence class $C_1 \in Q$ and (a_2, b_2) is any element in the equivalence class $C_2 \in Q$. For example, if

$$C_1 = \{(2, 3), (-2, -3), (4, 6), (-4, -6), (6, 9), \ldots\}$$

and

$$C_2 = \{(-3, 4), (3, -4), (-6, 8), (6, -8), (-9, 12), \ldots\},$$

then we choose an element from C_1, say $(4, 6)$, and an element from C_2, say $(-9, 12)$, and we compute:

$$
\begin{aligned}
C_1 + C_2 &= [4 \cdot 12 + (-9) \cdot 6, 6 \cdot 12] = [-6, 72] \\
&= \{(-1, 12), (1, -12), (-2, 24), \ldots, (-6, 72), \ldots\} \\
C_1 \cdot C_2 &= [4(-9), 6 \cdot 12] = [-36, 72] \\
&= \{(-1, 2), (1, -2), (-2, 4), \ldots, (-36, 72), \ldots\}
\end{aligned}
$$

We must still verify that the operations $+$ and $\cdot$ are binary operations; i.e., we must show that:

1. $(a_1 b_2 + b_1 a_2, b_1 b_2)$ and $(a_1 a_2, b_1 b_2)$ are pairs of integers whose second coordinate is nonzero (why is this so?).

2. The sum (product) of C_1 and C_2 is independent of the pairs (in C_1 and C_2) chosen for the computation.

For example, suppose that C_1 and C_2 are as above, but we decide to compute with the pairs $(-4, -6) \in C_1$ and $(-3, 4) \in C_2$. Then

$$
\begin{aligned}
C_1 + C_2 &= [(-4)4 + (-6)(-3), (-6)4] = [2, -24] \\
&= \{(-1, 12), (1, -12), \ldots, (2, -24), \ldots, (-6, 72)\} \quad \text{the same as} \\
&\quad \text{before,} \\
C_1 \cdot C_2 &= [(-4)(-3), (-6)4] = [12, -24] \\
&\quad \{(-1, 2), (1, -2), \ldots, (12, -24), \ldots, (-36, 72) \ldots\} \quad \text{as before.}
\end{aligned}
$$

"Why *must* the classes be the same as before?" is the question that needs to be answered to establish (2).

Now that we have verified that $+$ and $\cdot$ are binary operations, the next step is to *prove* the familiar properties of Q (the 11 properties listed on page 265). Again we get around the difficulty that $Q \not\supset I$ by identifying I with a special subset of Q:

. . .

$\{(-2, 1), (2, -1), (-4, 2), (4, -2), \ldots\}$ acts just like -2

$\{(-1, 1), (1, -1), (-2, 2), (2, -2), \ldots\}$ acts just like -1

$\{(0, 1), (0, -1), (0, 2), (0, -2), \ldots\}$ acts just like 0

$\{(1, 1), (-1, -1), (2, 2), (-2, -2), \ldots\}$ acts just like 1

$\{(2, 1), (-2, -1), (4, 2), (-4, -2), \ldots\}$ acts just like 2

. . .

EXERCISES 11-3

1. Verify the following:
   a) $(7, 2) \sim (-21, -6)$ b) $(-6, 8) \sim (3, -4)$
   c) $(5, 5) \sim (13, 13)$ d) $(6, 3) \sim (2, 1)$
   e) $(0, 1) \sim (0, 9)$ f) $(2, 7) \sim (-6, -21)$

2. Find an integer k such that
   a) $(k, 6) = (1, 3)$ b) $(10, 15) = (6, k)$ c) $(-1, 2) = (5, k)$
   d) $(1, k) = (k, 16)$ e) $(k, k) = (1, 1)$ f) $(3, 6) = (0, k)$

3. Prove that $\sim$ is an equivalence relation.

4. Are the following pairs of equivalence classes the same or different?
   a) $[9, 3]$ and $[3, 2]$ b) $[-6, 14]$ and $[3, -7]$
   c) $[14, 21]$ and $[-18, -27]$ d) $[2k, 5k]$ and $[2, 5]$, $k \neq 0$
   e) $[a^2, b^2]$ and $[a, b]$, $b \neq 0$ f) $[-1, 2]$ and $[1, -2]$

5. Compute the following:
   a) $[7, 8] + [-2, 6]$ b) $[-14, -16] + [1, -3]$
   c) $[7, 8] \cdot [-2, 6]$ d) $[-14, -16] \cdot [1, -3]$

6. a) Compare $[7, 8]$ and $[-14, -16]$.
   b) Compare $[-2, 6]$ and $[1, -3]$.
   c) Compare answers to 5(a), 5(b).
   d) Compare answers to 5(c), 5(d).

7. Complete the statement of the following general theorem:
   If $[a_1, b_1] = [a_2, b_2]$ and $[c_1, d_1] = [c_2, d_2]$, then

   i) ――――

   ii) ――――

   Prove it if you can.

8. a) Verify that $[3, 7] + [2, 7] = [5, 7]$.
   b) Verify that $[-11, 4] + [8, 4] = [-3, 4]$.
   c) Prove that $[a, b] + [c, b] = [a + c, b]$, $b \neq 0$.
   d) Verify that $[10, 12] = [5, 6]$.
   e) Verify that $[-16, 12] = [-4, 3]$.
   f) Verify that $[5, -3] = [-5, 3]$.
   g) Ponder the questions: What makes a pair "nice"? Is there one "nice" pair in each equivalence class?
   h) Compute by choosing nice pairs: $[5, 6] + [3, 18]$.
   i) Compute by choosing nice pairs: $[9, 12] + [-8, 12]$.

9. Verify the following:

   a) $[0, b] = [0, 1]$, $\forall b \neq 0$

   b) $[0, b] + [5, 3] = [5, 3]$

   c) $[0, b] + [c, d] = [c, d]$

   d) $[b, b] = [1, 1]$, $\forall b \neq 0$

   e) $[b, b] \cdot [5, 3] = [5, 3]$

   f) $[b, b] \cdot [c, d] = [c, d]$

   g) $\{[3, 4] + [-2, 6]\} + [7, -5] = [3, 4] + \{[-2, 6] + [7, -5]\}$

   h) $[3, 4] + [-2, 6] = [-2, 6] + [3, 4]$

   i) $[3, 4] + [-3, 4] = [0, 1]$

   j) $[a, b] + [-a, b] = [0, 1]$

   k) $\{[3, 4] \cdot [-2, 6]\} \cdot [7, -5] = [3, 4] \cdot \{[-2, 6] \cdot [7, -5]\}$

   l) $[3, 4] \cdot [-2, 6] = [-2, 6] \cdot [3, 4]$

   m) $[3, 4] \cdot [4, 3] = [1, 1]$

   n) $[a, b] \cdot [b, a] = [1, 1]$, $a, b \neq 0$

10. Find a solution (the equivalence class of a pair of integers) to each of the following equations:

    a) $[5, 1] \cdot x = [3, 1]$ b) $[2, 3] \cdot x = [-7, 5]$

    c) $[4, 11] \cdot x = [0, 93]$ d) $[2, 1] \cdot x = [12, 1]$

11. Verify $[m, 1] \cdot [n, m] = [n, 1]$. Which of the 11 properties of Q (on page 265) does this establish?

12. Prove that the function $f\colon I \to Q$ defined by $f(a) = [a, 1]$

    a) is 1–1,

    b) satisfies $f(a + b) = f(a) + f(b)$,

    c) satisfies $f(a \cdot b) = f(a) \cdot f(b)$.

    This is the "identification" function mentioned on page 343.

13. a) Graph $[4, 2]$ in the plane; i.e., plot

    $$\{(x, y) \in I \times I - \{0\} \mid (x, y) \sim (4, 2)\}.$$

    Now connect all the dots with a line.

    b) Repeat (a) for $[2, 4]$.

    c) Repeat (a) for $[-1, 3]$.

    d) Describe, in general, what the equivalence classes look like and where the lowest-terms fractions are located.

    e) From among all the possible vertical lines in the plane, select one that best deserves the name, "rational number line."

    f) Construct, using only a straightedge and a compass, a line through $(0, 0)$ which contains no other point with two integral coordinates.

14. a) Prove that if $(a, b) \sim (a, c)$ and $a \neq 0$, then $b = c$.

b) Conclude that the set of all ordered pairs of integers constituting a nonzero rational number is a function, in the strict sense of the word (cf. Exercise 8 page 42).

c) Does (b) convince you that the introduction of rational numbers as functions (the approach of Chapter 6) is a natural approach?

d) Contemplate and comment on the assertion: When we view rational numbers as functions, we note that our ordered-pair symbols should be reversed.

11–5   construction of R

As might be expected, constructing the real numbers is considerably more difficult than constructing the integers and rationals. There are, in fact, two standard constructions of R, and neither is easy. One involves defining a real number as an equivalence class of Cauchy sequences of rationals. We mentioned this approach briefly in Chapter 10 (pages 322, 323) and will not investigate it further. The interested (and courageous) reader is referred to the book, *Structure of the Real Number System*, Leon Cohen and Gertrude Ehrlich, Van Nostrand, Princeton, N.J., 1963, for a careful treatment of this approach. The other standard construction, which we shall sketch here, is by means of *Dedekind cuts* (named after their creator, Richard Dedekind, 1831–1916).

The problem of constructing the real numbers can be thought of geometrically as the problem of filling the holes in the rational line. Although one cannot talk sensibly about a "hole" in a "line," one can think of a hole as separating the line into two pieces and then talk sensibly about a pair (L, U) of subsets of Q.

For technical reasons it is much easier to work with subsets of the set of positive rationals, Q^+, rather than of Q itself (see also the aside following). The following definition is essentially the same as Dedekind's.

Definition   A pair (L, U) of subsets of Q^+ is called a (Dedekind) *cut* if

1. $L \neq \emptyset, U \neq \emptyset$,
2. $L \cup U = Q^+$,
3. $l < u, \quad \forall l \in L, \forall u \in U$,
4. L has no greatest element.

For example,

a) $L = \{x \in Q^+ \mid x < \frac{2}{3}\}$ and $U = \{x \in Q^+ \mid \frac{2}{3} \leq x\}$ form a cut.

b) $L = \{x \in Q^+ \mid x \le 1\}$ and $U = \{x \in Q^+ \mid 1 < x\}$ do not (4 is violated).

c) $L = \{x \in Q^+ \mid x < 2\}$ and $U = \{x \in Q^+ \mid 2 < x\}$ do not (2 is violated).

The set of positive real numbers R^+ is defined to be the set of all cuts; i.e., a positive real number *is* a cut. Binary operations $+$ and $\cdot$ are defined on R^+ by $(L_1, U_1) + (L_2, U_2) = (L_3, U_3)$, where

$$L_3 = \{l_1 + l_2 \mid l_1 \in L_1, l_2 \in L_2\}, \qquad U_3 = \{u_1 + u_2 \mid u_1 \in U_1, u_2 \in U_2\}.$$

Also: $(L_1, U_1) \cdot (L_2, U_2) = (L_4, U_4)$, where

$$L_4 = \{l_1 \cdot l_2 \mid l_1 \in L_1, l_2 \in L_2\}, \qquad U_4 = \{u_1 \cdot u_2 \mid u_1 \in U_1, u_2 \in U_2\}.$$

The order relation $<$ is defined by

$$(L_1, U_1) < (L_2, U_2) \text{ if } L_1 \subset L_2.$$

Finally Q^+ is identified with a subset of R^+ by means of the function $f: Q^+ \to R^+$, defined by $f(v) = (L, U)$, where

$$L = \{x \in Q^+ \mid x < v\}, \qquad U = \{x \in Q^+ \mid v \le x\}.$$

▶ *Aside.* We have tried to give something of the flavor of the Dedekind cut construction because of its geometric clarity. In fact, however, the Cauchy sequence construction is better suited to our plan of development,

$$W \to I \to Q \to R.$$

The Dedekind cut construction is more naturally suited to the plan,

$$N \to Q^+ \to R^+ \to R. \blacktriangleleft$$

EXERCISES 11–4

1. Which of the following pairs (L, U) are Dedekind cuts?
   a) $L = \{x \in Q^+ \mid x < \frac{13}{5}\}$, $U = \{x \in Q^+ \mid \frac{13}{5} \le x\}$.
   b) $L = Q^+$, $U = \emptyset$.
   c) $L = \{x \in Q^+ \mid x^2 < 2)$, $U = \{x \in Q^+ \mid 2 < x^2\}$.
   d) $L = \{x \in Q^+ \mid x^2 < 4\}$, $U = \{x \in Q^+ \mid 4 < x^2\}$.
   e) $L = \{x \in Q^+ \mid x \le \frac{1}{2}\}$, $U = \{x \in Q^+ \mid \frac{1}{2} \le x\}$.
   f) $L = \{x \in Q^+ \mid 2x < 3\}$, $U = \{x \in Q^+ \mid 2x \ge 3\}$.
   g) $L = \{x \in Q^+ \mid x < 2\pi\}$, $U = \{x \in Q^+ \mid x > 2\pi\}$.

h) $L = \{x \in Q^+ \mid x < 2\}, \qquad U = \{x \in Q^+ \mid 1 \le x\}.$

i) $L = \{x \in Q^+ \mid 2x + 4 < 3\}, \qquad U = Q^+ - L.$

j) $L = \{x \in Q^+ \mid 2x - 5 < x + 3\}, \qquad U = Q^+ - L.$

2. Among the Dedekind cuts in Exercise 1:

   a) For which does U have a least element?

   b) Which are identified with rationals?
      Deduce something from your answers to (a), (b).

3. Prove that if (L, U) is a cut, then $L \cap U = \varnothing$.

4. a) Write (as a cut) the sum of cuts 1(a), 1(f).

   b) Write (as a cut) the product of cuts 1(a), 1(f).

   c) Which cut is smaller, 1(a) or 1(f)?

5. Write the cuts identified with the rational numbers $\frac{1}{6}$, 1, 35.

6. Prove that addition of cuts is commutative.

SUMMARY

This chapter is our only contact with the Fifth Stage of the abstraction process. A careful treatment of the real number system requires this level of abstraction, because about the only way to make the concepts surrounding real numbers precise is to describe real numbers as sets.

In the first three stages of abstraction, we concerned ourselves only with *numerals*, that is, with symbols. These symbols denoted "things" in the physical world. For example, each use of $\frac{3}{5}$ denoted a function. Now we agree to use our numerals to denote abstract sets. These sets are our *numbers*. To add numbers, then, is to perform an operation on sets.

Note that all numbers in the real number system are ultimately defined in terms of the empty set. We repeat below definitions of typical whole numbers, integers, rationals, and reals.

$0 = \varnothing; \qquad 1 = \{0\}; \qquad 2 = \{0, 1\};$

$^+1 = \{(1, 0), (2, 1), (3, 2), \ldots\}; \qquad ^-1 = \{(0, 1), (1, 2), (2, 3), \ldots\}$

$\frac{1}{2} = \{(1, 2), (-1, -2), (2, 4), \ldots\}; \qquad -\frac{3}{5} = \{(-3, 5), (3, -5), (6, -10), \ldots\}$

$\sqrt{2} = (L_1, U_1), \quad \text{where} \quad L_1 = \{x \in Q^+ \mid x^2 < 2\}$

$U_1 = Q^+ - L_1; \qquad \text{that is, } U_1 \text{ is the complement of } L_1 \text{ in } Q^+.$

$\sqrt[3]{7} = (L_2, U_2), \quad L_2 = \{x \in Q^+ \mid x^3 < 7\}, \quad U_2 = Q^+ - L_2.$

The theoretical advantage of this fifth level abstraction is that now all the basic principles Assoc, Comm, etc., can be proved to hold. The proofs are based on set-theoretic and logical concepts.

12   number theory

12-1   introduction

At its simplest level, number theory can be thought of as the study of the whole number system W. Consequently many of the questions, concepts, and results of number theory are intelligible to the elementary school child.

Some of the results of number theory find immediate application to the child's other work in mathematics. For example, the Euclidean algorithm (a key result in number theory) provides him with a systematic procedure for reducing a fraction to lowest terms (cf. Section 12–3). Some of the concepts of number theory are very helpful in emphasizing the basic principles of ordinary arithmetic. For instance, the *finite* number systems discussed in Section 12–4 provide excellent examples to compare and contrast with the familiar number systems.

Most of all, however, number theory is fun. It is fascinating that such a simple question as the following should remain unanswered to this day. (It has defied mathematicians since it was posed in 1742.)

Question   (*The Goldbach Conjectures*)   Is every even number (greater than 2) expressible as the sum of two primes? Is every even number greater than 6 the sum of two distinct primes?

It is intriguing that

$2^7 - 2, 3^7 - 3, 4^7 - 4, 5^7 - 5, \ldots$, are all divisible by 7,

and

$2^5 - 2, 3^5 - 3, 4^5 - 4, 5^5 - 5, \ldots$, are all divisible by 5,

but

$2^4 - 2, 3^4 - 3, 4^4 - 4, 5^4 - 5, \ldots$, are not all divisible by 4.

What is more important (to you) is that many other interesting relationships among whole numbers (such as the one below) are within the power of the child to discover and prove (cf. Section 12–5).

$$1 = 1^2,$$
$$1 + 3 = 2^2,$$
$$1 + 3 + 5 = 3^2,$$
$$1 + 3 + 5 + 7 = 4^2.$$
$$\vdots$$

Even the young child should be given the opportunity to be original and creative. An enthusiastic and inquiring attitude toward mathematics can be fostered by a proper exposure to some number theory.

EXERCISES 12–1

1. Write each of the even numbers from 4 to 30 as the sum of two primes.
2. a) Prove that each of
   $2^2 - 2, 3^2 - 3, 4^2 - 4, 5^2 - 5, \ldots$ is divisible by 2.
   b) Prove that each of
   $2^3 - 2, 3^3 - 3, 4^3 - 4, 5^3 - 5, \ldots$ is divisible by 3.
   [*Hint:* Factor $x^3 - x$ into a product of three consecutive numbers.]

12–2   divisors and primes

We say that a is a *divisor* of b, and write $a \mid b$, if there is a c such that $b = ac$. (Other translations of the symbol $a \mid b$ are "a divides b," "a is a factor of b," "b is a multiple of a.") For example,

$1 \mid 6$ because $6 = 1 \cdot \underline{6}$, $2 \mid 6$ because $6 = 2 \cdot \underline{3}$,
$3 \mid 6$ because $6 = 3 \cdot \underline{2}$, $6 \mid 6$ because $6 = 6 \cdot \underline{1}$.

The divisors, 1 and 6, are called the improper divisors of 6. In general, if b is any whole number, the divisors 1 and b are called *improper divisors* of b. All other divisors are called *proper*. Therefore the only proper divisors of 6 are 2 and 3.

A whole number is called a *prime* if it is >1 and has no proper divisors. For example, 2, 3, 5, 7 are primes, while 0, 1, 4, 6 are not. Primes have received much attention because they are the building blocks of W, in the sense of the next theorem.

The Fundamental Theorem of Arithmetic   Every whole number >1 is expressible uniquely as a product of primes.

(See Chapter 8, pages 280, 281 for further discussion of this result.)

There is a very old method, known as the "*sieve of Eratosthenes*," for finding all the primes less than a given number. Suppose, for example, that you want to list all primes less than 50. Proceed as follows: List all the candidates.

② 3 A̸ 5 6̸ 7 8̸ 9 1̸0̸ 11 1̸2̸ 13 1̸4̸ 15 1̸6̸ 17 1̸8̸ . . .

Keep the first one, 2, and strike out all other multiples of 2 (every second number). Why could none of these be primes?

② ③   A̸ 5 6̸ 7 8̸ 9̸ 1̸0̸ 11 1̸2̸ 13 1̸4̸ 1̸5̸ 1̸6̸ 17 1̸8̸ . . .

Keep the first remaining one, 3, and strike out all other multiples of it (every third number). Some will have been stricken once already. Keep the first remaining one, 5, and strike out all other multiples of it (every fifth number), and so forth. (Why, at each step, must the first remaining number be a prime?)

The sieve of Eratosthenes allows us to list in order of increasing size as many primes as we wish. A theorem of Euclid tells us that we shall never be able to list them all.

Euclid's Theorem   There are infinitely many primes.

Proof   Suppose that there were only finitely many primes: $p_1, p_2, \ldots, p_N$. Consider the number $k = (p_1 p_2 \cdots p_N) + 1$. Clearly k is not divisible by any of $p_1, p_2, \ldots p_N$ because, for example, if $p_1 \mid (p_1 p_2 \cdots p_N) + 1$, then, since $p_1 \mid (p_1 p_2 \cdots p_N)$, p_1 would also have to divide 1 (cf. Exercise 12(g) below), which is absurd. Thus we have a positive whole number, k, not expressible as a product of primes. This contradicts the fundamental theorem of arithmetic. Our assumption that there are only finitely many primes is untenable.

Example $2 \cdot 3 + 1$ is not divisible by 2 or by 3.
$2 \cdot 3 \cdot 5 + 1$ is not divisible by 2 or 3 or 5.
$2 \cdot 3 \cdot 5 \cdot 7 + 1$ is not divisible by 2 or 3 or 5 or 7.

EXERCISES 12–2

1. List all the divisors of each of the following numbers, circling the improper ones.
   a) 15   b) 20   c) 24
2. Fill in the *factor trees* shown at the top of the next page. (The product of the entries in each row should be the bottom number.)

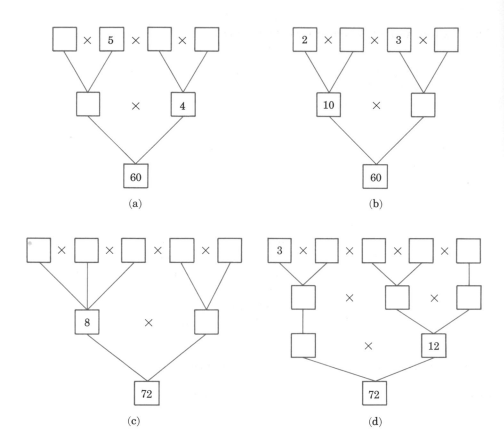

3. Factor each of the following into a product of primes:

    a) 10   b) 12   c) 16   d) 11   e) 36   f) 9   g) 30   h) 60

4. (a) through (h): List *all* divisors of each of the numbers in Exercise 3. [*Hint:* Be systematic; use your answers to Exercise 3, and don't worry about listing divisors in order of size. For example, the divisors of $2 \cdot 2 \cdot 7$ are 1, 2, 7, $2 \cdot 2$, $2 \cdot 7$, $2 \cdot 2 \cdot 7$.]

5. List all divisors of each of the following numbers (p, q, r denote distinct primes).

    a) p b) p^2 c) p^3 d) pq e) p^2q f) pqr

6. a) What kind of numbers have exactly 1 proper divisor?

    b) What kind of numbers have exactly 2 proper divisors?

    c) What kind of numbers have exactly 3 proper divisors?

7. a) How many divisors (proper and improper does $p^3 \cdot q^6 \cdot r^4$ have?

    [*Hint:* Each divisor is of the form $p^{?}q^{?}r^{?}$. How may each of the boxes be filled?]

   b) How many divisors has 1500?

   c) How many divisors has $64 \cdot 27 \cdot 625 \cdot 13$?

8. How many (rectangular) formations are possible for a marching band of 36 members? of 99 members?

9. a) List all the divisors of 12.

   b) Compute the sum of the divisors of 12.

   c) Compare your answer to (b) with: $(1 + 2 + 2^2) \cdot (1 + 3)$.

   d) Try to prove that the sum of the factors of $p^3 \cdot q^6 \cdot r^4$ is

$$(1 + p + p^2 + p^3)(1 + q + q^2 + q^3 + q^4 + q^5 + q^6)$$
$$(1 + r + r^2 + r^3 + r^4).$$

   [*Hint:* What does a typical term look like after you multiply out?]

10. The number 4 is called a *deficient number* because the sum of all its divisors other than itself is less than 4: $1 + 2 = 3 < 4$. The number 12 is called an *abundant number* because the sum of all its divisors other than itself is more than 12: $1 + 2 + 3 + 4 + 6 = 16 > 12$. The number 6 is called a *perfect number* because the sum of all of its divisors other than itself is 6: $1 + 2 + 3 = 6$.

   a) What sort of number is 10? 20? 28?

   b) Classify the numbers 2 through 20 as deficient, perfect, or abundant.

   c) What sort of number is any prime? square of a prime? cube of a prime? higher power of a prime?

   d) Verify that 496 is perfect.
   (It is not known whether there are any *odd* perfect numbers.)

   e) Prove that the sum of the reciprocals of *all* divisors of a perfect number is 2.

11. A number is *even* if it has 2 as a divisor. It is *odd* if it is of the form: even plus one.

   a) Describe the set of even numbers both in set-builder and roster notation.

   b) Describe the set of odd numbers both in set-builder and roster notation.

   c) What is the remainder after an odd number has been divided by 2?

   d) The sum of two even numbers is ———. Why?

   e) The sum of two odd numbers is ———. Why?

   f) The sum of an even and an odd number is ———. Why?

   g) The product of two even numbers is ———. Why?

   h) The product of two odd numbers is ———. Why?

   i) The product of an even and an odd number is ———. Why?

   j) If a is even and $a + b$ is odd, then ———.

   k) If ab is odd and a is odd, then ———.

l) If a/b is even and a is even, then ———.

m) If a/b is even and b is odd, then ———.

n) If the difference of two whole numbers is even, what can you conclude about the two numbers? What if the difference is odd?

o) Pick an odd number, square it, and subtract 1. Is the resulting number divisible by 8? Try this for some other odd numbers. Offer a conjecture and try to prove it.

p) Why is the sum of any number and its square even?

q) Prove that no integer can be both even and odd. [*Hint:* Use Exercise 2, page 268.]

12. Prove the following.

a) $a \mid 0$, $\forall a \in W$

b) $a \mid b$ and $b \mid c \Rightarrow a \mid c$

c) $d \mid a \Rightarrow d \mid ab$

d) $d \mid a$ and $d \mid b \Rightarrow d \mid a + b$

e) $d \mid a$ and $d \mid b \Rightarrow d \mid a - b$, $a \geq b$

f) If d divides any two of the numbers in the equation $a + b = c$, then it divides the third as well.

g) $d \mid a + b$ and $d \mid a \Rightarrow d \mid b$

13. a) Use the sieve of Eratosthenes to list all primes <100.

b) When you reached the stage of considering the prime 11, was there any more "striking out" left to be done?

c) If 11 were to be a factor of a number less than 121 $(= 11^2)$, how large could the *other* factor be? What *primes* could it possibly involve?

d) To decide whether a number n is prime, it suffices to check whether n is divisible by each prime less than ———.

e) Is 221 prime?

14. How long is the longest string of consecutive nonprimes (composites)

a) less than 11?

b) less than 31?

c) less than 100?

(It is known that, given any number n, there is a string of more than n consecutive nonprimes.)

d) Beginning with the number $(100 \cdot 99 \cdot 98 \cdots 3 \cdot 2) + 2$, at least ——— successive numbers will be composites?

15. Twin primes are pairs of primes with difference 2. For example: $(3, 5)$, $(5, 7)$, $(11, 13)$.

a) List the twin primes less than 100. (No one knows whether there are infinitely many twin primes. Some very large ones are known, though. For example, 8,482,259 and 8,482,261.)

b) Prove that (3, 5, 7) is the only "triple prime" by proving that, if you are given 3 consecutive odd numbers (for example, 17, 19, 21), one must be divisible by 3. [*Hint:* If the first is not divisible by 3, what is its remainder after it has been divided by 3?]

16. A famous theorem of Fermat states that every number is the sum of 4 squares (0 included). Express each of the following as the sum of 4 squares.

    a) 5   b) 10   c) 35   d) 187   e) 87

    f) Determine all numbers less than 50 which *cannot* be expressed as the sum of 3 squares, and make a conjecture.

    It is also true that every number is expressible as the sum of 9 cubes. Express each of the following as the sum of 9 cubes.

    g) 187   h) 215

17. The search for a usable formula which always produces primes has been fruitless.

    a) The formula $f(n) = n^2 - n + 41$ produces primes for $n = 1, 2, 3, \ldots,$ 40 but fails (why?) for $n = 41$. Compute $f(1), f(2), f(3), f(4), f(5), f(6)$. Also compute the differences: $f(2) - f(1), f(3) - f(2), f(4) - f(3), f(5) - f(4),$ $f(6) - f(5)$. Relate these calculations to the configuration below.

47	46	45	56
48	41	44	55
49	42	43	54
50	51	52	53

    b) Test the formula $f(n) = 2^n - 1$ for n a prime.

    c) Fermat hoped that $f(n) = 2^{2^n} + 1$ would work. Compute $f(1)$ and $f(2)$. [$f(1), f(2), f(3), f(4)$ are primes; $f(5)$ is not.]

18. A simple formula such as $f(n) = 5n + 3$ doesn't always produce primes, but it is known to produce infinitely many. Find 6 primes produced by it.

19. There is a well-known test (Wilson's theorem) for whether or not a number is prime:

    $$n \text{ is prime} \iff n \mid (n - 1)(n - 2) \cdots 3 \cdot 2 \cdot 1 + 1.$$

    For example, 4 is not a prime: $4 \nmid (3 \cdot 2 \cdot 1) + 1$, while 5 is prime $5 \mid (4 \cdot 3 \cdot 2 \cdot 1) + 1$. Verify Wilson's theorem for the prime 7 and the composite 8. How "practical" is this theorem?

20. It is known that for any *prime p*

    $$2^p - 2, 3^p - 3, 4^p - 4, 5^p - 5, 6^p - 6, \ldots$$

    are all divisible by p. Verify that 5 divides each of $2^5 - 2, 3^5 - 3, 4^5 - 4,$ $5^5 - 5$, and that $6 \nmid 2^6 - 2$.

12–3   more about divisibility; gcd and the Euclidean algorithm

One way of reducing the fraction $\dfrac{104{,}516}{14{,}790}$ to lowest terms is to factor both numerator and denominator into products of primes and then to cancel their "greatest common divisor":

$$\frac{104{,}516}{14{,}790} = \frac{\cancel{2}\cdot 2\cdot \cancel{17}\cdot \cancel{29}\cdot 53}{\cancel{2}\cdot 3\cdot 5\cdot \cancel{17}\cdot \cancel{29}} = \frac{2\cdot 53}{3\cdot 5} = \frac{106}{15}$$

Another way of doing it is sketched below. We shall soon see why it works.

```
            7                              15
14790 | 104516               986 | 14790
        103530    →                986      →    gcd is 986
          986                     4930
                                  4930
                                  ————
                                     0
```

```
          106
986 | 104516
      986
      ————
      5916        Answer:  106
      5916                 ———
      ————                  15
         0
```

We call d a *common divisor* of a and b if $d \mid a$ and $d \mid b$. For example, 1, 2, and 4 are all common divisors of 12 and 20. The greatest common divisor, gcd, of 12 and 20 is 4. Not only is it the greatest, it is also divisible by each of the other common divisors: $1 \mid 4$, $2 \mid 4$. It is a fact that:

Any two positive whole numbers a and b have a gcd, and this gcd is divisible by each of the common divisors of a and b.

▶ *Aside.* A straightforward definition of gcd is this: d is the gcd of a and b if

1. d is a common divisor of a and b, and

2. if c is a common divisor of a and b, then $c \leq d$.

Thus the first clause of the statement above is obvious (any two positive whole numbers have a gcd). The second is not. There is another definition of gcd which is even more widely used: d is a gcd of a and b if

1. d is a common divisor of a and b, and

2. if c is a common divisor of a and b, then $c \mid d$.

If we use this definition, the second statement in color above is superfluous. But now the first statement is not obvious. It must be proved! ◄

Example

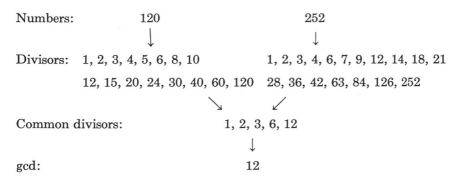

Numbers: 120   252

Divisors: 1, 2, 3, 4, 5, 6, 8, 10   1, 2, 3, 4, 6, 7, 9, 12, 14, 18, 21

           12, 15, 20, 24, 30, 40, 60, 120   28, 36, 42, 63, 84, 126, 252

Common divisors: 1, 2, 3, 6, 12

gcd: 12

[*Note:* 12 is divisible by 1, 2, 3, and 6]

In practice one never finds the gcd of two numbers as in the example. If factorization into primes is easy, then the gcd can be computed as follows.

Example 1 $120 = 2 \cdot 2 \cdot 2 \cdot 3 \cdot 5 = (2 \cdot 2 \cdot 3) \cdot (2 \cdot 5)$

                 $252 = 2 \cdot 2 \cdot 3 \cdot 3 \cdot 7 = (2 \cdot 2 \cdot 3) \cdot (3 \cdot 7)$

The gcd is $2 \cdot 2 \cdot 3$ because (a) $2 \cdot 2 \cdot 3$ is clearly a common divisor, and (b) no proper multiple of $2 \cdot 2 \cdot 3$ can divide both 120 and 252 (recall that the gcd is a multiple of each common factor), since there is no prime p such that both

        $2 \cdot 2 \cdot 3 \cdot p \mid 2 \cdot 2 \cdot 3 \cdot 2 \cdot 5$ (what would p have to be?)

and $2 \cdot 2 \cdot 3 \cdot p \mid 2 \cdot 2 \cdot 3 \cdot 3 \cdot 7$ (what would p have to be?)

Example 2   The gcd of $2^4 \cdot 3^3 \cdot 7 \cdot 13$ and $2 \cdot 3^5 \cdot 5 \cdot 7$ is

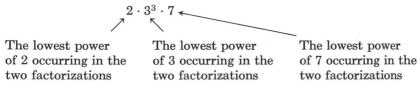

                        $2 \cdot 3^3 \cdot 7$

The lowest power   The lowest power   The lowest power
of 2 occurring in the   of 3 occurring in the   of 7 occurring in the
two factorizations   two factorizations   two factorizations

Is it clear that $2 \cdot 3^3 \cdot 7$ is a common factor? Is it clear that there is no prime p such that both

   $2 \cdot 3^3 \cdot 7 \cdot p \mid 2^4 \cdot 3^3 \cdot 7 \cdot 13$ and $2 \cdot 3^3 \cdot 7 \cdot p \mid 2 \cdot 3^5 \cdot 5 \cdot 7$,

and hence no (proper) multiple of $2 \cdot 3^3 \cdot 7$ can be a common factor?

If factorization into primes is not easy, as in the example on page 356, then one uses the Euclidean algorithm. We illustrate with a simple case, however.

Example   To find the gcd of 84 and 18, use the following procedure.

$$84 = 4 \cdot 18 + 12$$ Divide 84 by 18, get remainder 12

$$18 = 1 \cdot 12 + 6$$ Divide 18 by 12, get remainder 6

$$12 = 2 \cdot 6$$ Divide 12 by 6, get remainder 0

gcd is 6   Last nonzero remainder is gcd

Why does the algorithm work? The following diagram might make it geometrically plausible. Explain.

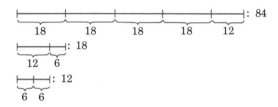

The algebraic justification depends primarily on the result of Exercise 12(f) on page 354. If $a + b = c$ and d divides any two of a, b, c, then d divides the third as well. Working from the bottom equation to the top in our example:

$6 \mid 6 \Rightarrow 6 \mid 2 \cdot 6 \Rightarrow 6 \mid 6$ and $6 \mid 12$

$6 \mid 6$ and $6 \mid 12$ and $18 = 1 \cdot 12 + 6 \Rightarrow 6 \mid 18$

$6 \mid 12$ and $6 \mid 18 \Rightarrow 6 \mid 12$ and $6 \mid 4 \cdot 18$

but

$84 = 4 \cdot 18 + 12$, so $6 \mid 84$; therefore $6 \mid 18$ and $6 \mid 84$

This proves that 6 is a common divisor of 18 and 84. To see that it is the greatest one, suppose that d is a common divisor. We work from the top down, and conclude that $d \mid 6$.

$d \mid 84$ and $d \mid 18 \Rightarrow d \mid 84$ and $d \mid 4 \cdot 18$

but

$84 = 4 \cdot 18 + 12$, so $d \mid 12$.

$d \mid 18$ and $d \mid 12$ and $18 = 12 + 6 \Rightarrow d \mid 6$.

Thus 6 is the greatest common divisor.

The following example gives a somewhat more complicated application of the Euclidean algorithm. Convince yourself that 2 really is the gcd of 86 and 68.

Example $\quad 86 = 1 \cdot 68 + 18$
$$68 = 3 \cdot 18 + 14$$
$$18 = 1 \cdot 14 + 4$$
$$14 = 3 \cdot 4 + \underline{2}$$
$$4 = 2 \cdot 2 \quad \text{Therefore the gcd of 86 and 68 is 2.}$$

Our original example on page 356 was much simpler!

$$104{,}516 = 7 \cdot 14{,}790 + 986$$
$$14{,}790 = 15 \cdot 986, \qquad \text{so the gcd is 986.}$$

Thus $\quad \dfrac{104{,}516}{14{,}790} = \dfrac{986 \cdot 106}{986 \cdot 15} = \dfrac{106}{15}.$

Although the Euclidean algorithm always works, it is not always the quickest way for finding the gcd of two numbers. Often factoring the numbers is quicker, especially if one knows a few tricks. Here are some common divisibility tricks, all closely related to the base 10 of our numeration system. If you work in another base you will need a new bag of tricks.

Divisibility by 2 A number is divisible by 2 if its last digit is divisible by 2 (that is, if the last digit is one of 0, 2, 4, 6, 8). Thus, $2 \mid 3976$ $(2 \mid 6)$ because

1. $3976 = 397 \cdot 10 + 6$ $\qquad\qquad$ 2. $2 \mid 10 \Rightarrow 2 \mid 397 \cdot 10$ (Why?)

3. $2 \mid 397 \cdot 10$ and $2 \mid 6 \Rightarrow 2 \mid 397 \cdot 10 + 6$ (Why?)

Divisibility by 5 A number is divisible by 5 if its last digit is divisible by 5 (that is, if the last digit is one of 0, 5). For example, $5 \mid 3975$ $(5 \mid 5)$ because

1. $3975 = 397 \cdot 10 + 5$ $\qquad\qquad$ 2. $5 \mid 10 \Rightarrow 5 \mid 397 \cdot 10$

3. $5 \mid 397 \cdot 10$ and $5 \mid 5 \Rightarrow 5 \mid 397 \cdot 10 + 5$

Divisibility by 3 A number is divisible by 3 if the sum of its digits is divisible by 3. For example, $3 \mid 7167$ $(3 \mid 21 = 7 + 1 + 6 + 7)$ because

1. $7167 = 7 \cdot 10^3 + 1 \cdot 10^2 + 6 \cdot 10 + 7$
$\qquad = 7(999 + 1) + 1(99 + 1) + 6(9 + 1) + 7$
$\qquad = (7 \cdot 999 + 1 \cdot 99 + 6 \cdot 9) + (7 + 1 + 6 + 7)$

2. $3 \mid (7 \cdot 999 + 1 \cdot 99 + 6 \cdot 9)$ (Why?)

3. $3 \mid (7 \cdot 999 + 1 \cdot 99 + 6 \cdot 9)$ and $3 \mid (7 + 1 + 6 + 7) \Rightarrow 3 \mid 7167$

Divisibility by 9 A number is divisible by 9 if the sum of its digits is divisible by 9. For example, $9 \mid 7164$ $(9 \mid 18 = 7 + 1 + 6 + 4)$ because

1. $7164 = 7 \cdot 10^3 + 1 \cdot 10^2 + 6 \cdot 10 + 4$
$\qquad = 7(999 + 1) + 1(99 + 1) + 6(9 + 1) + 4$
$\qquad = (7 \cdot 999 + 1 \cdot 99 + 6 \cdot 9) + (7 + 1 + 6 + 4)$

2. $9 \mid (7 \cdot 999 + 1 \cdot 99 + 6 \cdot 9)$ (Why?)

3. $9 \mid (7 \cdot 999 + 1 \cdot 99 + 6 \cdot 9)$ and $9 \mid 7 + 1 + 6 + 4 \Rightarrow 9 \mid 7164$

Divisibility by 4   A number is divisible by 4 if its last 2 digits represent a number divisible by 4.   For example, $4 \mid 3712$ $(4 \mid 12)$ because

1. $3712 = 37 \cdot 100 + 12$
2. $4 \mid 100 \Rightarrow 4 \mid 37 \cdot 100$
3. $4 \mid 37 \cdot 100$ and $4 \mid 12 \Rightarrow 4 \mid 37 \cdot 100 + 12$

Divisibility by 11   The rule here is easier to illustrate with examples than to express in words.

935 is divisible by 11 because $(9 + 5) - 3 = 14 - 3 = 11$ is.

4257 is divisible by 11 because $(4 + 5) - (2 + 7) = 9 - 9 = 0$ is.

69,482,919 is divisible by 11 because $(9 + 8 + 9 + 9) - (6 + 4 + 2 + 1) = 35 - 13 = 22$ is.

Before this rule can make any sense we need to observe that all of the following are divisible by 11.

$$10^0 - 1 = 0$$
$$10^1 + 1 = 11$$
$$10^2 - 1 = 99 \qquad\qquad [10^2 - 1 = 10(10^1 + 1) - 11]$$
$$10^3 + 1 = 1001 \qquad\quad [10^3 + 1 = 10(10^2 - 1) + 11]$$
$$10^4 - 1 = 9999 \qquad\quad [10^4 - 1 = 10(10^3 + 1) - 11]$$
$$10^5 + 1 = 100001 \qquad [10^5 + 1 = 10(10^4 - 1) + 11]$$
$$10^6 - 1 = 999999 \qquad [10^6 - 1 = 10(10^5 + 1) - 11]$$
$$10^7 + 1 = 10000001 \quad [10^7 + 1 = 10(10^6 - 1) + 11]$$
$$10^8 - 1 = 99999999 \quad [10^8 - 1 = 10(10^7 + 1) - 11]$$
$$\vdots \qquad\qquad\qquad\qquad\quad \vdots$$

Now $11 \mid 2763728$ $[11 \mid (2 + 6 + 7 + 8) - (7 + 3 + 2)]$ because

$$2763728 = 2 \cdot 10^6 + 7 \cdot 10^5 + 6 \cdot 10^4 + 3 \cdot 10^3 + 7 \cdot 10^2 + 2 \cdot 10 + 8.$$

$$
\begin{aligned}
&\quad\; 2(10^6 - 1 + 1) \qquad\qquad\qquad 2(10^6 - 1) + 2\\
&\;+7(10^5 + 1 - 1) \qquad\qquad\; + 7(10^5 + 1) - 7\\
&\;+6(10^4 - 1 + 1) \qquad\qquad\; + 6(10^4 - 1) + 6\\
=\;&\;+3(10^3 + 1 - 1) \qquad =\qquad + 3(10^3 + 1) - 3\\
&\;+7(10^2 - 1 + 1) \qquad\qquad\; + 7(10^2 - 1) + 7\\
&\;+2(10^1 + 1 - 1) \qquad\qquad\; + 2(10^1 + 1) - 2\\
&\;+8(10^0 - 1 + 1) \qquad\qquad\; + 8(10^0 - 1) + 8
\end{aligned}
$$

Thus $2763728 = k \cdot 11 + [(2 + 6 + 7 + 8) - (7 + 3 + 2)]$.

Since 2763728 is the sum of two terms, each divisible by 11, it too must be divisible by 11.

EXERCISES 12–3

1. a) List all the divisors of 24 and all the divisors of 30.

   b) List all the common divisors of 24 and 30.

   c) Pick out the gcd of 24 and 30 and verify that it is divisible by all the common divisors.

2. Find the gcd of each pair of numbers by factoring each into a product of primes.

   a) 20, 75   b) 144, 48   c) 12, 84   d) 12, 35

   e) 88, 90   f) 1326, 650

3. Reduce the following fractions to lowest terms:

   a) $\frac{20}{75}$ b) $\frac{144}{48}$ c) $\frac{84}{12}$ d) $\frac{12}{35}$ e) $\frac{88}{90}$ f) $\frac{650}{1326}$

4. Find the gcd of each pair of numbers by using the Euclidean algorithm.

   a) 1326, 650   b) 20, 75   c) 406, 343

   d) 117, 44   e) 1932,276

5. Find the gcd in any way you please. [*Hint:* The Euclidean algorithm will be helpful in (m) through (s).]

   a) 54, 72   b) 1, 72

   c) 100, 125   d) 198, 162

   e) 13, 1521   f) 13, 1242

   g) $2^3 \cdot 5 \cdot 3^2 \cdot 7$ h) $2 \cdot 3 \cdot 7^2 \cdot 13,\ 3^3 \cdot 5 \cdot 7 \cdot 13^3$

   i) $6 \cdot 9,\ 6 \cdot 15$ j) $6 \cdot 18,\ 6 \cdot 25$

   k) $6 \cdot 8,\ 4 \cdot 5$ l) p, q (p, q distinct primes)

   m) $n,\ n + 2$, where n is even   n) $n,\ n + 2$, where n is odd

   o) $n,\ n + 5$, where $5 \nmid n$ p) $n,\ n + 5$, where $5 \mid n$

   q) $n,\ n + 16$, where $8 \mid n$ but $16 \nmid n$ r) $n,\ n + 16$, where n is odd

   s) $n,\ n + 1$

6. The least common multiple, lcm, of 12 and 10 is 60 because (1) 60 is a common multiple of 12 and 10: $12 \mid 60$ and $10 \mid 60$; (2) $60 <$ any other common multiple of 12 and 10. One could find the lcm of 12 and 10 by listing the multiples of 12: 12, 24, 36, 48, <u>60</u>, 72, 84, 96, 108, <u>120</u>, ... ; the multiples of 10: 10, 20, 30, 40, 50, <u>60</u>, 70, 80, 90, 100, 110, <u>120</u>, ... ; the *common* multiples: 60, 120, ... ; and picking the smallest common multiple.

   In practice one never does it this way. Here is one practical way of finding the lcm. Observe that (1) $12 = 2^2 \cdot 3$, so any multiple of 12 must contain 2^2 and 3 as factors; (2) $10 = 2 \cdot 5$, so any multiple of 10 must contain 2 and 5 as factors. Thus any common multiple must contain $2^2 \cdot 3 \cdot 5$ as a factor. But $2^2 \cdot 3 \cdot 5$ is a common multiple and hence is the least. Notice that

$2^2 \cdot 3 \cdot 5$ is the product of the *highest* powers of the prime factors of 12 and 10. As another example,

The lcm of $2^2 \cdot 3 \cdot 11^3$ and $2 \cdot 3^4 \cdot 5 \cdot 11$ is

$$2^2 \cdot 3^4 \cdot 5 \cdot 11^3.$$

a) List some common multiples of 14 and 6 and find the lcm.

b) Factor 24 and 20 and find their lcm.

c) Factor 30 and 28 and find their lcm.

d) Prove that the lcm of two numbers *divides* any common multiple of them; in particular it divides their product.

e) Find the lcm of $2 \cdot 3^4 \cdot 5$ and $2^3 \cdot 7$.

f) Find the lcm of $2^2 \cdot 3^3 \cdot 5 \cdot 7$ and $2 \cdot 5 \cdot 7^4 \cdot 11$.

g) Find the gcd of $2^2 \cdot 3^3 \cdot 5 \cdot 7$ and $2 \cdot 5 \cdot 7^4 \cdot 11$.

h) Compute and ponder the product of your answers to (f) and (g).

i) Prove that

$$\text{the lcm of } m \text{ and } n = \frac{m \cdot n}{\text{gcd of } m \text{ and } n}.$$

(This is another way of finding the lcm, which avoids factoring if the gcd is computed by the Euclidean algorithm.)

j) Find the lcm of 1326 and 650.

k) Find the lcm of 406 and 343.

l) Find the lcm of p and q (p, q distinct primes).

m) Find the lcm of n, $n + 5$, where $5 \nmid n$.

n) Find the lcm of n, $n + 16$, where $8 \mid n$ but $16 \nmid n$.

o) $m \cdot n = 288$, the lcm of m and n is 72. What is the gcd of m and n? What could the numbers m and n be? (There are two possible answers.)

7. Find the least common denominators of the pairs of fractions

a) $\frac{3}{6}$, $\frac{4}{14}$ b) $\frac{9}{5}$, $\frac{8}{8}$,   c) $-\frac{3}{4}$, $\frac{5}{16}$

8. A car travels around a track in 90 seconds, a motorcycle in 132 seconds. If they begin together, how long will it take before they cross the finish line *together*? How many laps will each have driven?

9. a) A golfer can drive a ball 120 yards and can putt it 52 yards. Find the (least) number of drives and the (least) number of putts needed to advance the ball equal distances.

b) An angry golfer vows to break his driver and his putter into pieces, all of the same length. The driver is 40 inches long and the putter is 32 inches long. How can he minimize his effort?

10. The gcd of 48 and 18 is 6. The multiples of 48 are 48, 96, 144, ... ; the multiples of 18 are 18, 36, 54, 72, 90, ... 144, ... Consider a few selected differences:

$$54 - 48 = 6, \qquad 96 - 90 = 6, \qquad 144 - 144 = 0.$$

a) Could there be a multiple of 48 and a multiple of 18 having a *positive* difference less than 6? Why?
To see that the gcd *must* appear as a difference of a multiple of 48 and a multiple of 18, work backward up the Euclidean algorithm:

$$48 = 2 \cdot 18 + 12,$$
$$18 = 1 \cdot 12 + 6,$$
$$12 = 2 \cdot 6.$$

Second equation $\Rightarrow 6 = 18 - 1 \cdot 12$, First equation $\Rightarrow 12 = 48 - 2 \cdot 18$. Thus

$$6 = 18 - 1 \cdot (48 - 2 \cdot 18) = 3 \cdot 18 - 1 \cdot 48.$$

b) Express the gcd of 86 and 68 as the difference between multiples of 86 and 68.

c) Express the gcd of 3 and 5 as the difference between multiples of 3 and 5.

d) Find integers x and y such that

$$\frac{7}{15} = \frac{x}{5} + \frac{y}{3}.$$

[*Hint:* $\frac{7}{15} = 7 \cdot \frac{1}{15}$ and substitute for 1 from (c).]

e) Find integers x and y such that

$$\frac{10}{86 \cdot 68} = \frac{x}{86} + \frac{y}{68}.$$

f) Are there integers x and y such that

$$\frac{9}{86 \cdot 68} = \frac{x}{86} + \frac{y}{68} ? \qquad \text{Why?}$$

11. Given $a + b = c$. Prove that the gcd of a and b is equal to the gcd of b and c.

12. What is the rule for divisibility by 10?

13. Formulate rules for divisibility by
    a) 25   b) 8   c) 125   d) 16   e) 625
    Give an example for each.

14. How would you decide whether a number is divisible by
    a) 6?   b) 18?   c) 45?

15. a) Prove that a 2-digit number, ab, is divisible by 7 if $3a + b$ is divisible by 7.

    b) Prove that a 3-digit number, abc is, divisible by 7 if $2a + 3b + c$ is divisible by 7.

    c) Formulate and prove a rule for divisibility by 7 of a 4-digit number, $abcd$.

16. The last digit of a prime number (of more than one digit) must be one of the digits _____.

17. Factor the following numbers.

    a) 198   b) 1485   c) 4004   d) 1170   e) 137

18. a) Prove the following statement: If the sum of the digits of a base five numeral is divisible by 4, then the number is divisible by 4.

    b) What is the corresponding theorem for base twelve?

19. List the first sixteen even numbers in base 5 notation.

20. a) A base twelve numeral is divisible by 3 if its last digit is divisible by 3 (that is, if it is one of 0, 3, 6, 9). Prove this.

    b) Formulate and prove a rule for divisibility by 4 in base twelve.

    c) What is the test for divisibility by twelve in base twelve?

21. Convince yourself by looking at the rules for divisibility by 5 and 3 (in base 10) that our divisibility rules are "if and only if" rules. (This allows you to deduce that $3 \nmid 50713$ because $3 \nmid 5 + 7 + 1 + 3$.)

12–4   finite number systems; clock arithmetic

In our discussion of the Euclidean algorithm (and also earlier, see page 184), we made use of

The Division Theorem   Given that n and d are whole numbers, $d \neq 0$, then there are unique whole numbers q and r satisfying the two conditions

    1. $n = q \cdot d + r$,

    2. $0 \leq r < d$.

    This theorem is geometrically obvious. Algebraic proofs, however, are not easy and we do not attempt any.

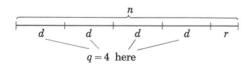

One consequence of this theorem is that when we divide by 12 each whole number yields a unique remainder in the set $\{0, 1, 2, \ldots, 11\}$. For example:

$17 \to 5$, $100 \to 4$, $2 \to 2$. We consider now the set

$I_{12} = \{0, 1, 2, \ldots, 11\}$,

define binary operations on it, and study the properties of the resulting system.
    Addition, $\oplus$, is defined on I_{12} by

$a \oplus b =$ the remainder when $a + b$ is divided by 12.

For example, $9 \oplus 7 = 4$, $11 \oplus 10 = 9$, $8 \oplus 4 = 0$.

▶ *Aside.* This definition suggests the name "clock arithmetic." If it is 9 o'clock now, in 7 more hours it will be 4 o'clock. If it is 11 o'clock now, in 10 more hours it will be 9 o'clock. If it is 8 o'clock now, in 4 more hours it will be 0 o'clock (0 o'clock is a much more natural name than 12 o'clock).

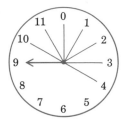 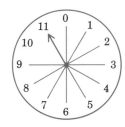 

Working with clocks may be helpful in understanding $\oplus$, but when we get to multiplication, $\otimes$, you will have to think in terms of the remainders after division by 12. ◀

    The binary operation $\oplus$ has all the usual properties.

Assoc $\oplus$ For example, $(8 \oplus 10) \oplus 9$ $\qquad$ $8 \oplus (10 \oplus 9)$
$$\| \qquad\qquad\qquad \|$$
$$6 \oplus 9 \;=\; 3 \;=\; 8 \oplus 7$$

Comm $\oplus$ For example, $8 \oplus 10 \;=\; 6 \;=\; 10 \oplus 8$

Add 0   For example, $7 \oplus 0 = 7$, $\quad 0 \oplus 11 = 11$

Negatives exist   For example,

$7 \oplus 5 = 0$, $\qquad 5 = \text{neg}(7)$
$9 \oplus 3 = 0$, $\qquad 3 = \text{neg}(9)$

    Multiplication, $\otimes$, is defined on I_{12} by

$a \otimes b =$ the remainder when ab is divided by 12.

For example: $9 \otimes 7 = 3$, $8 \otimes 4 = 8$, $11 \otimes 10 = 2$.

The binary operation $\otimes$ has most of the usual properties.

Assoc $\otimes$ For example, $(8 \otimes 10) \otimes 9$ $8 \otimes (10 \otimes 9)$

$$8 \otimes 9 \; = \; 0 \; = \; 8 \otimes 6$$

Comm $\otimes$ For example, $8 \otimes 10 = 8 = 10 \otimes 8$

Mult 1   For example, $7 \otimes 1 = 7, \quad 1 \otimes 11 = 11$

Dist $\otimes$ over $\oplus$ For example, $7 \otimes (5 \oplus 11) \quad (7 \otimes 5) \oplus (7 \otimes 11)$

$$7 \otimes 4 \; = \; 4 \; = \; 11 \oplus 5$$

One property, however, is conspicuously lacking: the cancellation law of multiplication.

$$8 \otimes 9 = 0 = 8 \otimes 0, \qquad \text{but } 9 \neq 0$$
$$6 \otimes 5 = 6 = 6 \otimes 7, \qquad \text{but } 5 \neq 7$$

Also lacking, of course, is its corollary:

$$a \neq 0, \quad b \neq 0 \Rightarrow a \otimes b \neq 0.$$

Complete addition and multiplication tables for the finite system $(I_{12}, \oplus, \otimes)$ are presented in the following tables.

$\oplus$	0	1	2	3	4	5	6	7	8	9	10	11
0	0	1	2	3	4	5	6	7	8	9	10	11
1	1	2	3	4	5	6	7	8	9	10	11	0
2	2	3	4	5	6	7	8	9	10	11	0	1
3	3	4	5	6	7	8	9	10	11	0	1	2
4	4	5	6	7	8	9	10	11	0	1	2	3
5	5	6	7	8	9	10	11	0	1	2	3	4
6	6	7	8	9	10	11	0	1	2	3	4	5
7	7	8	9	10	11	0	1	2	3	4	5	6
8	8	9	10	11	0	1	2	3	4	5	6	7
9	9	10	11	0	1	2	3	4	5	6	7	8
10	10	11	0	1	2	3	4	5	6	7	8	9
11	11	0	1	2	3	4	5	6	7	8	9	10

Addition table for I_{12}

⊗	0	1	2	3	4	5	6	7	8	9	10	11
0	0	0	0	0	0	0	0	0	0	0	0	0
1	0	1	2	3	4	5	6	7	8	9	10	11
2	0	2	4	6	8	10	0	2	4	6	8	10
3	0	3	6	9	0	3	6	9	0	3	6	9
4	0	4	8	0	4	8	0	4	8	0	4	8
5	0	5	10	3	8	1	6	11	4	9	2	7
6	0	6	0	6	0	6	0	6	0	6	0	6
7	0	7	2	9	4	11	6	1	8	3	10	5
8	0	8	4	0	8	4	0	8	4	0	8	4
9	0	9	6	3	0	9	6	3	0	9	6	3
10	0	10	8	6	4	2	0	10	8	6	4	2
11	0	11	10	9	8	7	6	5	4	3	2	1

Multiplication table for I_{12}

Of course, there is nothing special about 12. Any other positive integer will work as well, and some will lead to even nicer finite systems. Consider the system $(I_7, \oplus, \otimes)$, in which

$I_7 = \{0, 1, 2, 3, 4, 5, 6,\}$
$m \oplus n$ = remainder on dividing $m + n$ by 7
$m \otimes n$ = remainder on dividing $m \cdot n$ by 7

Again $\oplus$ and $\otimes$ satisfy all the properties they did before. But now the cancellation law of multiplication holds. In fact, a stronger result holds. Every nonzero element in I_7 has a multiplicative inverse.

$1 \otimes 1 = 1 \qquad 1 = \text{inv}(1)$
$2 \otimes 4 = 1 \qquad 4 = \text{inv}(2)$
$3 \otimes 5 = 1 \qquad 5 = \text{inv}(3)$
$4 \otimes 2 = 1 \qquad 2 = \text{inv}(4)$
$5 \otimes 3 = 1 \qquad 3 = \text{inv}(5)$
$6 \otimes 6 = 1 \qquad 6 = \text{inv}(6)$

Here, then, is a finite *field*. (See page 332 for the definition of field.) We give the addition and multiplication tables for I_7 at the top of the next page.

There are several good reasons for studying finite systems in the early grades. One reason is that in order to compute in such a system one needs to know how to add, subtract, multiply, and divide ordinary whole numbers.

⊕	0	1	2	3	4	5	6
0	0	1	2	3	4	5	6
1	1	2	3	4	5	6	0
2	2	3	4	5	6	0	1
3	3	4	5	6	0	1	2
4	4	5	6	0	1	2	3
5	5	6	0	1	2	3	4
6	6	0	1	2	3	4	5

Addition table for I_7

⊗	0	1	2	3	4	5	6
0	0	0	0	0	0	0	0
1	0	1	2	3	4	5	6
2	0	2	4	6	1	3	5
3	0	3	6	2	5	1	4
4	0	4	1	5	2	6	3
5	0	5	3	1	6	4	2
6	0	6	5	4	3	2	1

Multiplication table for I_7

For example, in I_{12}:

$6 \otimes 9 \xrightarrow{\hspace{2cm}} 54 \xrightarrow{\hspace{2cm}} 4 \cdot 12 + 6 \to 6$

      Ordinary   Ordinary

      multiplication   division by 12

$8 \oplus 11 \xrightarrow{\hspace{2cm}} 19 \xrightarrow{\hspace{2cm}} 7$

      Ordinary   Ordinary

      addition   subtraction of 12

Thus these finite systems provide new and interesting settings in which the child can sharpen his basic computational skills. Another reason is that an encounter with a system such as I_{12} puts a new light on the basic "laws" for W. It is not true that in any old system, $a \neq 0$ and $b \neq 0 \Rightarrow a \otimes b \neq 0$. Thus if we want it to be true of W, we must prove or assume it. A third reason is that the *finite* nature of these systems makes them especially nice for use as examples when new topics such as graphing and solving equations are introduced.

EXERCISES 12–4

1. Compute the following in I_{12}:

   a) $11 \otimes 9$ and $9 \otimes 11$ b) $8 \oplus 11$ and $11 \oplus 8$

   c) $(7 \oplus 9) \oplus 3$ and $7 \oplus (9 \oplus 3)$ d) $(5 \otimes 4) \otimes 3$ and $5 \otimes (4 \otimes 3)$

   e) $5 \otimes 5$ (which we'll abbreviate 5^2)   f) 6^2

   g) $9 \otimes (8 \oplus 5)$ and $(9 \otimes 8) \oplus (9 \otimes 5)$

   h) $0 \oplus 1 \oplus 2 \oplus 3 \oplus 4 \oplus 5 \oplus 6 \oplus 7 \oplus 8 \oplus 9 \oplus 10 \oplus 11$

   i) 3^2 j) 3^3 k) 3^4 l) 3^{5280} m) $10^{(10^{10})}$

2. Which elements of I_{12} have multiplicative inverses? How can you spot them by studying the multiplication table?

3. Some of the following equations have no solutions, some have a unique solution, and some have distinct solutions in I_{12}. Find all solutions when they exist. [*Hint:* Use the tables.]

   a) $x \oplus 4 = 11$ b) $x \oplus 11 = 4$ c) $3 \oplus x = 1$ d) $4 \otimes x = 8$

   e) $4 \otimes x = 6$ f) $5 \otimes x = 11$ g) $5 \otimes x = 0$ h) $x^2 = 1$

   i) $x^2 = 0$ j) $x^2 = 4$ k) $x^2 = 7$ l) $x^3 = 8$

4. Graph on axes like those given.

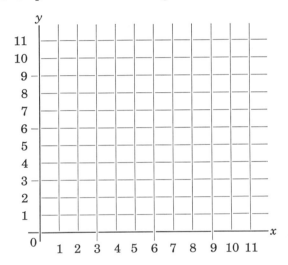

   a) $y = x^2$, that is, $\{(x, y) \in I_{12} \times I_{12} \mid y = x \otimes x\}$
   b) $y = 2x + 3$, that is, $\{(x, y) \in I_{12} \times I_{12} \mid y = 2 \otimes x + 3\}$
   c) $xy = 1$, that is, $\{(x, y) \in I_{12} \times I_{12} \mid x \otimes y = 1\}$

5. Show that $\oplus$ is a binary operation on I_{12} because $+$ is a binary operation on W and the remainder after division by 12 is unique. Explain (in terms of composition of functions).

6. Let $-a$ denote the additive inverse of a in I_{12}. Thus $-1 = 11$, $-2 = 10$, $-3 = 9, \ldots$ Compute the following:

   a) $-(3 \oplus 4)$ and $(-3) \oplus (-4)$ b) $(-3) \otimes (-5)$ and $3 \otimes 5$

   c) $-(-7)$ d) $(-1) \otimes 8$ and -8 e) $6 \otimes (-5)$ and $-(6 \otimes 5)$

7. Let $a - b$ denote $a \oplus (-b)$. Thus $6 - 4 = 6 \oplus (-4) = 6 \oplus 8 = 2$.
   Compute the following:

   a) $3 - 7$ b) $9 - 6$

   c) $-(8 - 5)$ and $(5 - 8)$ d) $9 - (5 - 2)$ and $(9 - 5) \oplus 2$

   e) $6 \otimes (3 - 8)$ and $(6 \otimes 3) - (6 \otimes 8)$

8. Compute the following in I_7.

   a) $5 \oplus 4$

   b) $2 \otimes 4$

   c) 3^2

   d) $0 \oplus 1 \oplus 2 \oplus 3 \oplus 4 \oplus 5 \oplus 6$

   e) $1 \otimes 2 \otimes 3 \otimes 4 \otimes 5 \otimes 6$

   f) 4^6

   g) 3^6

   h) 3^{12}

   i) 3^{5282}

9. Let $\frac{1}{a}$ denote the multiplicative inverse of a in I_7. Thus $\frac{1}{2} = 4$, $\frac{1}{3} = 5$, ...
   Compute the following:

   a) $\frac{1}{2} \otimes \frac{1}{3}$ and $\dfrac{1}{2 \otimes 3}$

   b) $\dfrac{1}{\frac{1}{5}}$

   c) $3 \otimes \frac{1}{3}$

10. Let $\frac{a}{b}$ denote $a \otimes \frac{1}{b}$ ($b \neq 0$). Compute the following (still in I_7).

    a) $\frac{2}{3}$ and $\frac{4}{6}$

    b) $\frac{3}{4}$ and $\frac{6}{1}$

    c) 1 and $\frac{5}{5}$

    d) $\frac{2}{3} \otimes \frac{1}{2}$

    e) $\dfrac{1}{\frac{3}{4}}$ and $\frac{4}{3}$

    f) $\dfrac{\frac{1}{2}}{\frac{3}{4}}$ and $\frac{1}{2} \otimes \frac{4}{3}$

    g) $\frac{2}{5} \oplus \frac{4}{5}$ and $\frac{6}{5}$

11. Give reasonable definitions of the following.

    a) $-a$,   where $a \in I_7$ Now compute the following.

    b) $a - b$,   where $a, b \in I_7$

    c) -4

    d) $6 - 3$

    e) $3 - 6$

    f) $-\left(\dfrac{2}{5}\right)$ and $\dfrac{-2}{5}$ and $\dfrac{2}{-5}$

    g) $\frac{6}{5} - \frac{2}{5}$ and $\frac{4}{5}$

    h) $1 - \frac{1}{6}$ and $\frac{5}{6}$

    i) $\frac{2}{3}(3 - \frac{5}{2})$ and $2 - \frac{5}{3}$

12. Describe the solutions in I_7 to the following equations.

    a) $x \oplus 4 = 6$

    b) $6 \oplus x = 2$

    c) $x - 2 = 3$

    d) $x - 5 = 6$

    e) $4 - x = 1$

    f) $x \oplus a = b$

    g) $5 \otimes x = 3$

    h) $5 \otimes x = 6$

    i) $2 \otimes x = 3$

    j) $3 \otimes x = 0$

    k) $a \otimes x = 0, a \neq 0$

    l) $a \otimes x = b, a \neq 0$

    m) $x^2 = 1$

    n) $x^2 = 4$

    o) $x^2 = 7$

    p) $x^3 = 6$

13. Graph on axes like those given. (The equations refer to I_7.)

    a) $y = x^2$

    b) $y = 2x + 3$

    c) $xy = 1$

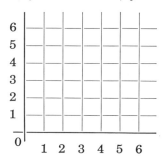

14. a) Make complete $\oplus$ and $\otimes$ tables for I_9.

b) Which elements have multiplicative inverses?

c) Do any of these elements contain the factor 3?

d) Must an element be prime to have a multiplicative inverse?

e) Compute a few products of elements having inverses. Draw a conclusion.

f) Find two nonzero elements whose product is 0. Draw a conclusion.

g) Find all solutions to $x^2 = 7$ in I_9.

h) Graph $y = x^2$.

15. Why should it be very easy to fill in the $\oplus$ and $\otimes$ tables for I_{10}?

16. Suppose that every nonzero element of I_n has a multiplicative inverse.

a) State the cancellation law for $\otimes$ and prove that it holds in I_n.

b) Prove that $a \neq 0$ and $b \neq 0 \Rightarrow a \otimes b \neq 0$.

c) Prove that n must be a prime number.

[*Hint:* Suppose that n is not prime. Then $n = ab$, where $a < n$ and $b < n$. Use (b).] There is a converse as well, but it is not easy to prove; namely, that if p is prime, then every nonzero element of I_p has a multiplicative inverse (that is, I_p is a field).

17. It is impossible to put an order relation $<$ on any of the finite systems and have it obey the usual order theorems. Let us suppose, on the contrary, that there is an order relation $<$ on I_7 which satisfies the usual order theorems. Supply the name of one of these order theorems in each blank in the following establishment of a contradiction. [$0 < 1$ because $1 = 1^2$; see Exercise 4 on page 264.]

a) $0 < 1$ and _____ $\Rightarrow 0 \oplus 1 < 1 \oplus 1$; that is, $1 < 2$

b) $0 < 1$ and $1 < 2$ and _____ $\Rightarrow 0 < 2$

c) $1 < 2$ and $0 < 2$ and _____ $\Rightarrow 1 \otimes 2 < 2 \otimes 2$; that is, $2 < 4$

d) $1 < 2$ and $2 < 4$ and _____ $\Rightarrow 1 < 4$

e) $2 < 4$ and $0 < 2$ and _____ $\Rightarrow 2 \otimes 2 < 4 \otimes 2$, that is, $4 < 1$

f) $1 < 4$ and $4 < 1$ contradicts _____.

18. Prove that our basic law concerning W, Cancel $\cdot$, is not a consequence of the other 8 basic laws.

19. Suppose that $a \in I_n$, $n \in N$.

a) Define "a is even."

b) Define "a is odd."

Define "a is prime" to mean (i) $a \neq 1$, (ii) only 1 and a divide a.

c) List the even elements of I_{12}.

d) List the odd elements of I_{12}.

e) List the primes of I_{12}.

f) List the even elements of I_7.

g) List the odd elements of I_7.   h) List the primes of I_7.

i) List the primes of I_4.   j) List the primes of I_6.

k) List the primes of I_3.   l) List the primes of I_5.

m) Is 4 factorable into primes in I_6?

n) Factor 5 into primes in I_6 two ways.

12–5 geometric numbers

Young children can discover interesting relationships among whole numbers by viewing them geometrically. The exercises below indicate a few possibilities.

EXERCISES 12–5

1. The perfect squares, or *square numbers*, 1, 4, 9, 16, 25, 36, ... can be represented by square arrays of dots.

$$1^2 = 1 \qquad 2^2 = 4 \qquad 3^2 = 9$$

a) Draw dot arrays for 4^2, 5^2, 6^2.

By partitioning these arrays in various ways, one can suggest different algebraic formulas.

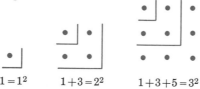

$$1 = 1^2 \qquad 1+3 = 2^2 \qquad 1+3+5 = 3^2$$

b) Partition the arrays for 4^2, 5^2, 6^2 as above, and write the corresponding algebraic formulas.

c) Write a general formula for n^2 suggested by the above.

d) Compute $1 + 3 + 5 + 7 + 9 + 11 + 13 + 15$.

e) Compute $1 + 3 + \cdots + 95 + 97 + 99$.

f) Partition the arrays for 4^2, 5^2, 6^2 as below, and write the corresponding algebraic formulas.

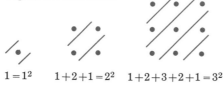

$$1 = 1^2 \qquad 1+2+1 = 2^2 \qquad 1+2+3+2+1 = 3^2$$

g) Write a general formula for n^2 suggested by the above.

h) Compute $1 + 2 + 3 + 4 + 5 + 6 + 5 + 4 + 3 + 2 + 1$.

i) Compute $1 + 2 + \cdots + 99 + 100 + 99 + \cdots + 2 + 1$.

j) Does $1 + 2 + \cdots + 99 + 100 + 99 + \cdots + 2 + 1$
$$= 1 + 3 + 5 + \cdots + 199?$$

2. The first three *triangular numbers* are as follows.

a) Draw dot arrays for $4^\triangle$, $5^\triangle$, $6^\triangle$ and compute their numerical values.

b) Partition the arrays for $4^\triangle$, $5^\triangle$, $6^\triangle$ as below, and write the corresponding algebraic formulas. Generalize.

$$1 = 1^\triangle \qquad 1+2 = 2^\triangle \qquad 1+2+3 = 3^\triangle$$

c) Express $1 + 2 + 3 + \cdots + 100$ as a triangular number.

d) Express $1 + 2 + 3 + \cdots + 99$ as a triangular number.

e) Express $1 + 2 + 3 + \cdots + 99 + 100 + 99 + \cdots + 2 + 1$ as a sum of two triangular numbers and as a square.

f) Partition the arrays for $6^\triangle, 7^\triangle$ as below and write the corresponding algebraic formulas.

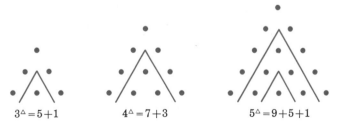

$$3^\triangle = 5+1 \qquad 4^\triangle = 7+3 \qquad 5^\triangle = 9+5+1$$

g) What is the first summand for $n^\triangle$?

h) Express $1 + 5 + 9 + 13 + 17 + 21$ as a triangular number.

i) Express $3 + 7 + 11 + 15 + 19$ as a triangular number.

j) Express $1 + 3 + 5 + \cdots + 19 + 21$ as a sum of two triangular numbers and as a square.

3. a) Partition the arrays for 4^2, 5^2, 6^2 as below, and write the corresponding formulas.

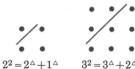

$2^2 = 2^\triangle + 1^\triangle$ $3^2 = 3^\triangle + 2^\triangle$

b) Write a general formula.

c) Express each of 49, 64, 81, 100 as the sum of two triangular numbers.

d) You've seen that each square number is expressible in terms of triangular numbers: $n^2 = n^\triangle + (n - 1)^\triangle$. The same formula can be used to express each triangular number in terms of square numbers. Prove the following:

$$n^\triangle = n^2 - (n - 1)^2 + (n - 2)^2 - (n - 3)^2 + \cdots \pm 1$$

[*Hint:* $n^\triangle = n^2 - (n - 1)^\triangle$; $(n - 1)^\triangle = (n - 1)^2 - (n - 2)^\triangle \ldots$]

e) Prove that

$$1 + 2 + \cdots + n = n^2 - (n - 1)^2 + (n - 2)^2 - \cdots \pm 1.$$

f) Compute $1^2 - 2^2 + 3^2 - 4^2 + 5^2 - 6^2 + 7^2$.

g) Compute $1^2 - 2^2 + 3^2 - 4^2 + 5^2 - 6^2 + 7^2 - 8^2 + 9^2 - 10^2$.

4. a) Extend and contemplate the following.

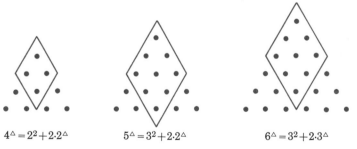

$4^\triangle = 2^2 + 2{\cdot}2^\triangle$ $5^\triangle = 3^2 + 2{\cdot}2^\triangle$ $6^\triangle = 3^2 + 2{\cdot}3^\triangle$

b) Extend and contemplate the following.

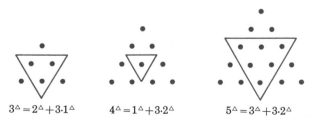

$3^\triangle = 2^\triangle + 3{\cdot}1^\triangle$ $4^\triangle = 1^\triangle + 3{\cdot}2^\triangle$ $5^\triangle = 3^\triangle + 3{\cdot}2^\triangle$

5. The first three hexagonal numbers are as follows.

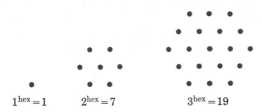

$1^{\text{hex}} = 1$ $2^{\text{hex}} = 7$ $3^{\text{hex}} = 19$

a) Draw arrays for 4^{hex}, 5^{hex} and compute their numerical values. Do you detect a pattern?

b) Extend and contemplate the following.

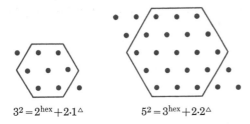

$3^2 = 2^{\text{hex}} + 2 \cdot 1^{\triangle}$ $5^2 = 3^{\text{hex}} + 2 \cdot 2^{\triangle}$

c) Extend and contemplate the following.

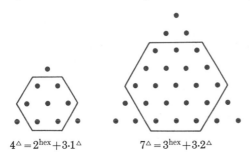

$4^{\triangle} = 2^{\text{hex}} + 3 \cdot 1^{\triangle}$ $7^{\triangle} = 3^{\text{hex}} + 3 \cdot 2^{\triangle}$

d) Extend and contemplate the following.

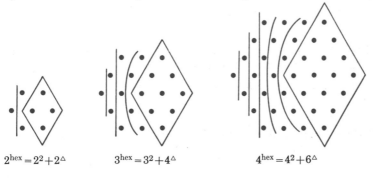

$2^{\text{hex}} = 2^2 + 2^{\triangle}$ $3^{\text{hex}} = 3^2 + 4^{\triangle}$ $4^{\text{hex}} = 4^2 + 6^{\triangle}$

6. Here is another somewhat different geometric approach to a problem.

a) To square systematically a sum of two terms, $a + b$, fill in the multiplication table and add all its entries

$$(a + b)^2 = a^2 + ab + ba + b^2 \; (= a^2 + 2ab + b^2).$$

	a	b
a	a^2	ab
b	ba	b^2

Square $9 + 6$ in this way.

b) To square a sum of three terms, $a + b + c$, fill in the multiplication table and add its entries.

	a	b	c
a	a^2	ab	ac
b	ba	b^2	bc
c	ca	cb	c^2

Square $7 + 3 + 5$ in this way.

c) How does one systematically square a sum of four terms? Square $1 + 2 + 3 + 4$ in this way.

d) Explain what is suggested by

1	2	3	4
2	4	6	8
3	6	9	12
4	8	12	16

=

$1 \times$	1	1	1	1
$2 \times$	1	2	2	2
$3 \times$	1	2	3	3
$4 \times$	1	2	3	4

e) Recalling that $1^2 = 1$, $2^2 = 1 + 2 + 1$, $3^2 = 1 + 2 + 3 + 2 + 1$, $4^2 = 1 + 2 + 3 + 4 + 3 + 2 + 1$, prove that

$$(1 + 2 + 3 + 4)^2 = 1^3 + 2^3 + 3^3 + 4^3.$$

f) Generalize (e).

g) Compute $1^3 + 2^3 + 3^3 + 4^3 + 5^3 + 6^3$.

7. Pascal's triangle is the following array of numbers.

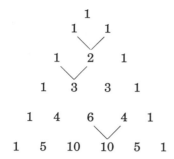

a) Look for a pattern and fill in the next 5 rows.

b) Locate the triangular numbers.

c) Locate the even numbers.

d) Locate the numbers divisible by 3.

e) Locate the numbers divisible by 5.

f) Show how to form all squares from numbers in the fourth diagonal.

g) Consider the set of 4 elements, $\{a, b, c, d\}$. How many subsets are there containing 0 elements? 1 element? 2 elements? 3 elements? 4 elements? Where do these numbers appear in the triangle?

h) Find the number of 7-element subsets of a set of 9 elements.

i) What is the total number of subsets of a set with 6 elements?

j) Compute and simplify: $(a + b)^1$, $(a + b)^2$, $(a + b)^3$. Now compare with the triangle.

k) Expand $(a + b)^{10}$.

l) Verify that $2^5 = 1 + 5 + 10 + 10 + 5 + 1$. Why should this be true? Generalize.

SUMMARY

In this chapter we return to W. Man has been fascinated by number theory for thousands of years. We list some of the ideas of the chapter below.

1. Divisibility terminology: $a \mid b$; a is a factor of b; a divides b; a is a divisor of b; b is a multiple of a.

2. Definition of prime numbers.

3. Fundamental theorem of arithmetic.

4. Sieve of Eratosthenes (this is sometimes treated in 5th or 6th grade).

5. Euclid's theorem on the infinitude of primes.

6. Factor trees (these occur in some elementary arithmetic texts).

7. The factored form of a number enables one to compute the number of divisors of the number and the sum of these divisors. For example,

$$2^3 \cdot 3^2 \cdot 5^4 \rightarrow 4 \cdot 3 \cdot 5 = 60 \text{ (divisors).}$$

$$2^3 \cdot 3^2 \cdot 5^4 \rightarrow (1 + 2 + 2^2 + 2^3)(1 + 3 + 3^2)(1 + 5 + 5^2 + 5^3 + 5^4)$$
$$= 15 \cdot 13 \cdot 781 \text{ (sum of all 60 divisors).}$$

8. Abundant, deficient, and perfect numbers.

9. Composites: There are strings of composites as long as you wish (contrast with point 5 above).

10. Twin primes.

11. The 4-square theorem. (Every number is also the sum of 9 cubes and of 19 fourth powers.)

12. Formulas that produce many primes.

13. The Euclidean algorithm and its use in determining the gcd of two numbers.

14. gcd and lcm. For any nonzero whole numbers a, b, $a \cdot b = (\text{gcd}) \cdot (\text{lcm})$.

15. Divisibility rules for 2, 3, 5, . . . in our base ten numeration system.

16. Finite number systems: In all these systems, Assoc $+$, Assoc $\cdot$, Comm $+$, Comm $\cdot$, Cancel $+$, Add 0, Mult 1, and Dist hold. Also negatives exist. If n is a prime, I_n is a field, that is, all nonzero elements have reciprocals and Cancel $\cdot$ holds. If n is composite, Cancel $\cdot$ does not hold and some elements fail to have reciprocals. Moreover one has $a \cdot b = 0$ with $a \neq 0$ and $b \neq 0$. For example, in I_{12}, $3 \cdot 4 = 0$; neither 3 nor 4 has a reciprocal; $8 \cdot 3 = 4 \cdot 3$.

17. Square, triangular, etc., numbers and formulas relating them. For example,

$$n^2 = 1 + 2 + \cdots + n + (n - 1) + \cdots + 1;$$

$$n^2 = 1 + 3 + 5 + \cdots + (2n - 1);$$

$$n^2 = (n - 1)^\triangle + n^\triangle; (1 + 2 + \cdots + n)^2 = 1^3 + 2^3 + \cdots + n^3.$$

13   geometry

13–1   historical background

The evolution of geometric thought beautifully exemplifies the process of mathematical abstraction. In the beginning geometry was a collection of practical rules used by the Egyptians and Babylonians for computing distances, areas, volumes, and directions. These rules were important to the carpenter, architect, surveyor, ship's pilot, and astronomer. The first geometric drawings in the sand and on papyrus scrolls were made in order to facilitate the solution of practical problems.

During the period from 600 B.C. to 300 B.C. the Greek mathematicians transformed geometry into a pure mathematical discipline. Thales of Miletus (seventh century B.C.) and Pythagoras (sixth century B.C.) are almost legendary figures. We have no written records of their work. Many geometers attended the famous academy of Plato, and it was there, during the fourth century B.C., that some of the major results of Greek geometry were obtained. Perhaps the greatest geometer of the Greek era was the mathematician-astronomer Eudoxus (370 B.C.).

About 300 B.C. Euclid, of Alexandria, produced the most famous textbook of all time, a summary of Greek mathematics (geometry and number theory) from the period of the Pythagoreans to his own day. The thirteen books of Euclid's *Elements* have appeared in more than a thousand editions. The school geometry taught all over the world today is still very closely related to the first six books of the *Elements*. Literal translations of parts of these books are still used in texts. Euclid organized geometry so that it could be treated deductively. He sought to show that one could derive all the theorems of geometry by applying logical reasoning to a small collection of basic axioms. Every school child encounters some of the axioms of Euclid.

Let it be postulated that one can:

   i) Draw a line segment from any point to any point.

  ii) Extend a line segment any distance.

 iii) Draw a circle with any center and any radius.

$$\vdots$$

Euclid's effort to place geometry on a purely logical basis was not quite successful, but it was approximately 2000 years before the growth of mathematical knowledge suggested improvements in the Euclidean treatment of geometry. To the Greek mathematicians, geometry belonged to the realm of the mind. They recognized the impossibility of drawing "perfectly straight lines" or "perfect circles," but they also recognized the possibility of *imagining* such geometric objects. In the present-day teaching of geometry each child roughly retraces the experience of the human race. In the beginning geometric language and geometric symbols are only tools to describe the real world. A *triangle* is something made by fastening three rods together. The rim of a can is a *circle*. A *sphere* is a ball. Gradually, encouraged by teachers and textbooks, the child begins to grasp the abstraction, until he feels that the *real* geometry is the geometry of his imagination and that physical objects are but imperfect copies of ideal geometric shapes. We may never *see* two sticks with exactly the same length, but we certainly can *think* of two line segments that are exactly alike.

EXERCISES 13-1

  1. What is the etymological meaning of the word geometry?

  2. Describe physical objects which suggest the following abstract geometric concepts.

a) point	b) line	c) ray	d) line segment
e) plane	f) angle	g) parallel lines	h) perpendicular lines
i) rectangle	j) square	k) circle	l) triangle
m) pyramid	n) cone	o) prism	p) sphere
q) parallelepiped	r) cube		

13–2 geometric figures

Everyone who thinks about geometry forms mental images of geometric figures. The pictures we draw are quite crude in comparison with our mental images, but even these images leave much to be desired. It is quite difficult to visualize a point. Lines and planes are just as difficult to visualize as points. How narrow is a line? How thick is a plane?

There are two standard ways to think about the relationships between points, lines, and planes. One way is to regard lines and planes as *supports* for points. We think of points on a line as if they were beads on a string, of points on a plane as if they were grains of sand resting on a table. The alternative (currently popular) viewpoint is to think of lines and planes (and other geometric figures as well) as sets of points. With this convenient viewpoint much of the language of set theory becomes useful in the study of geometry. We shall adopt this second point of view in the sequel.

We first consider some plane-geometric figures. Our universal set of points is a plane, the *Euclidean plane*. We denote this set by ε. Certain special subsets of ε are called lines (straight lines). Note that points are *elements* of ε; lines are *subsets* of ε. Note also that we do not formulate a definition of a line, but using points and lines as basic *undefined* objects, we define other geometric figures in terms of these.

We shall denote lines by small letters $l, m, n, \ldots$, and points by capitals, A, $B, C, \ldots$ This is a reversal of our customary notation used to indicate set membership. We write $A \in l$, $A \notin m$.

The diagrams indicate symbols we shall use to denote familiar geometric figures.

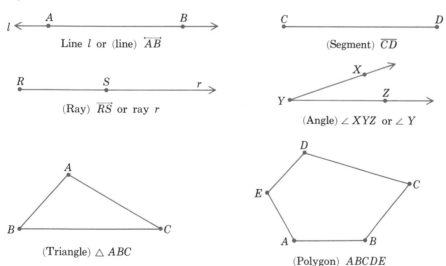

Line l or (line) $\overleftrightarrow{AB}$ (Segment) $\overline{CD}$

(Ray) $\overrightarrow{RS}$ or ray r (Angle) $\angle XYZ$ or $\angle Y$

(Triangle) $\triangle ABC$ (Polygon) $ABCDE$

Explain the following set-theoretic definitions.

$\overline{CD} = \{X \in \overleftrightarrow{CD} \mid X = C \text{ or } X = D \text{ or } X \text{ is between } C \text{ and } D\}$
$\overrightarrow{RS} = \{X \in \overleftrightarrow{RS} \mid R \text{ is not between } X \text{ and } S\}$
$\angle XYZ = \overrightarrow{YX} \cup \overrightarrow{YZ}$
$\triangle XYZ = \overline{XY} \cup \overline{YZ} \cup \overline{ZX}$
Polygon $ABCDE = \overline{AB} \cup \overline{BC} \cup \overline{CD} \cup \overline{DE} \cup \overline{EA}$

EXERCISES 13-2

1. State an axiom of geometry which assures us that if l and m are distinct lines of $\mathcal{E}$, then $l \cap m = \{P\}$ or $l \cap m = \varnothing$.

2. Let segments $\overline{AB}$ and $\overline{CD}$ be subsets of line l. Sketch figures showing the possibility of the following cases.

   a) $\overline{AB} \cap \overline{CD} = \varnothing$ b) $\overline{AB} \cap \overline{CD} = \{A\}$ c) $\overline{AB} \cap \overline{CD} = \overline{AB}$

   d) $\overline{AB} \cap \overline{CD} = \overline{CA}$ e) $\overline{AB} \cup \overline{CD} = \overline{AD}$ f) $\overline{AB} \cup \overline{CD} = \overline{AB}$

   g) $\overline{AB} \cup \overline{CD}$ is not a segment.

3. Given that the intersection of two segments contains at least two points:

   a) Are the segments necessarily subsets of the same line?

   b) Is the intersection of the two segments necessarily a segment?

   c) Discuss what would be involved in *proving* that your answers for (a) and (b) are correct.

4. Consider two distinct points A, B and rays $\overrightarrow{AB}$ and $\overrightarrow{BA}$.

   a) Describe the set $\overrightarrow{AB} \cup \overrightarrow{BA}$.

   b) Describe the set $\overrightarrow{AB} \cap \overrightarrow{BA}$.

   c) Discuss what would be involved in proving that your answers for (a) and (b) are correct.

5. Each polygon $ABCD$ has two *diagonals*, $\overline{AC}$ and $\overline{BD}$. Draw such a polygon for which:

   a) The intersection of the diagonals is $\varnothing$.

   b) The intersection of the diagonals is $\{P\}$.

6. Draw a triangle and a line whose intersection consists of (a) 0, (b) 1, (c) 2 points. If the intersection contains more than 2 points, what can you conclude?

7. Suggest symbols other than $\overleftrightarrow{AB}$, $\overline{AB}$, $\overrightarrow{AB}$, $\triangle ABC$, $\angle ABC$ as names for a line, a segment, etc. Why are we able to name geometric figures by naming only a few points?

8. $R \in \overleftrightarrow{PQ}$. Is it true that (a) $P \in \overleftrightarrow{RQ}$? (b) $Q \in \overleftrightarrow{PR}$?

9. $R \in \overrightarrow{PQ}$, $R \neq P$, and $R \neq Q$. Is it true that (a) $Q \in \overrightarrow{PR}$? (b) $P \in \overrightarrow{RQ}$?

10. $C \in \overline{AB}$, $C \neq A$, and $C \neq B$. Is it true that (a) $A \in \overline{BC}$? (b) $B \in \overline{AC}$?

11. What can you conclude if you know that $A \neq B$, $A \in l_1$, $B \in l_1$, $A \in l_2$, and $B \in l_2$?

12. What can you conclude if you know that $l_1 \neq l_2$, $A \in l_1$, $B \in l_1$, $A \in l_2$, and $B \in l_2$?

13. Name all the line segments determined by three points A, B, and C. How many line segments are determined by (a) 4 points, (b) 5 points, (c) 6 points?

14. Name all the rays determined by three noncollinear points A, B, and C. How many rays are determined by (a) 4 points, (b) 5 points, (c) 6 points, if no three points are collinear?

15. Answer the questions of Exercise 14 under the assumption that each set of points is a collinear set.

16. Sketch a figure showing that one ray can be a proper subset of a second ray.

17. $\angle ABC \subset \angle DEF$. What can you conclude?

18. Consider 3 rays from a point P. How many angles do these rays determine? How many angles are determined by 4 rays from P? 5 rays? 6 rays?

19. Verify that the following definitions of $\overrightarrow{RS}$ are equivalent to the one given in the text. $\overrightarrow{RS} = \{X \in \overleftrightarrow{RS} \mid X = R$ or X is between R and S or $X = S$ or S is between R and $X\}$; $\overrightarrow{RS} = \overline{RS} \cup \{X \in \overleftrightarrow{RS} \mid S$ is between R and $X\}$.

20. Is any segment so "long" that it contains every point of a line? One student argued: If A and B are *any* points on a line l, then there is a segment which contains them. So there is a segment which contains every point of l. A second student argued: Take the greatest segment of all the segments on l. This segment must contain every point of l, for otherwise it could be made longer. Comment on these "proofs."

The notation we use in naming geometric concepts is actually functional notation. We *associate* with each ordered pair of distinct points a line, a segment, and a ray. Ordinary function notation would be

$l(A, B);$ $s(A, B);$ $r(A, B).$

The letters l, s, r denote functions. Instead of these letters we use the symbols

$\leftrightarrow,$ $\overline{},$ $\rightarrow.$

In the symbol $\overrightarrow{AB}$, the symbol $\rightarrow$ denotes a *function*, the symbol AB represents the *ordered pair of points* (A, B), and the full symbol denotes the set of points (ray) that is matched with this ordered pair of points (A, B) by the function. This is just one more illustration of the extent to which function concepts permeate all of mathematics.

Problem   Explain the sense in which the symbols $\triangle$ and $\angle$ denote functions.

13–3   congruence and measurement

The concept of *congruence* is the primitive concept on which measurement is based. Intuitively, congruent figures have the same "size" and "shape." When we measure the distance between two points we "lay off" segments of the "same size." Hence a description of the measurement process requires the notion of congruence. In this sense the idea of congruence naturally precedes that of measurement, and distance can be defined in terms of congruence.

On the other hand, one can regard distance as the primitive concept and define a congruence as a 1–1 correspondence between two sets of points which *preserves distances.* Given that *f* is any congruence and *A, B* any two points in the domain of the congruence, then the points $f(A)$ and $f(B)$ are just as far apart as *A* and *B* are.

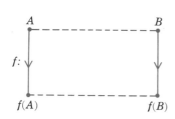

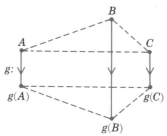

The sets $\{A, B\}$ and $\{f(A), f(B)\}$ are congruent sets. The distance from *A* to *B* is the same as from $f(A)$ to $f(B)$.

The sets $\{A, B, C\}$ and $\{g(A), g(B), g(C)\}$ are congruent sets. "Corresponding distances" are the same.

▶ *Aside.* Intuitive descriptions of congruences are as follows.

    i) A first set of points is congruent to a second if it can be *moved* so that it *coincides* with the second.

    ii) Congruent figures have the same *size* and *shape.*

    iii) Congruent figures are those figures which, when viewed separately, cannot be distinguished from one another.

These descriptions may be utilized in the elementary school by drawing figures on transparent paper and superimposing one figure on another. ◀

Measurement is a complex process by which one associates a real number with a set of points. For example, let $\overline{AB}$ be some segment and let $\overline{CD}$ be the chosen *unit segment.*

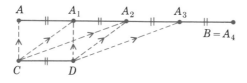

In real life $\overline{CD}$ would be a foot rule, a yardstick, an inch segment, etc. We would "pick $\overline{CD}$ up and lay it off repeatedly on AB," establishing "points" $A_1, A_2, \ldots$ In our geometry we think of points $A_1, A_2, \ldots$ such that consecutives pairs of points are "just as far apart" as are *C* and *D*. In other words, each of the point pairs $A, A_1; A_1, A_2; \ldots$ is congruent to the pair *C, D.*

In measuring the area of a region in terms of a chosen unit region, we "lay off" on the region to be measured congruent copies of a unit region.

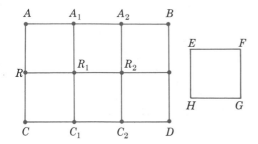

Each set of four points such as A, A_1, R_1, R; A_1, A_2, R_2, R_1; ... is congruent to the set E, F, G, H, the vertices of the unit square.

To measure the volume of a region in space we lay off congruent copies of a unit region.

In actual geometric work we deal mostly with triangle congruences.

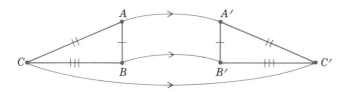

The markings on the sides assert that the corresponding segments are congruent, and we write $\overline{AB} \cong \overline{A'B'}, \overline{BC} \cong \overline{B'C'}, \overline{CA} \cong \overline{C'A'}$.

By our basic definition two angles are congruent if a one-to-one correspondence preserving *all* distances can be established. In any such correspondence, the vertices must correspond.

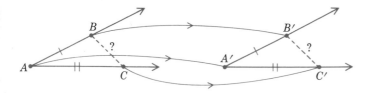

As the figure indicates, $\overline{AB} \cong \overline{A'B'}$ and $AC \cong \overline{A'C'}$.

Problem   a) If $\overline{BC} \not\cong \overline{B'C'}$, what can you conclude?

b) If $\overline{BC} \cong \overline{B'C'}$, what can you conclude?

c) Relate this diagram to some axiom or theorem which you encountered in school geometry.

Referring to the diagram below, of course we take for granted that if any two congruent pairs like B, C and B', C' can be found, then any two other corresponding pairs are also congruent. For if $\overline{BC} \cong \overline{B'C'}$ and $\overline{DE} \not\cong \overline{D'E'}$, then we would conclude that, simultaneously, $\angle A \cong \angle A'$ and $\angle A \not\cong \angle A'$.

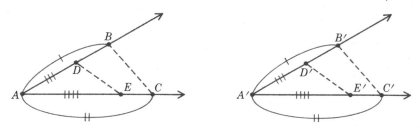

If $\overline{BC} \cong \overline{B'C'}$, then $\overline{DE} \cong \overline{D'E'}$

EXERCISES 13–3

1. For each pair of point sets below, explain why the first is not congruent to the second.

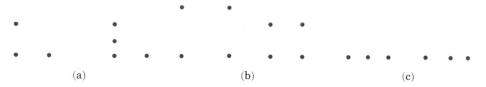

   (a)   (b)   (c)

2. For each pair of point sets below, select from the second set as many subsets as possible which are congruent to the first.

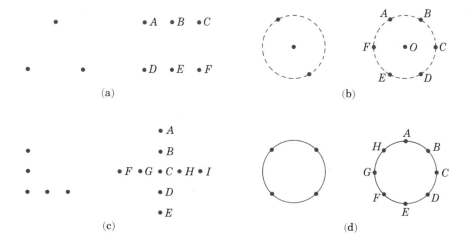

3. Explain why each function below is not a congruence and replace it by one which is a congruence.

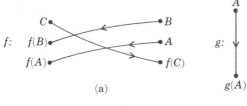

(a)

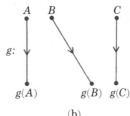

(b)

4. Each of the diagrams (a) and (b) below suggests a function which matches points of one segment 1–1 with points of a second. Describe each function and explain why you think it is or is not a congruence. Discuss similarly (c), (d), and (e).

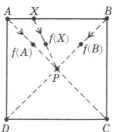

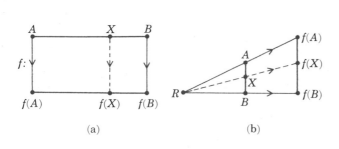

(a)   (b)

P is the intersection of the diagonals of square $ABCD$. For each $X \in ABCD$, $f(X)$ is the midpoint of $\overline{PX}$.

(c)

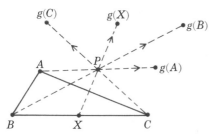

For each $X \in \triangle ABC$, $g(X)$ is the point such that P is the midpoint of $\overline{X\ g(X)}$.

(d)

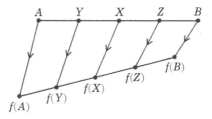

A is just as far from B as $f(A)$ is from $f(B)$. The midpoints of the two segments are matched [X with $f(X)$]. The midpoints of the resulting *two* half segments are matched. [$Y \rightarrow f(Y)$ and $Z \rightarrow f(Z)$]. The midpoints of the resulting *four* segments are matched, and so on endlessly.

(e)

5. Explain how congruence concepts are used in defining (a) right angle, (b) isosceles triangle, (c) square, (d) regular polygon.

We mentioned at the beginning of this section that the concept of congruence is more primitive than that of measurement. Ideas of *greater than* and *less than* for geometric figures are closely related to ideas of congruence.

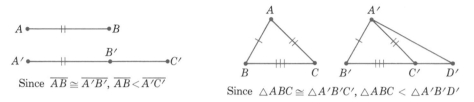

Since $\overline{AB} \cong \overline{A'B'}$, $\overline{AB} < \overline{A'C'}$

Since $\triangle ABC \cong \triangle A'B'C'$, $\triangle ABC < \triangle A'B'D'$

These diagrams should evoke memories of your school geometry days, when Euclid was quoted to you as having postulated:

The *whole* is greater than any of its *parts*.

It is intuitively clear that if we measure two congruent segments we get the same *lengths;* if we measure two congruent triangles we get the same *areas;* if we measure two congruent angles we get the same *angle measures*. Each term, *length, area, angle measure* refers to a real number obtained by repeatedly applying concepts of congruence. We illustrate this by considering the process of measuring an angle.

To measure an angle we choose a unit angle and "lay off" congruent copies on the angle to be measured.

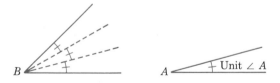

The figure indicates that the measure of $\angle B$ relative to unit $\angle A$ is 3. If we fail to "come out even" in the measurement process, we "chop up our unit" and use a fractional part as the new unit.

We have a natural unit for measuring angles, the straight angle:

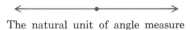

The natural unit of angle measure

When we use this angle as unit, all angles have measures from 0 to 1. The traditional unit of angle measurement is, however, $\frac{1}{180}$th of a straight angle.

If a ray from the vertex of a straight angle forms two congruent angles, each angle is called a *right angle*. If a right angle is subdivided into 90 congruent angles, each is called a *degree* (an angle of 1°). Each degree is subdivided into 60 congruent *minute* angles (1′). Each minute is subdivided into 60 angles of one *second* (1″). These are the traditional units of angle measurement.

$60'' = 1'$; $60' = 1°$; $90° = 1$ right angle;   2 right angles $= 1$ straight angle.

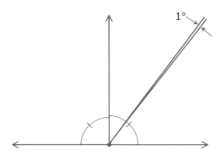

Right angles; a 1° angle

The standard protractor used for measuring angles lays off degree units on the angle being measured, just as a ruler lays off inch units on a segment. Instead of counting the units one can subtract.

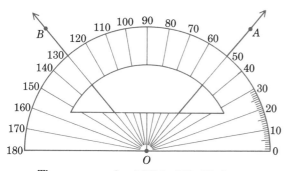

The measure of ∠AOB is 130−50 degrees.

It is easy to see that measurement of a line segment may produce an infinite decimal. (Cf. the figure at the top of the next page.)

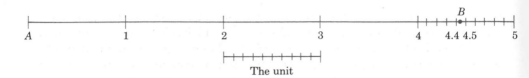

The unit

Laying off the unit, the length is between 4 and 5.
Laying off tenths of the unit, the length is between 4.4 and 4.5.
Laying off hundredths of the unit, the length is between 4.43 and 4.44.
Laying off thousandths of the unit, the length is between 4.437 and 4.438.

Practically, of course, it is impossible to repeatedly subdivide a unit of length and make finer and finer measurements. In the imaginary world of geometry, however, this measurement process may continue endlessly, generating an infinite decimal, perhaps repeating, perhaps not. For example, if one measures a segment that is one-third of the unit, then the subdivision into tenths, hundredths, . . . produces the repeating decimal

0.333 . . .

For the diagonal of a unit square, the decimal fails to repeat. It begins

1.414213562373 . . .

Sometimes the length of a segment $\overline{AB}$ is denoted by $m(\overline{AB})$ (measure of $\overline{AB}$). The symbols $|AB|$ and AB are also used.

Measurement of areas and volumes also produces decimals because of the repeated subdivision of unit squares and unit cubes.

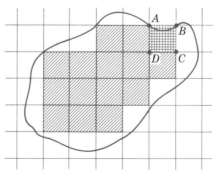

Region R includes 14 unit squares.

The diagram above pictures a region which includes 14 unit squares of the grid. Now, as the subdivision of unit square $ABCD$ into 100 small congruent squares suggests, each unit square which contains both points of R and points outside R is subdivided, and small squares in R are counted. This subdivision process proceeds interminably. For example, for region R one might have:

1st stage	14 unit squares	14.
2nd stage	783 hundredths	7.83
3rd stage	2175 ten thousandths	0.2175
4th stage	7391 millionths	0.007391

Termination of the measurement process at this fourth stage would yield the approximation 22.054891.

EXERCISES 13–4

1. The unit usually chosen for measuring area is a square. Squares "fill up" the plane nicely. Suggest other geometric figures that have this property of filling the plane.

2. Actually it is not necessary that the unit regions chosen for measuring area fit together. For example, one could use a circle as unit, then fit into extra space circles of $\frac{1}{10}$ the radius of the unit, $\frac{1}{100}$ of the radius, ... Sketch a figure picturing this way of measuring the area of a square.

3. The diagram indicates lengths of segments relative to unit segment $\overline{AB}$.

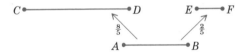

a) Give the length of $\overline{AB}$ if $\overline{CD}$ is the unit.

b) Give the length of $\overline{EF}$ if $\overline{CD}$ is the unit.

c) Give the length of $\overline{CD}$ if $\overline{EF}$ is the unit.

d) Explain how to manipulate the fractions mechanically in computing answers for (a), (b), and (c).

4. The diagram indicates areas of squares relative to unit square $ABCD$.

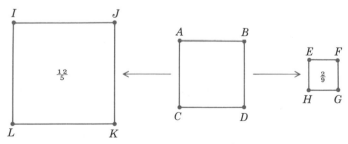

a) Give the area of *ABCD* if *EFGH* is the unit square.

b) Give the area of *IJKL* if *EFGH* is the unit.

c) Give the area of *EFGH* if *IJKL* is the unit.

5. The diagram indicates measures of angles relative to a unit angle ∠ *A*.

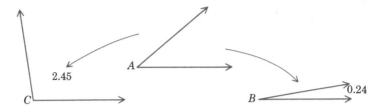

2.45

0.24

a) Give the measure of ∠ *C* in terms of ∠ *B* as unit.

b) Give the measure of ∠ *A* in terms of ∠ *C* as unit to the nearest hundredth.

6.

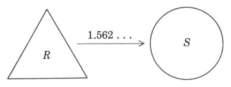

1.562 ...

R   *S*

As the figure indicates, the area of region *S* in terms of unit region *R* is approximately 1.562. Compute to the nearest hundredth the area of *R* if region *S* is chosen as the unit region.

7. The figures below recall for the reader certain minimal conditions for triangle congruence. For example, figure (a) calls attention to the theorem that two triangles are congruent if side-angle-side of one are congruent, respectively, to side-angle-side of the other. State the theorems associated with the other figures.

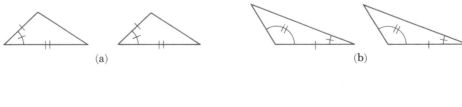

(a)   (b)

(c)   (d)

13–4   separation and convexity

Each point in a line partitions the line into three sets.

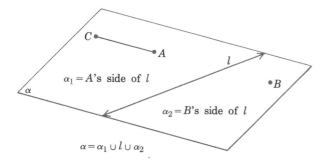

$$l = l_1 \cup \{P\} \cup l_2$$

Each of the sets l_1, l_2 is a *half line*. (Note that a half line is a ray with endpoint deleted.) Each half line is *convex*. A set S of points is convex if it has the property that

$$A \in S \text{ and } B \in S \Rightarrow \overline{AB} \subset S.$$

Note that $A \in l_1$, $C \in l_1$, and $\overline{AC} \subset l_1$.

Each line in a plane partitions the plane into three convex sets.

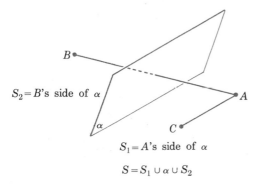

Each of the sets α_1, α_2 is a *half plane*. The common edge l belongs to neither half plane. Each half plane is convex. Note that $A \in \alpha_1$, $C \in \alpha_1$, and $\overline{AC} \subset \alpha_1$.

Each plane partitions the three-dimensional space S into three sets.

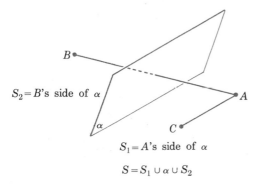

Each of the sets S_1, S_2 is a *half space*. The common boundary α belongs to neither half space. Each of S_1, S_2 is convex. Note that $A \in S_1$, $C \in S_1$, and $\overline{AC} \subset S_1$.

One important property of convex sets is that the intersection of two convex sets is itself a convex set. (Can you prove this?) Many important geometric figures are formed by the intersection of convex sets. As an example, consider $\angle ABC$ below.

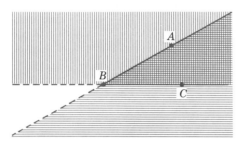

We have shaded C's side of $\overleftrightarrow{AB}$ horizontally, A's side of $\overleftrightarrow{BC}$ vertically. The cross-hatched region is the *interior* of $\angle ABC$. This is a convex region. The angle $\angle ABC$ partitions the plane into three sets, the set of points comprising the *angle* (the points of rays $\overrightarrow{BA}$ and $\overrightarrow{BC}$), the *interior* of $\angle ABC$ noted above, and the remaining points of the plane, the *exterior* of $\angle ABC$.

EXERCISES 13-5

1. The interior of $\triangle ABC$ is the intersection of three half planes. One of these half planes is A's side of $\overleftrightarrow{BC}$. Name the others.

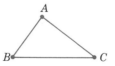

2. The interior of the convex polygon $ABCDE$ shown here is the intersection of half planes. Name these half planes.

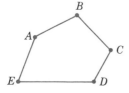

3. For a one-dimensional bug who lives on a line, two points can form a "jail."

Bug

a) What is the least number of lines required to form a jail in the plane?

b) What is the least number of planes required to form a jail in space?

4. Note that 1 point on a line splits the line into 2 pieces; 2 points . . . One line in a plane splits the plane into 2 pieces; 2 lines can split it into 4 pieces; 3 lines . . .

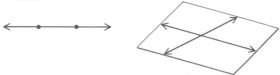

One plane in space splits space into 2 pieces; 2 planes can split space into 4 pieces; 3 planes can split space into 8 pieces (explain); 4 planes . . . Complete the table below. [*Hint:* Look for arithmetical and geometrical relationships.]

Number of points	Subsets of the line	Number of lines	Subsets of the plane	Number of planes	Subsets of space
0	1	0	1	0	1
1	2	1	2	1	2
2		2	4	2	4
3		3		3	8
4		4		4	
5		5		5	
6		6		6	

5. What is the least number of regions into which 2 lines can split a plane? 3 lines? n lines?

6. Note that if 2 points on the circumference of a circle are connected by a segment, the interior of the circle is separated into 2 pieces. If 3 points are connected, each to the other two, 4 pieces are formed. Compute the maximum number of pieces into which the interior of a circle can be separated by similarly connecting 4, 5, and 6 points on the circumference. Justify the use of the word "maximum."

7. When Venn diagrams utilizing circles are employed, 1 circle partitions the universal set into 2 subsets; 2 circles can form 4 subsets.

 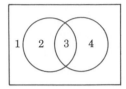

Compute the maximum number of subsets into which the universal set can be partitioned by 3 circles; 4 circles; 5 circles. This result illustrates that Venn diagrams have limited usefulness in picturing logical concepts (explain). Can you replace the circles by triangles and, using 4 triangles, partition the universal set into 16 regions?

8. Three houses, A, B, C, are each to be connected to outlets G, W, E for gas, water, and electricity, respectively. Can nine paths be drawn forming these connections, with no two paths intersecting?

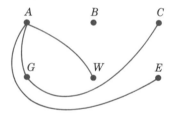

9. In coloring a map the cardinal rule is that two countries with a common boundary must be colored differently. Consider a map whose boundaries are all formed by straight lines running completely across the map as shown below. In all three of these diagrams two colors, red and green, suffice. Will two colors be sufficient to color any such map, no matter how many lines may be drawn?

2 countries   4 countries   7 countries

10. Relax the conditions that boundaries must be straight lines running across the map, and present a map which requires for its coloring (a) 3 colors, (b) 4 colors. Can you construct a map requiring 5 colors? (Each country must be one connected piece.) No one has ever been able to do this.

11. **Which of the following point sets are convex?**
    a) The empty set   b) A set of 1 point
    c) A set of 2 points   d) A line segment
    e) A ray   f) A line
    g) An angle   h) A triangle
    i) The interior of a triangle j) The interior of a circle

12. **Describe the smallest convex set which includes each figure below as a subset.**

(a) 2 points

(f) A line and a point not on the line

(b) 3 noncollinear points

(g) Two parallel planes

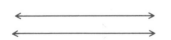

(c) Two segments

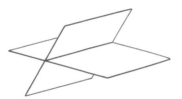

(h) Two intersecting planes

(d) Two parallel lines

(i) Four points not in one plane

(e) Two intersecting lines

(j) A circle and a point not in the plane of the circle

13. Draw a figure showing that the intersection of two half planes can be each of the following sets.

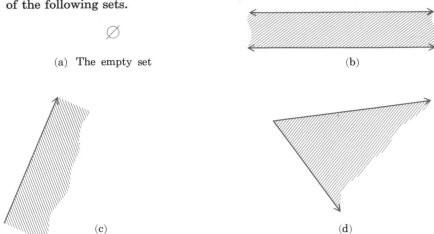

(a) The empty set   (b)

(c)   (d)

14. Of course the intersection of three half planes can be any of the four sets of points above, but there are other possibilities. Show all other possible types of intersections for three half planes.

13–5   similarity

Congruence is a special case of *similarity*. That is, all congruences are similarities. Intuitively, we say that two geometric figures are *similar* if they have the same *shape*. If they have also the same *size*, the figures are congruent. Every segment is similar to every segment, every square to every square, every circle to every circle. A photograph that does not distort presents a figure similar to the object photographed.

A similarity from one line segment to a second one *twice* as long is pictured below. Note that a similarity is a *function*.

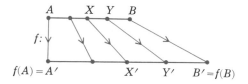

Every similarity f has associated with it a positive real number k. For all points X, Y in the domain of f, if $X' = f(X)$ and $Y' = f(Y)$, then $m(\overline{X'Y'}) = k \cdot m(\overline{XY})$ (where $m(\overline{AB})$ denotes the measure of $\overline{AB}$). In our example, $k = 2$. A similarity may either "blow up" or "shrink" a figure. Scale drawings and maps are the most obvious applications of similarity concepts.

Given any point P and any geometric figure F of two or more points, there is a standard technique for using P to construct figures similar to F. We used this technique in an earlier example.

1. Choose a positive real number k. (In the diagram $k = \frac{1}{2}$.)

2. For each $X \in F$, consider $\overrightarrow{PX}$.

3. Match X with the point X' on $\overrightarrow{PX}$ such that $m(\overline{PX'}) = k \cdot m(\overline{PX})$. The set F' of all such points X' is similar to F.

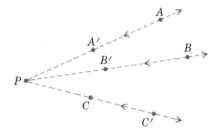

The symbol for similarity is $\sim$. We read $F \sim F'$ as "F is similar to F'." Note that the congruence symbol combines $=$ and $\sim$. Congruent figures are both "equal" (in length, area, or volume) and similar.

EXERCISES 13–6

1. Given that $k = 1$, what is the relationship between F' and F?

2. Take F to be the vertexes of a triangle and apply the construction above for $k = 2$ and also $k = \frac{1}{2}$. (Choose P outside the triangle determined by F.)

3. Take F to be a square and apply the construction above for $k = 3$ and $k = \frac{1}{3}$. (Choose P inside the square F.) For each construction:

   a) How does the perimeter of F' compare with the perimeter of F?

   b) How does the area of F' compare with the area of F?

4. Procure a map of your home state. Let F be a set of 20 or more points, wisely selected, on the boundary of the map. Use the technique above to construct a similar map taking k to be either $\frac{1}{2}$ or 2.

5. Explain how one might use ideas of the above exercises in making a map of some region.

6. A scale drawing of a mammal is about 1 inch long and shows the scale 1:1000. What mammal is represented?

7. A scale drawing of a living creature is about 2 inches long and shows the scale 250:1. What is the actual length of the creature?

8. A map of the world is to be about six feet wide. Approximately what scale should be used?

9. The figure below shows that a similarity can "turn a figure over" as well as shrink it. Explain how the image points are chosen.

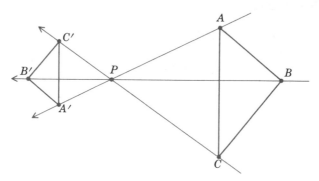

10. If we choose the point P, the *center* of the similarity, to be one of the points of F, we get interesting special cases. For example, let F be a triangle, $\triangle ABC$, and P one of its vertexes. Estimate the value of k that produces each of the triangles $\triangle A'B'C'$, $\triangle A''B''C''$, $\triangle A'''B'''C'''$.

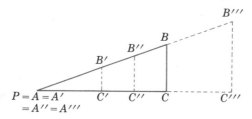

11. The theory of similarity is the basis of indirect measurement and the practical applications of trigonometry. Determining heights of objects by measuring their shadows is a simple application of the ideas.

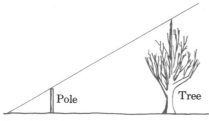

Explain the diagram above and compute the height of the tree, given that its shadow is 80 feet long, and a 12-foot pole throws a shadow of 20 feet.

12. A rectangle has length 16 and width 12. Determine x such that cutting off the region R as shown leaves a rectangle similar to the original rectangle. See the figure at the top of the next page.

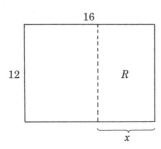

13. The Greeks considered the most beautifully proportioned rectangle to be one with the property that cutting off a square from one end left a rectangle similar to the original one. *EBDF* is a square. *AEFC* ~ *ACDB*. If *AB* is 100 units long, compute *AC* to the nearest unit.

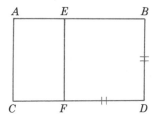

14. Is similarity of geometric figures a reflexive relation? a symmetric relation? a transitive relation?

13-6 symmetry

We think of congruence and similarity as relations between pairs of figures, but every geometric figure is congruent to itself in at least one way. The identity function which maps each point on itself is a congruence of any figure on itself.

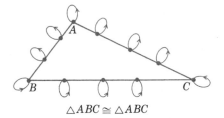

$$\triangle ABC \cong \triangle ABC$$

If a figure is congruent to itself in more than this one trivial way we say that the figure possesses *symmetry*. Symmetries are special congruences of figures with themselves.

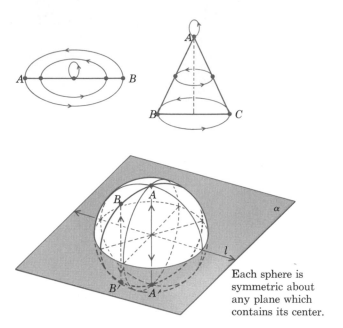

Each sphere is
symmetric about
any plane which
contains its center.

In terms of motion, you can think of *reflecting* a line segment in its mid-point. The isosceles triangle can be *reflected* in the altitude from vertex A. The sphere is *reflected* in the plane α so that top and bottom hemispheres interchange. Explain the use of the term *reflected*, and show that the reflections of the segment and the triangle can be viewed instead as 180° rotations about an axis. Can the reflection in α shown above for the sphere be interpreted as a rotation about an axis?

A figure may have a *center* (point) of symmetry, an *axis* (line) of symmetry, or a *plane* of symmetry. It is interesting to consider all the symmetries of certain figures. For convenience, when we discuss the symmetries of a figure we shall refer to the identity congruence as a symmetry also.

An isosceles triangle has just two symmetries, the identity and a 180° rotation about its altitude to the base. We use the symbols below to denote these symmetries.

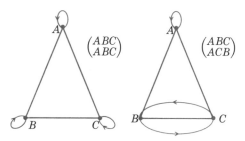

The symbol $\begin{pmatrix} ABC \\ ACB \end{pmatrix}$ is to be read "downward." It is an abbreviation for the functional notation

$$f: A \rightarrow A; \quad f: B \rightarrow C; \quad f: C \rightarrow B.$$

Of course, points of the triangle on side $\overline{AC}$ are mapped into points on side $\overline{AB}$, but so long as we know what happens to the vertexes we know what happens to all points of the triangle. Explain.

A rectangle has four symmetries:

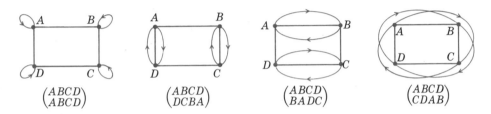

$$\begin{pmatrix} ABCD \\ ABCD \end{pmatrix} \qquad \begin{pmatrix} ABCD \\ DCBA \end{pmatrix} \qquad \begin{pmatrix} ABCD \\ BADC \end{pmatrix} \qquad \begin{pmatrix} ABCD \\ CDAB \end{pmatrix}$$

Explain how each of

$$\begin{pmatrix} ABCD \\ DCBA \end{pmatrix} \quad \text{and} \quad \begin{pmatrix} ABCD \\ BADC \end{pmatrix}$$

may be viewed geometrically as a 180° rotation about an axis through the midpoints of opposite sides, while

$$\begin{pmatrix} ABCD \\ CDAB \end{pmatrix}$$

is a rotation of 180° about an axis perpendicular to the plane of the rectangle.

EXERCISES 13–7

1. Has a man a center of symmetry? an axis of symmetry? an approximate plane of symmetry?

2. Show that a ray is not a symmetric figure, while a line has infinitely many central symmetries, one for each point on the line.

3. Show that an angle has an axis of symmetry. Relate this fact to the symmetries of an isosceles triangle.

4. Show that, in general, two intersecting lines have four symmetries. Relate these to the symmetries of a rectangle.

5. Using the notation

$$\begin{pmatrix} ABC \\ ABC \end{pmatrix}, \qquad \begin{pmatrix} ABC \\ CAB \end{pmatrix}, \qquad \cdots$$

exhibit the six symmetries of an equilateral triangle and interpret each as a rotation about an axis. (Cf. the left-hand figure below.)

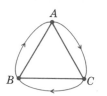

6. Using the notation of Exercise 5, exhibit all the symmetries of a square (you should find 8), and interpret each symmetry geometrically. (Cf. the right-hand figure above.)

7. Show that two perpendicular lines have the same number of symmetries as does a square.

8. Show that a circle has infinitely many symmetries.

9. Since each symmetry is a function mapping a geometric figure on itself, we can form the composition of two symmetries. For example, the symmetries

$$\begin{pmatrix} ABCD \\ BCDA \end{pmatrix} \qquad \text{and} \qquad \begin{pmatrix} ABCD \\ CBAD \end{pmatrix}$$

for a square $ABCD$ can be interpreted respectively as a 90° "clockwise" rotation in the plane of the square and a 180° "flip" about the diagonal line $\overleftrightarrow{BD}$.

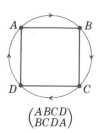 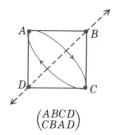

$$\begin{pmatrix} ABCD \\ BCDA \end{pmatrix} \qquad\qquad \begin{pmatrix} ABCD \\ CBAD \end{pmatrix}$$

The composition, first the 90° rotation and then the 180° flip, may be computed as below.

$$\begin{pmatrix} ABCD \\ CBAD \end{pmatrix} \begin{pmatrix} ABCD \\ BCDA \end{pmatrix} = \begin{pmatrix} ABCD \\ BADC \end{pmatrix}$$

$$(A \to B \to B; \ B \to C \to A; \ C \to D \to D; \ D \to A \to C)$$

Reversing the order of operations, we get

$$\begin{pmatrix} ABCD \\ BCDA \end{pmatrix} \begin{pmatrix} ABCD \\ CBAD \end{pmatrix} = \begin{pmatrix} ABCD \\ DCBA \end{pmatrix}$$

$(A \rightarrow C \rightarrow D;\ B \rightarrow B \rightarrow C;\ C \rightarrow A \rightarrow B;\ D \rightarrow D \rightarrow A)$

Note that composition of symmetries is not a commutative operation.

a) Interpret each of the two compositions above geometrically.

b) Compute several other compositions of symmetries of the square. Decide whether the 180° rotation

$$\begin{pmatrix} ABCD \\ CDAB \end{pmatrix}$$

commutes with every symmetry.

13–7   geometric construction

In many respects Greek geometry was a ruler-compass geometry. One can describe it as follows. Visualize a geometric plane as an infinite set of points, say an infinite, flat desert with grains of sand so small that single grains are invisible. Now visualize Euclid's postulated geometric constructions:

1)   To *draw* a line segment from *any* point to *any* point

2)   To *extend* a line segment

3)   To *draw* a circle with *any* center and *any* radius

It is as if the geometer possesses a magic wand that enables him to indicate any two grains of sand and bring into view the segment with these grains as endpoints (Axiom 1). If the segment is not long enough, with a second gesture our geometer can extend it beyond either endpoint as far as he wishes (Axiom 2). Choosing any first point A and any second point B, he can summon into view the circle with A as center containing B (Axiom 3).

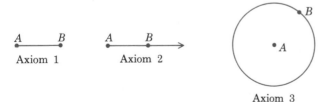

Axiom 1   Axiom 2   Axiom 3

Now we can describe the essential problem of the Greek geometers.

   i)   Start with *two* points A, B, and "draw" the segment and two circles that Axioms 1 and 3 permit. Extend the segment (Axiom 2) to cut the circles. Note that 4 new points are located as intersections of these two circles and lines.

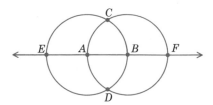

ii) Using the six points of (i), repeat the process, drawing all lines and circles determined by these points.

We imagine an endless repetition of these constructions. The plane begins to "fill up" with points, lines, and circles. Our task is to describe *all* types of geometric configurations that are obtained by this unending process.

Proposition 1, Book 1 of Euclid's *Elements* is:

To construct on a given line segment an equilateral triangle.

Note that the equilateral triangle on *AB* appears at step (ii). Hence at least by step (iii) there will appear all equilateral triangles on all other segments determined by the 6 points of step (i).

Propositions 2 and 3 of Book 1 are, respectively:

To place at a point a line (segment) equal to a line (segment).
To cut off from a line segment, or the segment extended, a segment equal to a given segment.

Other propositions are: To bisect an angle; to erect a perpendicular at a point; to bisect a segment; to construct an angle at a point on a line, and on a given side of the line, equal to a given angle; to construct a parallel to a line through a point not on the line; to construct a square; to construct a regular hexagon; to construct a regular pentagon; . . .

Of course it is not enough to describe the construction of a certain figure. One must prove that the construction yields the desired result. Here other axioms of Euclid are needed.

EXERCISES 13–8

1. Referring to the diagram above, with its 6 points labeled *A, B, C, D, E, F,* at what stage of the construction process does each of the following geometric figures first appear?

   a) The perpendicular bisector of $\overline{AB}$ b) The perpendicular bisector of $\overline{ED}$
   c) The perpendicular bisector of $\overline{DB}$ d) A 60° angle

e) A 30° angle   f) A 15° angle

g) A rhombus   h) A line parallel to $\overline{DF}$ through A

i) A line parallel to $\overline{EF}$ through D j) A regular hexagon

k) A square   l) The perpendicular to $\overleftrightarrow{EF}$ at B

2. At the end of Stage 2 of the sequence of constructions described above, how many lines, circles, and points will be in evidence?

3. Look up a geometric construction for a regular pentagon and try to decide at what stage of the construction process the first regular pentagon appears.

What cannot be done by ruler-compass constructions is about as interesting as what can be done. At the second step 90°, 60°, and 30° angles occur. When a regular pentagon is constructed, 72° angles appear (explain). Every angle is eventually bisected and every pair of angles is eventually "added" and "subtracted." From the 72° angles come angles of 36°, 18°, 9°, . . . When we subtract 30° and 18° angles, 12° angles are formed. From the 12° angles we obtain 6° and 3° angles. Many angles are *trisected*, among them angles of 180°, 90°, 72°, 36°, 18°, 9°. But in the infinite chain of constructions, no 20° angle will occur. No 60° angle will ever be trisected. One of the famous problems of antiquity, which baffled the Greek geometers and was not solved until the nineteenth century, was the *angle trisection* problem. The Greeks knew that some angles could be trisected by ruler and compass, and they felt that it should be possible to trisect every angle. Not until the beginning of the nineteenth century was it proved that for some angles there is no ruler-compass trisection. The 60° angle is the simplest example.

It is quite obvious that *regular* 3-sided polygons (equilateral triangles), 4-sided polygons (squares), and 6-sided polygons (hexagons) turn up in our chain of constructions. We have mentioned that regular 5-sided polygons occur. But no regular 7-, 9-, 11-, or 13-sided polygons are constructible. In the early part of the nineteenth century, the mathematician Gauss showed that a 17-sided regular polygon can be constructed by ruler and compass. Those prime numbers for which a ruler-compass construction of a regular polygon of p sides is possible are the famous *Fermat primes*, and have the form $2^{(2^n)} + 1$. Only the five numbers listed below are known to be Fermat primes.

$$2^{(2^0)} + 1 = 3; \qquad 2^{(2^1)} + 1 = 5; \qquad 2^{(2^2)} + 1 = 17; \qquad 2^{(2^3)} + 1 = 257;$$
$$2^{(2^4)} + 1 = 65{,}537; \ldots$$

The three dots here need explanation. The next number of this form

$$2^{(2^5)} + 1 = 4{,}294{,}967{,}297$$

is *not* a prime. It is divisible by 641. No one has ever discovered a Fermat prime beyond the one for $n = 4$. A regular polygon of 65,537 sides can be constructed by ruler and compass and certainly appears at some stage of the construction process we have described, but no one has ever constructed one. Someone did try though (cf. J. R. Newman, *The World of Mathematics*, Simon and Shuster, page 502).

Another famous problem that concerned the Greek geometers was the *squaring of the circle*. Given any polygon, the Greeks could construct a square whose area was equal to that of the polygon. But they could not devise a ruler-compass technique for constructing a square equal in area to a given circle. This problem was also settled in the nineteenth century. In our infinite sequence of constructions, no square and circle of equal area occur.

Another problem which baffled the Greeks was *duplicating a cube*. The Delphian oracle, when consulted during a pestilence, advised that the (cubical) altar of Apollo be doubled in size to appease the god. The Greeks built a new altar with each edge double the edge of the old one and the pestilence raged on. Returning to the oracle, they learned that the new altar was to have exactly twice the volume of the old. This required the construction of a line segment of length $\sqrt[3]{2}$ times the edge of the old altar. The geometers of the time could find no construction for this segment. Again in the nineteenth century, it was shown that in the sequence of geometric constructions described above there occurs no pair of segments such that the length of one is $\sqrt[3]{2}$ times the other.

EXERCISES 13-9

1. Assuming that we choose our initial segment $\overline{AB}$ as unit, show that segments will be constructed of length

   a) $\frac{1}{2}, \frac{1}{3}, \frac{1}{4}, \frac{1}{5}, \frac{1}{6}, \ldots \frac{1}{n}, , \ldots$

   b) $\sqrt{2}, \sqrt{3}, \sqrt{4}, \sqrt{5}, \sqrt{6}, \ldots, \sqrt{n}, \ldots$

   [*Hint:* For (b), you need the Pythagorean theorem.]

2. Show that in our sequence of geometric constructions none of the following angles will occur. You may assume that a 20° angle never occurs.

   a) 40°   b) 16°   c) 7°   d) 1°

3. Show that regular polygons of the following number of sides occur in our sequence of constructions.

   a) 8   b) 10   c) 15   d) 51

4. Show how to perform the following ruler-compass constructions.

   a) Given two points, bisect the segment they determine.

   b) Given two points A, B, construct the perpendicular to $\overleftrightarrow{AB}$ at A.

   c) Given three noncollinear points A, B, C bisect $\angle ABC$.

   d) Given three points A, B, C, construct the perpendicular to $\overleftrightarrow{AB}$ from C.

e) Given five points A, B, C, D, E, construct a ray $\overrightarrow{DF}$ such that we have $\angle FDE \cong \angle ABC$.

f) Given three points A, B, C, with $C \notin \overleftrightarrow{AB}$, construct the line l on C and parallel to $\overleftrightarrow{AB}$.

g) Given two points A, B, construct points C, D which trisect $\overline{AB}$.

h) Given three noncollinear points A, B, C, construct the circle through these points.

i) Given two points A, B, construct a regular pentagon with $\overline{AB}$ as side.

5. Show that if you are presented with a 7° angle, that is, if you begin your geometric construction with 3 points which form a 7° angle, then you can trisect a 60° angle.

13–8 proof

A careful treatment of the theorems of Euclidean geometry is not one of our aims. We sketch below a few proofs done in the spirit of Euclid. We make no pretense of indicating all axioms needed for the proofs of these theorems. We shall assume the famous *pons asinorum* (Euclid's Proposition V, Book 1) which asserts that *the base angles of an isosceles triangle are congruent.*

Theorem 1   A triangle with two congruent angles is isosceles.

Proof   If $\overline{AB} \not\cong \overline{AC}$, then one is greater. Let $\overline{AB}$ be greater, and cut off from $\overline{BA}$ segment $\overline{BX} \cong \overline{CA}$. Let $\overline{CX}$ be drawn.

Now, clearly, $\triangle XBC \cong \triangle ABC$ (here we use the side-angle-side theorem), and $\angle XCB \cong \angle ABC$ (why?). But $\angle ABC \cong \angle ACB$ and hence $\angle XCB \cong \angle ACB$. But this last is absurd. Hence the assumption that $\overline{AB} \cong \overline{AC}$ is untenable, and it must be the case that $\overline{AB} \cong \overline{AC}$.

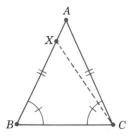

Theorem 2   Any exterior angle of a triangle is greater than each of the remote interior angles.

Proof   We shall prove that the exterior angle at C, namely $\angle ACD$, is greater than both $\angle B$ and $\angle A$, the interior angles *other* than $\angle C$. For let $\overline{AC}$ be bisected at M. Let $\overline{BM}$ be extended to P so that $\overline{BM} \cong \overline{MP}$. Let $\overline{CP}$ be drawn. Then $\angle BMA \cong \angle PMC$, for they are vertical to one another.   Hence $\triangle BMA \cong \triangle PMC$ (why?) and $\angle MCP \cong \angle MAB = \angle A$.   But clearly $\angle MCP < \angle ACD$, and so $\angle A < \angle ACD$.   Similarly one can show that $\angle B < \angle ACD$. (Do this.)

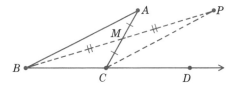

Theorem 3   There are not two perpendiculars from any point outside a line to the line.

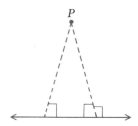

Proof   If there were two perpendiculars from a point P to a line l, then a triangle would be formed having an exterior angle congruent to a remote interior angle (explain).   But this is impossible, and so there are not two perpendiculars from P to l.

Theorem 4   In any triangle the greater side subtends the greater angle.

Proof   In $\triangle ABC$ let $\overline{AC}$ be greater than $\overline{AB}$. Then $\angle B$ is greater than $\angle C$; for, cut off from $\overline{AC}$, segment $AX \cong \overline{AB}$. Then

$$\angle ABC > \angle ABX \cong \angle AXB > \angle C \text{ (why?)}$$

Hence $\angle B > \angle C$.

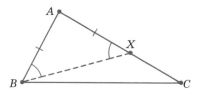

Theorem 5 In any triangle the greater angle is subtended by the greater side.

Proof If $\angle B > \angle C$, then $\overline{AC} > \overline{AB}$. For it must be the case that (1) $\overline{AC} \cong \overline{AB}$ or (2) $\overline{AC} < \overline{AB}$ or (3) $\overline{AC} > \overline{AB}$. Now clearly (1) is not the case, for then we should have $\angle B \cong \angle C$ (why?). And (2) cannot hold, for then by Theorem 4 we should have $\angle C > \angle B$. Therefore (3) holds.

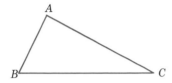

Theorem 6 In any triangle the sum of any two sides taken together is greater than the third.

Proof We claim that in $\triangle ABC$, sides $\overline{AB}$, $\overline{AC}$ together are greater than $\overline{BC}$. For let $\overline{BA}$ be extended to D so that $\overline{AD} \cong \overline{AC}$. Then $\angle BCD > \angle ACD \cong \angle D$ (why?). Hence $\angle BCD > \angle D$. But in $\triangle DBC$ the angle C subtends $\overline{BD}$ and $\angle D$ subtends $\overline{BC}$. And since $\angle C > \angle D$, the side $\overline{BD} > \overline{BC}$. But $\overline{BD}$ is the sum of sides $\overline{BA}$ and $\overline{AC}$, and so these two sides together are greater than $\overline{BC}$.

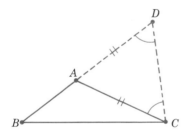

Theorem 7 It is not true that every triangle has an angle sum of 179°.

Proof If the angle sum of $\triangle ABC$ were 179°, and the angle sum of $\triangle ABD$ were 179°, then the angle sum of $\triangle ADC$ would be 180°.

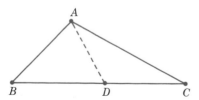

Problem Supply the details omitted in the above proof, and prove similarly that it is not true that every triangle has an angle sum of 181°. Now argue that *if* all triangles have the same angle sum, then this sum is a straight angle.

▶ *Aside.* In non-Euclidean geometries, different triangles may have different angle sums. For example, a spherical triangle whose sides are great circle arcs may have any angle sum between 180° and 540°. For example, the prime meridian, the equator, and the 90° W meridian form a triangle on the earth whose angle sum is 270°. (Draw a figure to illustrate this.) In hyperbolic geometry, the creation of Gauss, Lobachevsky, and Bolyai, triangles can have every angle sum between 0° and 180°, but none has an angle sum as great as 180°. ◀

Theorem 8   Each diagonal of a parallelogram divides the parallelogram into congruent triangles and hence triangles of equal area.

Proof   We must show that $\triangle ADB \cong \triangle CBD$. Assume one of (i) and (ii) below:

  i) Opposite sides of a parallelogram are congruent.

  ii) Parallels cut by a transversal have "alternate interior" angles congruent.

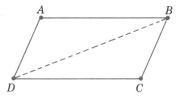

Also assume necessary theorems of triangle congruence and complete the proof.

Theorem 9   Parallelograms in the same parallels and on the same base are equal in area.

Proof   Show that $\triangle DAE \cong \triangle CBF$. "Subtract" from each $\triangle BGE$. "Add" to the remainders $\triangle DGC$. (What axioms of Euclid are you using?)

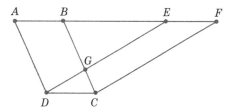

Theorem 10   Parallelograms in the same parallels and on congruent bases are equal in area.

Proof   Look at the figure at the top of the next page.

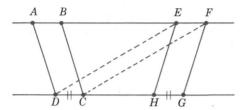

Theorem 11 Triangles in the same parallels and on congruent bases are equal in area.

Proof Use Theorems 8 and 10.

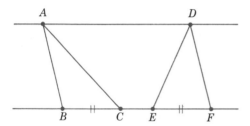

Theorem 12 (Pythagoras) In any right triangle the square on the hypotenuse is equal (in area) to the sum of the squares on the legs.

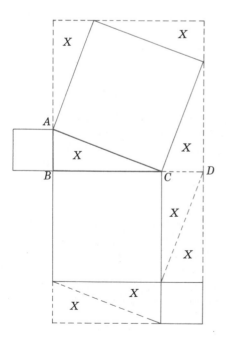

Proof Note that if we "add" to the square on $\overline{AC}$ four copies of $\triangle ABC$, and also add to the sum of the squares on $\overline{BC}$ and $\overline{AB}$ four copies of $\triangle ABC$, then we obtain congruent squares on $\overline{BD}$. Now, when we "subtract equals from equals," our result follows.

Explain the "algebraic" proof associated with the figure on the right below.

$$(a + c)^2 - 4m(X) = b^2$$

[by $m(X)$ is meant the measure (area) of $\triangle ABC$]. But

$$m(X) = \frac{ac}{2}$$

so that

$$a^2 + 2ac + c^2 - 2ac = b^2,$$

$$a^2 + c^2 = b^2.$$

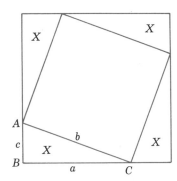

SUMMARY

Over 2000 years ago, the Greeks abstracted mathematical geometry from the physical world. Properties of physical objects were idealized and ascribed to imaginary objects: points, lines, planes, triangles, etc.

We have stressed the role played by functions in geometry. Geometric figures are viewed as sets of points. A congruence from one figure to another is a one-to-one correspondence that preserves shape and size. A similarity is a one-to-one correspondence that preserves shape. A symmetry is a congruence that maps a figure on itself.

Ideas of measurement and congruence are interlaced. Measure functions assign numbers to various figures: lengths to segments, areas to polygonal regions, etc. Children should view measurement as a process of laying off congruent copies of a unit (unit segment, unit region, or unit angle) and counting.

The nonmetric ideas of separation and convexity were briefly treated. These notions lead to interesting problems unrelated to measurement; for example, the map-coloring problems and the 3-houses, 3-outlets problem.

We viewed the general problem of constructions in geometry as determining what figures can be brought into existence if we begin with two points and utilize the basic constructions of drawing lines and circles repeatedly.

No formal axiomatic treatment of geometry was attempted. The few proofs given were selected from the first book of Euclid's *Elements*. Except for the algebraic proof of the Pythagorean theorem, these arguments are much as Euclid made them.

14   probability

14-1   introduction

One of the most important applications of mathematics is to the organization and interpretation of statistical information. In this application one is dealing with uncertainties, for rarely are the statistical data complete. The branch of mathematics that forms the basis for statistical work is *probability*.

In everyday speech, a comment that something will *probably* happen has a wide range of interpretations. Usually the speaker believes that the event is more likely than not to happen. Such comments are based on past experience. For example if someone remarks in the morning, "It will probably rain today," he means that in the light of his experience most days that start out like today turn out to be rainy. Weather forecasters make predictions of this type: "There is a 30% chance of rain tomorrow." This sort of statement is based on careful observation and accurate records. The forecaster may know that out of 100 days in past years with approximately the same temperature, prevailing winds, barometric pressure, humidity, . . . as today, it rained on 30 of those days.

EXERCISES 14-1

1. A bowl contains red marbles and white marbles. You are told that if you draw one marble it will probably be red. What do you conclude?

2. To estimate the result of a school election, you ask your 10 best friends how they plan to vote. Is this satisfactory information on which to base your judgment of the election results?

3. An urn contains 5 red marbles and 3 white ones.

   a) If you plan to draw 1 marble, which color are you more likely to draw?

   b) If you plan to draw a pair of marbles, will you probably get 2 reds? 1 red and 1 white? 2 whites?

4. You have 4 coins in a cup and will shake them and pour them on a table. Do you think you will probably get 2 heads and 2 tails? Explain your answer.

5. If instead of 4 coins you have 10, do you think a throw will probably result in 5 heads and 5 tails?

6. You toss an "honest" coin 6 times and it comes up heads every time. On the 7th toss, which do you think will probably turn up, heads or tails?

7. You are interested in checking 1000 light bulbs. You select 10 of these bulbs and screw each into a light socket. You record G (for good) and B (for bad) according as the bulb lights or does not light. You secure the following record: *GGGGGGGBGG*.

   a) Do you think the 11th bulb will probably be good?

   b) If you estimated the number of bad bulbs in the lot of 1000, what would your estimate be?

8. A biologist injects a vaccine into several rats and then exposes them all to the same disease. He records S if a rat gets sick, W otherwise. His record is: *SWWWWWSSWWWW*. Now he exposes several unvaccinated rats to the same disease. For them the record is *SSWSSSSSSWWWWSS*. Do you think that the vaccine affords some protection from the disease? Explain your answer.

9. There are 5 colored marbles in a container. A friend is blindfolded. He draws a marble, holds it up for you to see, returns it to the container, mixes the marbles, and repeats the process. You record the following colors in order, B (black), R (red), G (green): *BGBGRRRBBGBBRBRRGBR*. How many marbles of each color are probably in the container?

10. Ten students have a gift exchange. Gifts are put into a box and drawn. Do you think that some student will probably get his own gift? (Cf. Section 14–3.)

11. Think of a classroom with 40 students. Do you think that there are probably two persons in the class whose birthdays fall on the same day of the year? (This is a classic example which illustrates that the average person is betrayed by his intuition when he considers questions of probability.)

14–2   sample spaces

We refer to a situation in which we perform an act that can have several different outcomes as an *experiment*. For example, if we toss a coin, 2 outcomes are possible; if we draw a card from a bridge deck, there are 52 outcomes. The set of all possible outcomes for an experiment is called a *sample space*. For tossing a coin, the sample space is $\{H, T\}$. If a coin is to be tossed twice, the sample space is the set below:

$$\{(H, H), (H, T), (T, H), (T, T)\}.$$

Interpret the elements of this sample space.

The simplest situation to analyze is one in which all outcomes are believed to be equally likely. For example, if we are to make a single toss of an honest coin, then we have no reason to believe that either heads or tails is more likely to turn up. We say that the probability of each event, H and T, is $1/2$. In general, if a sample space for an experiment has n elements and all n outcomes are believed to be equally likely, then we assign the probability $1/n$ to each outcome. Note that the sum of the probabilities for all the elements of a sample space is 1. This agrees with ordinary terminology. When we say that the probability that an event will happen is 1, we mean that it is certain to happen.

We illustrate the ways we use sample spaces by considering the sample space for an experiment in which we are to toss 3 coins, a penny, a nickel, and a dime. The sample space S is listed below, where (H, T, H) represents the event of the penny falling heads, the nickel tails, and the dime heads.

$$S = \{(H, H, H), \quad (H, H, T), \quad (H, T, H), \quad (T, H, H), \quad (H, T, T), \quad (T, H, T),$$
$$(T, T, H), \quad (T, T, T)\}.$$

The probability of each event is $1/8$.

The probability that the event (H, T, H) will occur is $1/8$.

The probability that (H, H, H) or (T, T, T) will occur is $2/8$.

The probability that at most two heads will occur is $7/8$.

These examples illustrate the fundamental formula:

$$\text{Probability of an occurrence} \ = \ \frac{\text{number of favorable outcomes}}{\text{total number of possible outcomes}}.$$

This is the definition of *the probability of an occurrence in an experiment in which all outcomes are equally likely*. The word "favorable" is interpreted in the obvious way.

EXERCISES 14–2

1. List elements of the sample space S for the experiment of tossing 4 coins.

2. With S as in Exercise 1, compute the following:

   a) The probability of tossing 3 heads and 1 tail.

   b) The probability of tossing more than 2 heads or more than 2 tails.

   c) The probability of tossing more than 1 head.

   d) The probability of tossing more than 1 tail.

   e) The probability of tossing more than 1 head *and* more than 1 tail.

   f) The probability of tossing more than 1 head *or* more than 1 tail.

   g) Add your answers to (e) and (b). Comment.

3. Let A and B be subsets of the sample space S of Exercise 1 such that A contains 5 elements, B contains 8 elements, and $A \cap B$ contains 2 elements. Let A', B' be the complements of A, B in S. Compute the probability that on a particular toss the outcome will fall in

a) A b) B c) $A \cap B$ d) $A \cup B$ e) $A' \cap B'$ f) $A' \cup B'$.

4. Two dice, a red die and a blue die, are to be thrown. On each die occur the numbers 1, 2, 3, 4, 5, 6. The experiment consists of throwing the dice and totaling the numbers that turn up. Given that x denotes this sum,

$$x \in [2, 3, 4, 5, 6, 7, 8, 9, 10, 11, 12].$$

Note that these outcomes are not all equally likely. We denote the probability that $x = k$ by Pr $(x = k)$. Compute:

a) Pr $(x = 2)$ b) Pr $(x = 3)$ c) Pr $(x = 4)$

d) Pr $(x = 5)$ e) Pr $(x = 6)$

[*Hint:* Consider the sample space $\{(1, 1), (1, 2), (1, 3), \ldots, (6, 5), (6, 6)\}$.]

5. For the experiment of Exercise 4, show that for $x = 8, 9, 10, 11, 12$, the probabilities are the same as for 6, 5, 4, 3, 2, respectively.

6. Use the diagram below as an aid in computing the following probabilities for the experiment of Exercise 4. Note that in parts (c) ff. the sample space is restricted.

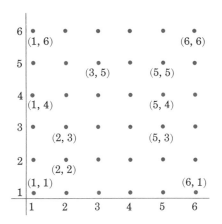

a) Pr $(x > 8)$, Pr $(x \leq 8)$

b) Pr $(x < 5$ or $x > 10)$

c) Pr $(x = 6,$ given that exactly one die has a 4)

d) Pr $(x = 6,$ given that at least one die has a 4)

e) Pr $(x = 6,$ given that $x = 6$ or 7)

f) Pr (a 6 is faced, given that $x > 8)$

g) Pr ($x = 8$, given that at least one die has a 4)

h) Pr ($x = 8$, given that exactly one die has a 4)

i) Pr ($x = 8$, given that 4 turns up on the red die)

j) Pr (a 5 is faced, given that $x = 9$)

k) Pr (a 5 is faced, given that $x = 10$)

l) Pr ($5 < x < 9$)

m) Pr ($x = 6$, given that $5 < x < 9$)

7. Whole numbers 1, 2, 3, 4 are written on slips of paper and placed in a container. The following experiment is to be performed. One slip will be drawn, the number recorded, and the slip returned to the container. Call this number x. A slip will again be drawn. Call the resulting number y. Compute:

a) Pr ($x + y$ is even)   b) Pr ($x + y$ is odd)

c) Pr ($x \cdot y$ is even)   d) Pr ($x \cdot y$ is odd)

e) Pr ($x + y$ is odd and $x \cdot y$ is odd)   f) Pr ($x + y$ is even and $x \cdot y$ is even)

8. Slips numbered 1, 2, 3, 4, 5 are placed in a hat. Four slips are to be drawn successively without replacement. Call the numbers drawn in order x, y, z, w. Compute.

a) Pr (x is even)   b) Pr (y is even)

c) Pr (y is even, given that x is even)   d) Pr ($x + y$ is odd)

e) Pr ($x \cdot y$ is odd)   f) Pr ($x \cdot y \cdot z$ is odd)

g) Pr ($x + y + z + w$ is even)

h) Pr ($x \cdot y \cdot z \cdot w$ is even)

i) Pr ($z + w$ is even, given that $x + y$ is even)

j) Pr ($z + w$ is odd, given that $x + y$ is even)

k) Pr ($z \cdot w$ is odd, given that $x \cdot y$ is odd)

l) Pr ($z \cdot w$ is odd, given that $x \cdot y$ is even)

m) Pr ($x > y > z > w$)

n) Pr ($x + y = z + w$)

14–3 counting

Several of the exercises in the above lists call attention to a fundamental difficulty that surrounds probability problems. Theoretically, if one can establish a sample space for an experiment and assign a probability to each element of the sample space, then one can answer questions by examining the sample space. But often the sample space contains so many elements that it is impossible to list them all. For example, consider the gift-exchange problem for ten students mentioned in the first problem list of this chapter. Elements of the sample space are naturally denoted by symbols like the one below. Interpret this symbol.

$$\begin{pmatrix} 1 & 2 & 3 & 4 & 5 & 6 & 7 & 8 & 9 & 10 \\ 2 & 7 & 1 & 5 & 8 & 3 & 4 & 10 & 9 & 6 \end{pmatrix}$$

Now we need to know the number of different symbols of this type and also in how many of these some number is matched with itself. The first requirement is met without too much difficulty. We look at the situations for 2, 3, and 4 students.

$$\begin{pmatrix} 1 & 2 \\ 1 & 2 \end{pmatrix}, \qquad \begin{pmatrix} 1 & 2 \\ 2 & 1 \end{pmatrix} \longrightarrow 2$$

$$\begin{pmatrix} 1 & 2 & 3 \\ 1 & 2 & 3 \end{pmatrix}, \qquad \begin{pmatrix} 1 & 2 & 3 \\ 1 & 3 & 2 \end{pmatrix}, \qquad \begin{pmatrix} 1 & 2 & 3 \\ 2 & 1 & 3 \end{pmatrix}, \qquad \begin{pmatrix} 1 & 2 & 3 \\ 2 & 3 & 1 \end{pmatrix},$$

$$\begin{pmatrix} 1 & 2 & 3 \\ 3 & 1 & 2 \end{pmatrix}, \qquad \begin{pmatrix} 1 & 2 & 3 \\ 3 & 2 & 1 \end{pmatrix} \longrightarrow 6$$

$$\begin{pmatrix} 1 & 2 & 3 & 4 \\ 1 & \_ & \_ & \_ \end{pmatrix}, \quad \begin{pmatrix} 1 & 2 & 3 & 4 \\ 2 & \_ & \_ & \_ \end{pmatrix}, \quad \begin{pmatrix} 1 & 2 & 3 & 4 \\ 3 & \_ & \_ & \_ \end{pmatrix}, \quad \begin{pmatrix} 1 & 2 & 3 & 4 \\ 4 & \_ & \_ & \_ \end{pmatrix} \longrightarrow 4 \cdot 6 = 24$$

6 of these	6 of these	6 of these	6 of these
(Why?)	(Why?)	(Why?)	(Why?)

Note that

$$6 = 3 \cdot 2 \cdot 1 = 3!; \qquad 24 = 4 \cdot 3 \cdot 2 \cdot 1 = 4!$$

In general, the symbol $n!$ is defined by

$$n! = n \cdot (n - 1) \cdots 3 \cdot 2 \cdot 1$$

and is read *n factorial*. Show that for 5 students there are

$$5 \cdot 24 = 5 \cdot 4 \cdot 3 \cdot 2 \cdot 1 = 5!$$

ways that the gifts can be drawn.

Now we can settle the matter for 10 students. Explain the computation below.

$$\begin{pmatrix} 1 & 2 & 3 & 4 & 5 & 6 & 7 & 8 & 9 & 10 \\ \_ & \_ & \_ & \_ & \_ & \_ & \_ & \_ & \_ & \_ \end{pmatrix}$$

$$10 \cdot 9 \cdot 8 \cdot 7 \cdot 6 \cdot 5 \cdot 4 \cdot 3 \cdot 2 \cdot 1 = 10!$$

Counting the number of cases in which at least one student draws his own gift is much more difficult. The result (and we shall not explain how it is obtained) is:

$$10! - \frac{10!}{2!} + \frac{10!}{3!} - \frac{10!}{4!} + \frac{10!}{5!} - \frac{10!}{6!} + \frac{10!}{7!} - \frac{10!}{8!} + \frac{10!}{9!} - \frac{10!}{10!}$$

Verify that the probability that at least one student will draw his own gift is

$$\frac{2,293,839}{3,628,800}.$$

It is convenient to introduce the terms *permutation* and *combination*. A permutation of a set is a 1–1 function mapping the set onto itself. Note that in the gift problem above we had to count all the ways in which a 10-element set could be matched with itself. Often instead of *permutation* the term *arrangement* is used, and we say that 3 objects can be arranged in 3! ways, 4 objects in 4! ways, etc. Instead of denoting each permutation (function) by a symbol like

$$\begin{pmatrix} 1 & 2 & 3 & 4 \\ 3 & 2 & 1 & 4 \end{pmatrix},$$

which is an abbreviation for

$$f(1) = 3, \qquad f(2) = 2, \qquad f(3) = 1, \qquad f(4) = 4,$$

we can write simply

$$(3\ 2\ 1\ 4),$$

where the top row, 1, 2, 3, 4, is understood, and call (3 2 1 4) an *arrangement* of the set {1, 2, 3, 4}.

By *the number of permutations of a set of* 4 *things taken* 2 *at a time is* meant the total number of arrangements of 2 elements that can be formed. As the list below shows, there are 12 = 4 · 3 of these.

$$\{A, B, C, D\} \rightarrow (A, B),\ (A, C),\ (A, D),\ (B, A),\ (B, C),\ (B, D),$$
$$(C, A),\ (C, B),\ (C, D),\ (D, A),\ (D, B),\ (D, C).$$

We can count the number of permutations of 10 things 3 at a time, as indicated below:

$$(A,\ B,\ C,\ D,\ E,\ F,\ G,\ H,\ I,\ J)$$
$$\downarrow \qquad \downarrow \qquad \downarrow$$
(10 choices, 9 choices, 8 choices) $\rightarrow 10 \cdot 9 \cdot 8 = 720$

Explain this diagram.

The symbol P_k^n denotes the number of different arrangements of n things taken k at a time. We have seen, for example, that

$$P_3^3 = 3!; \qquad P_4^4 = 4!; \qquad P_{10}^{10} = 10!; \qquad P_2^4 = 4 \cdot 3; \qquad P_3^{10} = 10 \cdot 9 \cdot 8.$$

In general,

$$P_k^n = n(n-1) \cdots (n-k+1) = \frac{n!}{(n-k)!}.$$

Often we are more interested in subsets of a set than in arrangements. For example, given that a committee of 3 persons is to be chosen from a set of 5 people, $\{A, B, C, D, E\}$, we can consider all permutations of 5 things 3 at a time.

$$\begin{cases} (ABC) \\ (ACB) \\ (BAC) \\ (BCA) \\ (CAB) \\ (CBA) \end{cases} \begin{cases} (ABD) \\ (ADB) \\ (BAD) \\ (BDA) \\ (DAB) \\ (DBA) \end{cases} \quad \ldots$$

Each group of three of these people appears in 6 different arrangements. There are 6 arrangements for each possible committee. There are $P_3^5 = 60$ arrangements. Hence there are

$$\frac{P_3^5}{6} = \frac{60}{6} = 10$$

possible committees. Note that this can be written as

$$\frac{P_3^5}{3!} \qquad \text{(Explain.)}$$

We denote the number of k element subsets of a set of n elements by

$$C_k^n.$$

This symbol is traditionally read as *the number of combinations of n things k at a time.*

$$k! \cdot C_k^n = P_k^n$$

or

$$C_k^n = \frac{n!}{k!(n-k)!}$$

The arrangement of numbers below, known as *Pascal's triangle*, exhibits the values of the function C_k^n. (Explain why the symbol C_k^n denotes a function. What is its domain?) The notation $\binom{n}{k}$ is frequently used instead of C_k^n.

Pascal's triangle.   Values of C_k^n, $n \geq k$.

n \ k	0	1	2	3	4	5	6	...
0	1							
1	1	1						
2	1	2	1					
3	1	3	3	1				
4	1	4	6	4	1			
5	1	5	10	10	5	1		
6	1	6	15	20	15	6	1	
⋮								

The first row shows that the empty set has 1 empty subset.

The second row shows that a set of 1 element has 1 empty subset; 1 subset of 1 element.

The third row shows that a set of 2 elements has 1 empty subset; 2 subsets of 1 element; 1 subset of 2 elements.

EXERCISES 14–3

1. Interpret the rows for $n = 3$ and $n = 4$ and verify the table of entries using the sets

    $\{A, B, C\}$ and $\{1, 2, 3, 4\}$.

2. Explain how each entry of each row after the first seems to be formed from entries of the row above.

3. In the row $n = 6$ interpret the meaning of each entry 15.

4. Consider any set of 20 objects

    $\{A, B, C, \ldots, T\}$.

    The symbols C_7^{20} and C_{13}^{20} denote the number of 7-element and 13-element subsets of this set. Prove that there are exactly the same number of each by explaining how to match the collection of 7-element subsets 1–1 with the collection of 13-element subsets. [*Hint:* What is the complement of a 7-element set?]

5. Note the symmetry of each row in Pascal's triangle. This is described by the equation

$$\forall n, k, \qquad C_k^n = C_{n-k}^n.$$

Verify this formula for at least 5 pairs of values of n and k. Prove it in general.

6. Continue Pascal's triangle through the row for $n = 10$ and use it to answer the following questions.

a) How many 3-member committees can be chosen from 8 people?

b) On a test of 10 problems, a student is to work any 7. How many choices has he?

c) On a test of 10 problems, a student can omit any 3. How many choices has he?

d) A child has enough money to buy 3 candy bars. There are 9 varieties to choose from. How many choices has he if he will not buy two of the same kind?

e) From 10 boys, a coach must choose 5 players to start a game. How many choices has he? (For each set of 5 players, in how many ways can he assign them playing positions, if all playing positions are considered distinct?)

7. What would be the first three numbers in the $n = 17$ row of Pascal's triangle? The last three numbers?

8. Note that if we ignore the 1's, all other entries in the rows for n a prime, namely 2, 3, 5, 7, are respectively divisible by 2, 3, 5, and 7. Make a conjecture and test it for $n = 11$.

9. How many 98-element subsets are included in a set of 100 elements?

10. a) How many subsets of 3 digits can be chosen from {1, 2, 3, 4, 5, 6, 7}?

b) How many 3-digit numbers, all digits different, can be formed from the digits 1, 2, 3, 4, 5, 6, 7?

11. Use symbols C_k^n, P_k^n, and $n!$ to answer the following questions.

a) In how many ways may 13 cards be drawn from a deck of 52 cards?

b) In how many different ways can one sort (arrange) a hand of 13 cards?

c) How many different bridge hands (each of 13 cards) are there?

d) In how many ways can a president, vice president, secretary, and treasurer be chosen from a group of 30 persons?

e) How many 4-man committees can be selected from 30 persons?

f) How many different sets of 9 players can be chosen from 25?

g) In how many different ways can the 9 positions on a baseball team be filled from 25 players?

h) In how many orders can 7 persons seat themselves in 7 chairs in a row?

i) In how many clockwise orders can 7 persons seat themselves at a round table with 7 chairs?

j) One can put 3 keys on a key ring in only 1 way (explain). In how many ways can one arrange 4 keys on a key ring? 5 keys? 6 keys? 7 keys? Relate to part (i).

12. How many 5-card hands can be drawn from a deck of 52 cards?

13. Among the hands of Exercise 12, how many:

a) Contain 4 aces?   b) Contain exactly 3 aces?

c) Contain exactly 2 aces?   d) Contain no ace?

e) Contain exactly 2 aces and exactly 2 kings?

f) Contain 3 eights and 2 fours?

g) Contain 3 cards of one rank and 2 of another?

h) Contain 5 spades?

i) Contain 4 spades and 1 heart?

j) Contain at least one card of each suit?

k) Have no card higher than a 5? (Consider the ace high.)

l) Have no card lower than a Q?

14. A motorist driving to work crosses 2 intersections with traffic lights. At each intersection the cycle is 1 minute. At the first intersection the light shows green on the highway for 30 seconds. At the other intersection it is green for 40 seconds. If the motorist obeys the traffic laws, what is the probability he will be stopped by (a) neither light? (b) both lights? (c) exactly one light?

15. The probability that a man of age 50 will live another year is 0.987. How large a premium should an insurance company charge him for a $10,000 term life insurance policy for one year? (Ignore extra charges for company expenses.)

16. A coin is to be tossed 5 times. What is the probability that on some 3 consecutive tosses either 3 heads or 3 tails will occur?

17. A pair of dice is rolled. You are told that the sum of the numbers is less than 6. What is the probability that the sum is 4?

18. In a set of 4 light bulbs, 2 are good and 2 bad. You test them one by one. What is the probability that you will find the last defective bulb with the third bulb that you test?

19. In a room are two chests of drawers. There are two drawers in each chest. In each drawer in one of the chests is a silver ball. In the other chest there is a silver ball in one drawer and a gold ball in the other. You are to enter the room, choose a chest, and open a drawer. If you find a silver ball in the drawer opened, what is the probability that the other drawer in the chest will contain the gold ball?

20. The following is a description of an experiment for approximating the value of π. It is to be carried out with the aid of an adding machine.

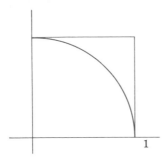

Consider the figure shown here. The quarter circle has area $\pi/4$. The square region has area 1. Thus if 100 points are chosen randomly in the square, then

$$\frac{\text{number inside circle}}{100} \quad \text{ought to be} \quad \approx \frac{\pi/4}{1}.$$

That is,

$$\pi \approx \frac{4 \times \text{the number inside}}{100}.$$

Choose 200 ordered triples of digits in a random fashion (for example, the last 3 digits of randomly chosen telephone numbers), and pair them to form 100 ordered pairs, such as $(217, 783)$. To see whether the pair $(217, 783)$ represents a point inside the circle, check whether

$$(.217)^2 + (.783)^2 < 1.$$

Compute

$$\frac{4 \times \text{the number inside}}{100}.$$

and compare with known approximations to π.

SUMMARY

The basic procedure for handling probability problems dealing with some experiment is to list all possible outcomes and assign a probability to each. The sum of the probabilities must be 1. In many practical situations we cannot be sure what probability should be assigned to particular outcomes, and must make estimates.

It is convenient to introduce the symbols C_k^n and P_k^n:

$$C_k^n = \frac{n!}{k!\,(n-k)!}\;; \qquad P_k^n = k!\,C_k^n = \frac{n!}{(n-k)!}\,.$$

C_k^n is the number of k-element subsets of an n-element set. P_k^n is the number of *ordered* k-element subsets of an n-element set. The numbers C_k^n appear in Pascal's triangle.

index

index

ABCDE69